International Management Series

The Carnegie Bosch Institute
International Conference on Closed-Loop Supply Chains

Business Aspects of Closed-Loop Supply Chains

May 31 - June 2, 2001

Pittsburgh, Pennsylvania

International Management Series

The Carnegie Bosch Institute
International Conference on Closed-Loop Supply Chains

BUSINESS ASPECTS OF CLOSED-LOOP SUPPLY CHAINS

May 31 - June 2, 2001

Pittsburgh, Pennsylvania

V. Daniel R. Guide, Jr. and Luk N. Van Wassenhove, Editors

Carnegie Mellon University Press
Pittsburgh, Pennsylvania
2003

Library of Congress Control Number 2003100706

ISBN 0-88748-402-6

Carnegie Mellon University Press
4902 Forbes Avenue
Pittsburgh, Pennsylvaina 15213-3799

Table of Contents

Introduction

Closed-loop supply chains have traditional forward supply chain activities and a set of additional activities required for the reverse supply chain. These additional activities include:

- *product acquisition* – the activities required to obtain the products from the end-users,
- *reverse logistics* – the activities required to move the products from the points of use to a point(s) of disposition,
- *test, sort and disposition* – the activities to determine the condition of the products, and the most economically attractive reuse option,
- *refurbish* – the activities required to execute the most economically attractive option: direct reuse, repair, remanufacture, recycle, disposal,
- *distribution and marketing* – the activities required to create and exploit markets for refurbished goods and distribution.

The major difference between closed-loop supply chains and traditional forward supply chains is for a forward supply chain, the customer is at the end of the processes, and for a closed-loop supply chain, there is value to be recovered from the customer or end-user. The value to be recovered is significant, current estimates of annual sales of remanufactured products are in excess of $50 billion in the United States alone. There are no worldwide estimates of the economic scope of reuse activities, but the number of firms engaged in these activities is growing rapidly in response to the opportunities to create additional wealth, and in response to the growth in extended producer responsibility legislation in the European Union and in many Asian countries.

We posit that the best way to address the extended producer responsibilities requirements imposed on businesses is to approach the problem from a business perspective. Simply put, we believe that economic incentives (increased profits) provide the strongest argument in favor of firms developing closed-loop systems. This distinction is important since we believe that closed-loop supply chains should not be confused with 'green' supply chains, or sustainable development, or mandated waste-recovery systems.

We view closed-loop supply chains as a business proposition where profit maximization is the objective. This is a rational point of view since no firm can engage in business practices that destroy rather than create shareholder value. We are not taking an anti-environmental position, and we hypothesize that closed-loop supply chains provide many of the desired benefits of 'green' supply chains. However, the primary purpose of closed-loop supply chains is to create sufficient shareholder wealth to be economically attractive.

Commercial returns from retail and Internet-based sales are a concern in North America and a growing concern in Western Europe. In 2001, the cost of returns for Internet sales was averaging twice the value of the product. The returns process, from an operational and financial view, overwhelmed many dot-com firms. Distributed forward supply chains are being rapidly adopted by many firms, and with strategic partners responsible for manufacturing and sourcing, it remains unclear for many firms exactly which partner, if any, will be responsible for managing the returns processes.

In addition to the growing trend toward distributed forward supply chains, there are many reuse activities best managed by partners in a cascade reuse relationship. Cascade reuse opportunities are based on the fact that small firms usually have a lower cost of capital, and the smaller profits from some value recovery activities may be readily acceptable for smaller specialized companies rather than the supply chain captain. There are more parties involved in closed-loop supply chains and this makes the managerial tasks of coordinating activities more complex. Firms may enter into a variety of contractual agreements with specialized providers to manage the various processes required in a closed-loop supply chain. Original equipment manufacturers may form partnerships for any or all of the specialized reverse supply chain activities. The additional firms in the supply chain may amplify the bullwhip effect making activities at every stage of the supply chain more difficult to manage and control. These activities are boundary spanning and require a multidisciplinary approach for the design of profitable systems.

The product life cycle for many consumer goods is continually shrinking. Many consumer electronics, such as mobile telephones, have less than six months between new model introductions. The management of the product returns process in a timely and effective manner in the case of short life cycle goods presents enormous difficulties for firms managing agreements with contract manufacturers on different continents and global distribution.

The global nature of closed-loop supply chains requires creative, innovative information technology (IT). The rate of technology diffusion varies from country to country and even within counties, and this provides opportunities for marketing remanufactured or refurbished goods in a cascade reuse system. The challenge is in having good market information about buyers and sellers globally. Additionally, information technology may become incorporated into product designs, as was the case with the Bosch data logger, to facilitate product recovery efforts. The data logger was developed for use with Bosch hand tools and shows whether the motor is recoverable. IT devices have the promise of reducing the uncertainty about the condition of the returned product, and even in reducing the timing uncertainty in product returns.

We have attempted to take a multidisciplinary approach with the development of this book. We asked the leading academic experts to write chapters for a workshop sponsored by the Carnegie Bosch Institute and held at Carnegie Mellon University in May/June of 2001. These chapters were presented initially at plenary sessions, and participants then selected breakout groups for each of the topic areas for in-depth discussions on the research needs and key issues. We recognize and acknowledge the contribution of each of the participants as well as the individual authors. A complete list of participants and the workshop program is provided in the appendix.

Loosely speaking, the book chapters are structured along the following major issues: product design, consumer behavior, and supply chain actors.

This book covers a number of issues, outlines the similarities and differences with classical forward supply chains, suggests approaches, frameworks, and points out venues for further research. It also points to major gaps in our knowledge:
- how design influences the ease of recovery and the recoverable value,
- how consumers react (marketing),
- how information technology may be used to facilitate product re covery, and
- how we (firms and society) should understand the value (or loss) associated with these activities (accounting).

Product Design	• Recoverable value • Form factor • Ease of recovery	Product, modules, components, parts, materials Transportation costs Design for X, economies of scale	
Consumer Behavior	• Reuse options • Reusability	Consumer behavior Markets Return quality Return percentage Return delay	• Maturity • Technology diffusion • IT • Incentives
Supply Chain Actors	• Profitable for whom? • Length of the chain	OEM, 3rd parties Coordination ñ delays, bullwhip effect, batching	

Table 1: Major Issues in Closed-Loop Supply Chains

The largest gaps exist outside the field of operations, and this points to the need for interdisciplinary research.

This book does not cover green issues (environmental, Life Cycle Assessment, etc.). It focuses on supply chains. However, there are a number of issues that arise from simply considering environmental concerns and how they fit with the supply chain problems. Many tools developed for environmental (green) analysis do not provide any connectivity to the classic tools (finance, accounting, economics, etc.) for managing supply chains. This again points to potentially insightful research issues to be resolved.

If we focus on supply chain issues and use the same rough breakdown of product, consumers, and actors (Table 1), one may ask the following questions about reuse opportunities:

1. Does the product stay intact (e.g., from a photocopier to a photocopier), or not (e.g., use for spare parts, cascade reuse opportunities)?
2. Does the customer make a distinction (e.g., cannibalization, different secondary markets) or not?
3. Do the actors remain the same (e.g., brokers, third parties) or not?

The complexity of the supply chain clearly increases along the three dimensions:

- Higher costs
- More need to coordinate (e.g., incentives, information asymmetry)
- Longer chains (amplified bullwhip effect, obsolescence, risk)

We hypothesize that short closed-loop supply chains with the correct quantity and quality and smooth flows are more profitable. However, more complex situations offer greater business opportunities, provided one could enhance and control the activities with the right business model. We hope our first chapter discussing closed-loop supply chains in various industries provides the foundation for such models.

Perhaps the greatest need is to reduce the uncertainty inherent in closed-loop supply chains to enhance the recovery profitability. We see the following trends developing and as having great promise:

- Design – not just of the product, but the entire service process associated with the design of the delivery of the product benefits. Consumers may be offered the choice of buying the function of the product, but not the product itself. This is a familiar concept for office managers leasing photocopiers and having the lease contract include routine maintenance and service. The same concept is possible for automobile tires, where the consumer purchases the tread life but the casing is leased. There are endless scenarios possible and almost no research conducted at this point.

- Intelligent IT devices – these devices enable the product to tell you everything a firm needs to know about the product and the use of the product.

These two areas offer tremendous research possibilities.

We recognize that some recovery opportunities will remain difficult to exploit for any company. These areas are where policymakers can design appropriate regulations or incentives structures. For example, it has long been recognized that recycled materials often cost more than virgin materials, and a way to resolve the short-run problem is to place a tax on virgin materials to provide an equal playing field for a period that would allow recyclers to improve their process (economy of scale effects). This would provide the opportunity for recyclers to become competitive, and would place long-term pressure on recyclers to reduce the costs of recycled materials so as to be competitive with virgin materials without the tax differential. Another, less draconian, policy would be to offer tax incentives to firms investing capital in closed-loop supply chain processes. This will reduce the firm's weighted cost of capital and may make many programs attractive from a financial perspective.

Each of the chapters includes a more detailed discussion of the research needs for each of the areas we address in the book. We hope that these ideas and questions will generate further academic research into closed-loop supply chains, and that this represents the beginning of research in this area.

Finally, we would be remiss if we did not acknowledge the efforts and financial assistance that made the workshop and this book possible. Professor Michael Trick of Carnegie Mellon University and President of the Carnegie Bosch Institute provided the funding and arranged for the workshop meeting space at the Graduate School of Industrial Administration; Cathy Burstein of the Carnegie Bosch Institute made all the local arrangements, managed the budgets, and generally made the workshop a reality; Dean James Stalder of Duquesne University, for financial support; Charles Corbett, The Anderson School, UCLA and Rommert Dekker of Erasmus University Rotterdam both provided additional assistance on editing this book and planning the workshop activities.

V. Daniel R. Guide, Jr.
Luk N. Van Wassenhove

PART I – SETTING THE STAGE

BUSINESS ASPECTS OF CLOSED-LOOP SUPPLY CHAINS

V. Daniel R. Guide, Jr., Pennsylvania State University, USA*
Luk N. Van Wassenhove, INSEAD, France

1. Introduction

Successful development of waste-free supply chains is a foundation of sustainable development; however, all businesses have the responsibility of returning profits for investors. We focus on the business aspects of developing and managing profitable closed-loop supply chains. We identify the common processes required by a closed-loop supply chain: product acquisition, reverse logistics, inspection, testing and disposition, remanufacturing, and selling and distribution. However, the management activities and focus in these common processes are not the same among all closed-loop supply chains. In the following sections, we document a number of diverse products that are presently being remanufactured and describe their supply chains. After each case, we summarize and discuss the distinguishing features of the supply chains. Finally, we discuss the management of each of the different supply chain systems, and identify the key research issues.

2. Waste-free Supply Chains

There are some well-known examples of closed-loop supply chains; many people are familiar with the refillable milk and soft drink bottle systems. However, these systems have disappeared in the United States, chiefly because of the shift to regional bottling centers rather than local facilities and the added transportation expense of refillable glass containers. A more recent example of an economically viable closed-loop supply chain is the Xerox waste-free supply chain program. The two keys to the success of the Xerox program are a systems view and a value-creating set of activities.

In 1991, the Xerox Corporation started a program to enable the company to be waste-free. Xerox cites a number of reasons for requiring the development of a waste-free company, including financial benefits, to provide a competitive

---

* In 2001, Dr. Guide was at Duquesne University. In 2002, Dr. Guide moved to Pennsylvania State University.

edge, to comply with legislative regulation, and to meet customer requirements. Proactive leadership is Xerox's goal in its environmental programs, and all Xerox products are required, at a minimum, to comply with government standards and meet Xerox's internal environmental standards. The internal standards dictated by Xerox are, in many cases, more stringent than existing legislative requirements.

Design for disassembly, durability, reuse, and recycling has enabled Xerox to maximize the end-of-life potential of products and components. Today, 90 percent of Xerox-designed equipment is remanufacturable. Equipment remanufacture and the reuse and recycling of parts prevented more than 145 million pounds of waste from entering landfills in 1998. Since 1991, parts reuse has reduced the use of raw materials and energy needed to manufacture new parts. The financial benefits of equipment remanufacture and parts reuse amount to several hundred million dollars a year.

Xerox has developed an encompassing program of design for the environment that explicitly considers the logistics activities required for an active product take-back and asset recovery program. Xerox's customer supply chain incorporates a supply network dedicated to reuse activities. These activities include removal of Xerox equipment from the end-user to regional distribution centers, the testing and grading of returned copiers, equipment and parts repair, remanufacturing, and recycling. Xerox also reuses toner cartridges in a program composed of remanufacturing and recycling. The asset management program in Europe alone resulted in over $76 million in cost savings in 1999.

Xerox takes a system view of reuse activities and recognizes that economics dictate the best option for product reuse. Value-added recovery, in the forms of repair and remanufacturing is preferred when conditions allow, but Xerox also practices recycling with supply chain partners.

In the following section we present specific details about the closed-loop supply chain with industrial remanufacturing managed by Xerox-Europe. This type of closed-loop supply chain is a foundation to the waste-free systems that Xerox has emphasized.

3. Xerox-Europe

Xerox-Europe is part of the Xerox Corporation accounting for 25 percnet of

Xerox's worldwide business, reporting $53 billion in revenue from sales, leasing, and service. Xerox-Europe serves 600,000 customers with 1.5 million installed machines, and makes over 1 million deliveries per year through distribution channels. Xerox-Europe has a supply chain that facilitates the reuse of copiers, printers, and office products (Figure 1). The first step is obtaining the used products from customers that will serve as the inputs to the remanufacturing processes. After the products are obtained, they must be moved from their present location to where the remanufacturing facility is located. This is accomplished via reverse logistics activities. Decisions regarding the disposition of the returned products determine the appropriate reuse activity and at what level. Finally, the remanufactured products must be sold and distributed. Xerox relies on leasing to predict more accurately the timing and quantities of product returns.

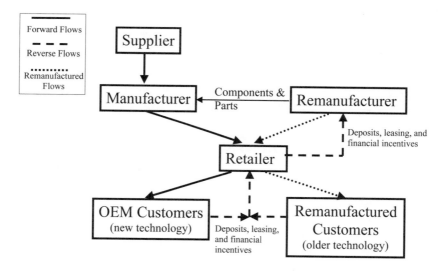

Figure1: A Closed-Loop Supply Chain for Photocopiers

A foundation of the asset recovery program is value-added remanufacturing operations. Xerox-Europe provides returns service for any product (photocopiers, commercial printers, and supplies) they sell or lease, and the return rate for all products was 65 percent. Table 1 shows the volumes of copiers and the reuse alternatives in 1999.

	Repaired	Remanu-factured	Stripped for parts	Materials Recycled
Units	2,500	8,209	13,935	91,664
Percentage	2.14	7.06	11.98	78.82

Table 1: Reuse Options and Volumes for Photocopiers

After products are collected from Xerox customers and returned to one of four centralized logistics return centers, the returned units are inspected, tested, and assigned to one of four grades. The inspection process is complex and requires the examination and testing of each component and part. The grades represent the most economically attractive use of the returned product and are based on economic conditions, the physical condition, the age of the asset and the demand for particular copier models. The grades and brief descriptions are shown in Table 2. Grade 1 products are virtually unused machines requiring only minor servicing. Grade 2 machines are in good condition and are remanufactured, requiring parts and components to be replaced during the process.

Grade	Description	Reuse Alternative
1	Dust-off	Repair
2	Good	Remanufacture
3	Good	Parts remanufacture
4	Dispose	Recycle

Table 2: Product Recovery Grades and Recovery Options

Grade 3 machines are in good condition, but not economically fit for remanufacturing. Machines may be classified as grade 2 or 3 based, in part, on the demand for remanufactured machines and the levels of reused parts inventories. Grade 4 machines are economically fit only for materials recycling. After machines have been inspected and graded, they are disassembled and the parts and components enter reused parts inventories. These inventories may be used with new parts and components to produce additional copiers, or to meet demand for spare parts.

Repaired and remanufactured copiers and copiers containing remanufactured components are distributed to customers through the traditional forward logistics channel. The service network is responsible for repair and maintenance activities and relies on a flow of quality remanufactured parts and components.

One of the barriers to the success of Xerox' equipment remanufacture and parts reuse program over the years has been the misperception among some customers that products with recycled-part content are inferior to those built from all-new parts. Xerox' unique processes and technologies ensure that all of the products, regardless of remanufactured content, meet the same specifications for performance, quality, and reliability.

4. Closed-Loop Suppy Chains with Industrial Remanufacturing

Industrial remanufacturing is an outgrowth of product life extension, where very expensive products with very long expected lifetimes are routinely remanufactured. Typical products that are subject to product life extensions include aircraft, ships, and railroad locomotives. The main differences between product life extension and industrial remanufacturing are very low volumes, often a single unit, and there is no need to balance supply and demand for product life extension since the operating firm retains ownership of the item.

Xerox-Europe's remanufacturing operations provide an example of industrial remanufacturing. Table 3 shows the distinguishing characteristics of closed-loop supply chains for industrial remanufacturing. Xerox is in the minority in industrial remanufacturing since less than 5 percent of remanufacturing in the United States is done by OEMs (Guide 2000). Additionally, Xerox relies heavily on leasing to enable the firm to forecast the timing and quantities of product returns. Product returns from leasing, for non-OEM remanufacturers, represent less than 5 percent of total returns, and this makes the tasks of forecasting product returns timing and quantities much more difficult. This forecasting problem manifests itself as product imbalances since matching return rates with demand rates is complex and difficult. OEMs have another distinct advantage in the area of product design, because most products must be designed for reuse, i.e., a modular design and clearly labeled materials.

Marketing is more complex for the remanufactured products since customers may require significant education and assurances to convince them to purchase remanufactured products. Market cannibalization is also a significant concern since little is known about how remanufacturing sales affect new products sales.

Characteristic
High variances
Stable production technology
Limited volumes
Modular design
Imbalances in supply and demand
Cannibalization

**Table 3: Characteristics of Closed-Loop
Supply chains for Industrial
Remanufacturing**

5. Closed-Loop Supply Chains with Tire Retreading

The closed-loop supply chain for tire retreading has some elements in common with industrial remanufacturing; however, the volume of tires in use is enormous. Additionally, tires are bulky and expensive to transport, and the residual value remaining may be low, especially when compared to the cost of new replacements. Tire remanufacturing is rarely profitable for passenger tires, but financially attractive for commercial tires. Illustrating the two supply chains and their characteristics provides some insights into this situation. We present a brief overview of the closed-loop supply chains for commercial (Figure 2) and passenger (Figure 3) tire retreading.

In passenger tire retreading, casing collectors consolidate tires from retailers and garages, and broker tires to retreaders. The casing collectors place a disposal bin on tire retailers and garages sites. Old tires are simply placed in the bin by the resellers and the casing collector routinely empties the bin. The casing collector charges a fee for maintaining the bin and for removing the used passenger tires. The used tires are then sold in batches to the tire retreader. The batches of tires are composed of a variety of tire makes, sizes, and quality. The tire retreader has no way of knowing the composition of the batch offered and must decide whether to purchase the entire batch. Balancing supply and demand is difficult since some models of tires may be preferred by the retreader to meet demand, and other models of tires may be undesirable (no demand or casings unfit for retreading). Finally the selling of retreaded passenger tires is quite difficult since retreaded tires may cost more than inexpensive new tires in some cases, and the image of retreaded tires may be poor in many locations.

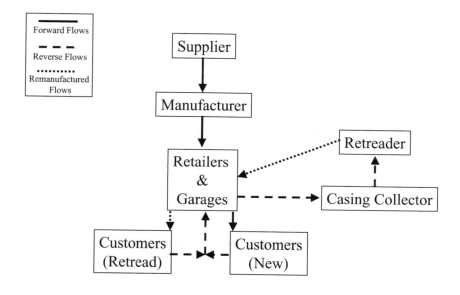

Figure 2: A Closed-Loop Supply Chain for Passenger Tire Retreading

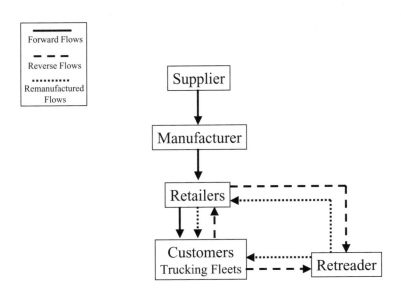

Figure 3: A Closed-Loop Supply Chain for Commerical Tire Retreading

Commercial tire retreading is, by contrast, a simpler closed-loop supply chain. Product acquisition is very easy for commercial tire retreading. A trucking fleet manager arranges for retreading of casings from their trucks. The fleet manager, for large truck fleets, may make arrangements directly with the tire retreader. For smaller trucking fleets, the manager will contract via a reseller or dealer, that will then make the arrangements with the retreader. The retreader receives the casings, retreads the same casing and then returns them to the reseller or trucking fleet. The problem of balancing supply and demand is greatly simplified.

Passenger tires	Commercial tires
High variance in returns timing	Low variance in returns timing
High variance in quality	Low variance in quality
Difficult to sell	Easy to sell
High logistics costs	Intermediate logistics costs

Table 4: Characteristics of Closed-Loop Supply Chains with Tire Retreading

There are differences in closed-loop supply chains for tire retreading and closed-loop supply chains incorporating industrial remanufacturing (Table 4). Potential volumes for both passenger and commercial tire retreading are higher relative to most industrial remanufacturing situations. The retreading processes are not as complex as those required for industrial remanufacturing.

6. Closed-Loop Supply Chains with Container Remanufacturing

Historically, container remanufacturing may be one of the oldest forms of product reuse. In the past, drink bottles were regularly refilled after being acquired from the consumer. Product acquisition was done directly from the consumer, e.g., milk bottles, or at resellers (soft drink bottles) who participated in a deposit system to encourage returns. While bottle refilling is not commonly practiced in the United States anymore, there are a number of products that utilize the same principles. We discuss two such products: toner cartridges and single-use cameras.

6.1 Xerox Copy/Print Cartridge Return Program

Xerox introduced their program for copy/print cartridge returns in 1991 and, at present, it covers 80 percent of the toner/print cartridge line. In 1998 Xerox expanded the program to include the recycling of waste toner from high-speed copier and commercial production publishing systems. The return rate for cartridges in Europe and North America was greater than 60% for 1998. This equates to over 2.86 million kilograms of material remanufactured or recycled just from cartridges. Xerox reports avoiding almost 23 million kilograms of landfill because of their reuse programs. The cartridges are designed for remanufacturing and recycling of materials not fit for remanufacture.

Customers return the cartridges by placing the spent cartridge into the packaging used for a full cartridge and attaching a prepaid postage label provided by Xerox. The returned cartridges are cleaned, inspected, and then parts are reused or materials recycled. The full cartridges are then distributed through normal distribution channels to customers. The final cartridge product containing remanufactured parts or recycled materials is indistinguishable from cartridges containing exclusively virgin materials. Figure 4 shows the supply chain, in simplified form, for a cartridge. Xerox is presently testing the use of 'ecoboxes' to allow bulk returns from high-volume users in Europe. Xerox will arrange for regular pick-ups of the boxes by its own carrier network. A bulk returns process allows each high-volume user to batch cartridges and may lower the returns costs absorbed by Xerox (the information in this section was obtained from Xerox 1999).

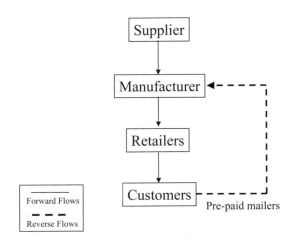

Figure 4: A Closed-Loop Supply Chain for Cartridge Reuse

6.2 Kodak Single-Use Cameras

Kodak, in 1990-91, began a program to redesign completely their single-use cameras to make possible the recycling and reuse of parts. This effort involved the integration of business development, design, and environmental personnel. The first stage featured new designs that facilitated the reuse of parts and components. The entire line of single-use cameras may be remanufactured or recycled, and the amount of materials per camera that are reusable range from 77-80 percent. The second stage involved forging agreements with photofinishers to return the cameras to Kodak after consumers had turned them in for processing. Kodak now enjoys a return rate greater than 70 percent in the United States and almost 60 percent worldwide. Since 1990, Kodak has reused over 310 million cameras, and has active programs in over 20 countries. The Kodak single-use camera program has become a centerpiece in Kodak's widespread efforts in recycling, reuse, and product stewardship.

The process flow for the reuse of cameras, after the sale of the camera, starts with the consumer returning the camera to a photofinisher to develop the film.

The photofinisher then batches the cameras into specially designed shipping containers and sends them to one of three collection centers. Kodak has entered into agreements with other manufacturers (Fuji, Konica and others) of single-use cameras that allow for the use of common collection centers. At the collection center, the cameras are sorted according to manufacturer and then by camera model.

After the sorting operations, the cameras are shipped to a subcontractor facility. There, all packaging is removed along with the front and back covers and batteries. The cameras are then cleaned and transferred to an assembly line where they are disassembled, and inspected. Some parts are routinely reused, some are replaced (batteries) and the frame and flash circuit board are carefully tested following rigorous quality testing procedures.

These subassemblies are then shipped to one of three Kodak facilities that manufacture single-use cameras. At the Kodak facility, the cameras are loaded with film and a fresh battery (flash models only), and, finally, new outer packaging. The final product is now distributed to retailers for resale. By leveraging excellent customer relationships with photofinishers around the world, Kodak established a variety of marketing and promotional programs to get the camera shells back to the company once the customer's film had been removed. For a Kodak single-use camera, the time from collection back to the store shelf can be as short as 30 days.

The final product containing remanufactured parts and recycled materials is indistinguishable to consumers from single-use cameras containing no reused parts. Figure 5 shows the supply chain network for reusable cameras (the information in this section was obtained from Kodak, 1999).

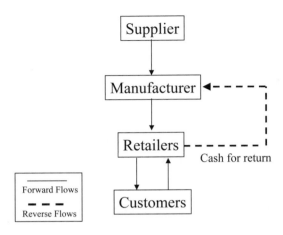

Figure 5: A Closed-Loop Supply Chain for Single-Use Cameras

7. Characteristics of Refillable Container Closed-Loop Supply Chains

These products, toner/printer cartridges and single-use cameras, are both containers required to sell the contents. Consumers do not distinguish between a new and a remanufactured/reused product since the purpose of buying the container is to gain access to the contents, which are toner ink and film, respectively. Additionally, the customer also has no way of determining, aside from labeling, whether the container has been remanufactured or that it contains reused materials. The returned containers in both cases are blended with new materials so there is no distinguishing between new and reused products. This is possible because the technology is extremely stable for toner/print cartridges and single-use cameras. The markets for the remanufactured products are exactly the same as for the new products becasuse the two are indistinguishable. The characteristics of the supply chain for container reuse are listed in Table 5. The volumes are very high, in the millions for both products, and the annual returns quantities are stable or have a known growth rate. In both cases, the OEM controls the reverse logistics network and the reuse alternatives.

Characteristic
Commodity goods
Containers for consumables
High volume
Low variance
Non-distinguishable products
Simple products
OEM-controlled
Short lead times

Table 5: Characteristics of Closed-Loop Supply Chains for Refillable Containers

8. Closed-Loop Supply Chains for Reuse of Cellular Telephones

Our last case discusses the reuse of consumer electronics equipment and details the supply chain and remanufacturing operations.

Cellular Telephone Reuse at ReCellular, Inc.

ReCellular, Inc. was founded in 1991 in Ann Arbor, MI by Charles Newman to trade new, used, and remanufactured cellular handsets. The business grew from a venture that provided cellular telephones for leasing, and alternative sources for handsets were required to reduce costs (hence the discovery of the used handset market). ReCellular is a trading operation that refurbishes cellular phones when necessary to add value for existing orders, and buys and sells wireless handsets of all technologies. At present, ReCellular estimates it has remanufactured over 1.3 million cellular phones. One of the goals of the company is to be the "first in the second" in the wireless exchange plan. The company offers remanufactured (refurbished) products as a high quality, cost effective alternative to new cellular handsets. Customer services include: grading and sorting, remanufacturing, repackaging, logistics, and trading and product sourcing (all services are specific to cellular handsets and accessories). ReCellular operates globally with a presence in South America, the Far East, Western Europe, Africa, the Middle East, and North America. The company has plans to expand operations to provide better coverage throughout the world.

The cellular communications industry is a highly dynamic market where the demand for telephones changes daily. Demand may be influenced by the introduction of new technology (e.g., digital and analog), price changes in cellular airtime, promotional campaigns, the opening of new markets, churn (customers leaving present airtime providers), and the number of new cellular telephones manufactured. Additionally, there is no worldwide standard technology (e.g., Europe uses GSM, but the United States does not support this wireless technology at the same frequency) and this necessitates dealing in a number of often disparate technologies and standards. These global technology differences make regional remanufacturing activities difficult since there may be no local market for certain types/models of phones, requiring a firm to manage global sales and procurement. Additionally, cellular airtime providers may limit the number of telephones supported by their system, and the dropping of a phone model by a major carrier can greatly affect a local market. These factors make competition for an original equipment manufacturer challenging. However, a company offering used or remanufactured equipment faces numerous factors affecting the supply of used cellular phones. The same factors that complicate demand affect the availability of used handsets. Further, identifying and taking actions to reduce the uncertainties in the reverse flows as early as possible is an important issue in this business. The supply of used handsets is a volatile market, with volumes and prices in a constant state of flux.

In order to fully understand the nature of the market, both forward and reverse flows of materials must be considered. Figure 6 shows the supply chain system for cellular telephone reuse. The forward movement of materials consists of the traditional flows from suppliers to manufacturers, manufacturers to airtime providers (retailers in this case since the sale of a cellular phone is tied to airtime activation) and airtime providers to the customers. The reverse flows are more complex. Remanufacturers of cellular telephones do not collect handsets directly from the end-user, but rather rely on airtime providers or a variety of third-party collectors (we discuss the specifics of product acquisition in the next section). Airtime providers and third-party collectors act as consolidators who then broker the units to remanufacturers. ReCellular then sorts and grades the handsets, and sells the handsets as-is or remanufactured to airtime providers and third-party dealers working with airtime providers. Some handsets may be obsolete or damaged beyond higher-order recovery and these products are sold to scrap dealers and recyclers (note this flow may come from both remanufacturers and third party collectors). Recyclers recover polymers and other materials in the handset assemblies, and base materials in batteries. Scrap dealers may separate the handsets into materials and resell individual parts for reuse in other applications, and offer the other sorted materials to recyclers. Suppliers may then purchase the recycled materials for use in new products.

The acquisition of used telephones is central to the success of a remanufacturing firm. The nature of product acquisitions is driven by what future demands (unknown) will be for phones. The lead times for delivery after used phones have been purchased are often lengthy and subject to a large amount of variability. This has caused remanufacturers to have stocks on-hand to compete for sales. ReCellular obtains used phones in bulk from a variety of sources, including cellular airtime providers and third-party collectors. Third-party collectors are often charitable foundations (e.g., the Wireless Foundation)

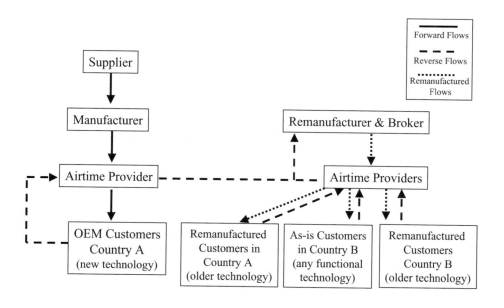

Figure 6: A Closed-Loop Supply Chain for Cellular Telephones

that act as consolidators by collecting used handsets and accessories from individuals. Cellular airtime providers also act as consolidators by collecting used phones from customers who have returned the phones at the end of service agreements, or customers upgrading to newer technology. Both these and other sources worldwide may offer a variety of handsets and accessories in varying condition for a wide range of prices and quantities. Due to the low cost (approximately $0.50 per phone using air transport) of bulk transportation of phones, using a worldwide network of suppliers of used phones is practical and cost-efficient. No individual returns are accepted since the channels required for direct returns from the consumer have too high a cost to be effective at this time. Obtaining the best grade of used products for the best price is one of the key tasks necessary for the success of ReCellular. Deciding on a fair price to offer for the used phones is a difficult and complex task. At present, the acquisition staff devotes much of their time to identifying reliable and reputable sources of used phones and establishing a working relationship with these suppliers. New suppliers usually require a physical visit to ensure the quality of the used phones.

The value of a used handset is highly dependent on future market demand for that particular model either in remanufactured or as-is form. The present demand for a graded as-is used cellular phone or a remanufactured phone is known for that instant in time, but due to the highly dynamic nature of the industry, the prices are not stable. The market forces discussed earlier may cause the value of a particular model of phone to drop or rise with little warning. An additional factor is that the selling price for remanufactured phones tends to drop over time, making the used phones a perishable product.

This nature of the product reuse market necessitates a fast, responsive supply chain that identifies sources of used phones for a fair price, and future buyers of these phones in either graded as-is or remanufactured condition. Additionally, the system must procure the phones in a timely manner, sort and grade the telephones, have the capability to rapidly remanufacture the phones to order, and provide a fast, accurate transportation method to ensure timely delivery of the phones. ReCellular is developing an e-Commerce site strictly for business to business in order to facilitate matching suppliers and buyers of equipment. The present e-Commerce site shows the current stocks (model, price, grade, and quantity) available and what models are needed (but not the prices offered). The site is being upgraded to allow real-time transactions by sales and procurement agents. Future considerations also include using the e-Commerce site to facilitate on-line auctions for used and remanufactured products.

9. Characteristics of Closed-Loop Supply Chains for Cellular Telephones

The volume of cellular telephones in use worldwide is enormous, with over 55 million cellular subscribers in the United States alone (U.S. Central Intelligence Agency 2000). One of the first requirements for a remanufacturer in this environment is global coverage. Because the rate of technology diffusion is different for each country in the world, phones, which may be technically obsolete in Norway, may be current technology in Ecuador. This imbalance in the diffusion of technology makes having global operations and intelligence crucial for a profitable operation. Tightly tied to the concept of global markets is the problem of acquisition, or obtaining the best-used product for the best price. The prices for cellular telephones are highly dynamic and are based on future expected prices for remanufactured handsets. The problem is further complicated by the market for graded as-is cellular telephones where a selling price is known, as opposed to an expected price in the future for a remanufactured item.

Cellular telephones are perishable items because of the high clockspeed in new product development. Electronics industries have the highest clockspeed, an average of 18 months, and this makes responsive systems crucial to making a profit. Remanufacturers cannot afford to remanufacture to stock in this environment since the value of the items drops daily.

Characteristic
Dynamic spot markets for supply and demand
High volumes
Perishable goods
Cascade reuse opportunities (worldwide market)
High information requirements
High variability

Table 6: Characteristics of Supply Chains for Consumer Electronics Reuse

10. Management of Closed-Loop Supply Chains

In the simplest, terms all closed-loop supply chains do have a common set of activities. The recovery process consists of several highly inter-related sub-processes: product acquisition, reverse logistics, inspection and disposition (consisting of test, sort, and grade), reconditioning (which may include remanufacturing), and distribution and selling of the recovered products. However, the previous cases illustrate that while there are common processes, not all closed-loop supply chains are alike. Each different supply chain system has different characteristics and management concerns. The majority of the literature on closed-loop supply chains is focused on value-recovery (remanufacturing), with some of the more recent literature examining reverse logistics (the collection process), but research has missed one of the key tasks: matching supply and demand (product acquisition management). In the following subsections we discuss each of the processes for the different types of closed-loop supply chains.

10.1 Industrial Remanufacturing Closed-Loop Supply Chains

Of the closed-loop supply chains, the industrial remanufacturing sector is most likely the best documented, but the most difficult to plan, manage, and control. Table 7 summarizes the critical success factors for managing these types of closed-loop supply chains.

Product acquisition refers to product acquisition management, and is actually a number of related processes (Guide and Van Wassenhove, 2000). Product acquisition activities for industrial remanufacturing may be based on leasing, in which case the product will be either returned at the expiration of the lease, or the lease renewed with the same item. Product acquisition in the case of leasing may be viewed as relatively simple; however, only a small number (5 percent) of industrial remanufacturers report using leasing (Guide, 2000). Remanufacturers report using a number of other techniques (deposits, rebates, and cash refunds) with varying degrees of success, and this indicates that the problem of obtaining sufficient quantities is more difficult than for refillable containers.

Keys to Success – Industrial Remanufacturing Closed-Loop Supply Chains

- Ability to forecast and control the timing, quantity, and quality of product returns (Information Systems)
- Design for reuse (recycle, repair, and remanufacture) (engineering)
- Customer education (remanufactured as good as new)
- New relationships with suppliers (fewer parts and components, design)
- Complex production planning and control problems

Table 7: Key Factors Industrial Remanufacturing

The reverse logistics process is most often difficult since the remanufacturer must arrange for pick-ups from many geographically diverse facilities. Many used industrial items are also regarded as hazardous waste and must be treated as such during transportation. The process of testing, sorting, grading, and inspection is time-consuming and complex, with the possibility of a single product containing tens of thousands of parts and components. The screening process must be rigorous since products of poor quality may be expensive to remanufacture, or dangerous to reuse. The remanufacturing/reconditioning processes are most often complex and difficult to plan, manage, and control (Guide, 2000). Distribution and selling, which requires balancing return and demand rates for industrial remanufacturing, is more difficult since there may be distinct and separate markets for new and remanufactured goods. Customers may require the newest technology or may simply perceive remanufactured products as inferior. These separate markets may affect the distribution and selling of remanufactured products. Market cannibalization may be a concern for manufacturers providing remanufactured products and, consequently, the retail markets may be disparate.

10.2 Product Life Extension Closed-Loop Supply Chains

Product life extension programs represent some of the earliest remanufacturing programs for very expensive industrial goods such as jet engines, airframes, and railroad locomotive engines. The volumes of items remanufactured are often very low, with each product being an essentially new project to plan (for example, the US Navy required over three years to completely overhaul the carrier the USS *Enterprise*). The supply chains are often owned and controlled by the equipment owner; there are no uncertainties in the timing of returns, and return quantities are known with certainty. Product acquisition is a matter of scheduling the unit for testing and the required remanufacturing operations. Reverse logistics activities are limited to delivering the asset to the remanufacturing facility, and in many cases, the asset may be used to deliver itself (as with the cases of aircraft, railroad locomotives, and ships).

However, the complex nature and physical size of the products makes testing and remanufacturing operations very difficult. Jet engines are composed of several thousand modules and each module may be composed of hundreds of parts. The critical nature of the product makes testing mandatory and requires a high degree of accuracy in detecting worn parts that require replacement prior to failure. Remanufacturing operations are complex and require careful coordination to produce parts for reassembly at the proper time. Reassembly often requires that parts be returned to the same product, and this requires remanufactures to have systems to perfectly trace every part.

There are no distribution or selling problems since the original owner retains ownership of the asset during the product life extension.

10.3 Tire Remanufacturing Closed-Loop Supply Chains

Tire remanufacturing, or retreading, has enjoyed periods of popularity during times of economic crisis or during wartimes when rationing has been in effect. The European Union recently passed legislation requiring extended producer responsibility for tire manufacturers. In order to comply with this new legislation, tire manufacturers will have to arrange for economic end-of-life disposition for all their products.

The main difference between the two types of tire retreading is the degree of difficulty in distribution and selling of the remanufactured tires. Tires retreaded for commercial trucking applications have a ready market since tires are often one of the largest expenses for trucking fleet owners. The lower cost of remanufactured tires makes them attractive for fleet managers. However, retreaded passenger tires have a much more limited market. In addition to the poor image retreaded tires have, the retail cost of many Asian imports is lower than the price of a retreaded tire. This key difference in market perception makes one application profitable and the other relatively unattractive.

10.4 Refillable Container Closed-Loop Supply Chains

In the case of single-use cameras, the OEM controls product acquisition and reverse logistics by using cash incentives to motivate the photofinisher to return the empty cameras to Kodak's reuse facility. Xerox also directly controls the returns process for toner/print cartridges. Xerox supplies each customer with a pre-paid mailer and appeals to customers to send back the spent cartridge. Both strategies are extremely successful at ensuring constant volumes of containers, and are examples of market-based returns strategies. Market-based strategies are active strategies to encourage product returns, in contrast to waste stream systems where returns are passively accepted from the waste stream (Guide and Van Wassenhove, 2000). Both firms enjoy stable return flows with predictable volumes each period.

In both examples of refillable containers, reverse logistics activities are simple. The photofinisher acts as a consolidator for Kodak and eliminates the need for Kodak to deal with individual customers. Xerox has minimized their contact with end-users by using a pre-paid mailer, which the customer may then use to arrange for pick-up and transportation.

The disassembly, test and inspection processes, and the remanufacturing processes for refillable containers are simple. The product itself is simple, the costs are low, and products that may be questionable may be recycled with little or no concern about replacement materials. Finally, the distribution and selling processes are simple since traditional distribution networks are used, and the customer base is the same as for new products.

Distribution and selling of remanufactured tires requires balancing return and demand rates. A refillable container closed-loop supply chain is a relatively easy process, in part because the customer cannot differentiate between reused and new products. We do not mean that the processes involved in balancing return and demand rates are simplistic (see Toktay, et al. 2000 for a complete discussion of this process), but rather that the process is simple in comparison with the other types of closed-loop supply chains. The technology contained in these products is stable and there are very limited secondary markets available for the used containers. There are secondary markets for the refilling of printer cartridges and single-use cameras; these are small localized operations that are considered more of a nuisance since the remanufacturing may be substandard and damage the firm's reputation. The returned products are mixed with new (replacement) materials as needed, and then repackaged and sent back out through traditional distribution channels. There is no need to segment demand by product type (remanufactured vs. new) or for a manufacturer to consider market cannibalization.

10.5 Consumer electronics reuse

These types of closed-loop supply chains may hold the greatest promise due to the volume of products available for reuse, but at the same time, these types of supply chains represent some of the greatest challenges. We list the key factors for success in Table 8.

Keys Factors - Consumer Electronics Closed-Loop Supply Chains

- Ability to forecast and control the timing, quantity, and quality of product returns, and reseller opportunities in a global market (information systems)
- Fast response (perishable items)
- e-Commerce to identify buyers and sellers
- Identify and exploit cascade reuse
- Identify and exploit technology diffusion differences

Table 8: Key Factors to Consumer Electronics

Product acquisition is very difficult for this form of closed-loop supply chains. The products are used globally, but the rate of technical diffusion is different in various geographic areas. This requires that a successful operation will have worldwide collection and distribution markets, and these markets will not be in the same geographic areas. Supply and demand rates and prices are extremely volatile. The products are also perishable items since the value of a remanufactured item may drop daily because of the rapid rate of technological progress and the rate of technology diffusion. There are also multiple options for reuse since products may be sold in graded as-is condition or remanufactured. Each option has a different selling price, which is quite dynamic.

However, there are several of the major processes that may be characterized as easy to intermediate. The nature of the products, with very few mechanical parts, makes them simple to test, sort and grade and remanufacture/recondition. The reverse logistics processes are somewhat hard to coordinate since there are so many national borders with customs regulations to manage. However, the handsets are small and light and may be shipped in bulk with commercial air carriers for an inexpensive price (approximately $0.50 as of the summer of 2000). The distribution and selling processes involve a number of different nations, and require knowledge of the cellular technology in use and who are the airtime providers. The selling process is, for reasons discussed previously, tightly intertwined with the acquisition process.

11. Conclusions

Table 9 shows the distinctions between closed-loop supply chains and offers some insights into why some closed-loop supply chains are economically attractive. If crucial subprocesses are difficult to plan, control, and manage, the processes may not be able to generate sufficient returns. The table also clearly shows what processes require close attention by managers and should be addressed in future research.

	Product Acquisition	Reverse Logistics	Test Sort Grade	Recondition	Distribution and Selling
Product Life Extension ⇒ **Jet engines**	Easy	Easy	Hard	Hard	Easy
Refillable Containers ⇒ **Toner cartridges**	Easy	Easy	Easy	Easy	Easy
Tire Retreading ⇒ **Commercial**	Easy	Inter mediate	Inter-mediate	Inter-mediate	Easy
Consumer Electronics Reuse ⇒ **Cellular Phones**	Hard	Easy	Easy	Easy	Inter-mediate
Industrial Remanufacturing ⇒ **Copiers**	Inter-mediate	Inter-mediate	Hard	Hard	Hard
Tire Retreading ⇒ **Passenger**	Easy	Hard	Inter-mediate	Inter-mediate	Hard

Table 9: Key Distinctions Between Closed-Loop Supply Chains

Product life extension and industrial remanufacturing both share high degrees of difficulty in testing, sorting, grading, and reconditioning processes. The important differences in these two types of closed-loop supply chains are that the product acquisition and distribution and selling subprocess are more difficult in closed-loop supply chains for industrial remanufacturing. Industrial remanufacturing is perhaps the best-documented closed-loop supply chain. It is somewhat surprising to find all of the processes classified as intermediate or hard. The high amount of recoverable value in industrial products may help explain why firms will allocate higher amounts of resources to make the processes manageable.

All of the activities required for closed-loop supply chains for container reuse may be classified as easy. This form of closed-loop supply chain is controlled by OEMs and it may be that these managerial activities, due to the lower uncertainty in the processes, are more similar to traditional supply chains. The value remaining in the products is much lower than for products typically in industrial remanufacturing systems, but the volumes of refillable containers numbers in the millions of units.

The difficulties of product acquisition and distribution and selling of reused consumer goods make consumer electronics reuse less attractive. There are profits to be made in consumer electronics, but the processes require more sophisticated planning and control mechanisms. There are higher amounts of value to be recovered from the individual units and the volumes available for reuse are very large.

The difference between the successful development of closed-loop supply chains for commercial tire retreading and the unsuccessful development of profitable passenger tire retreading is distributing and selling. Both commercial and passenger tire retreading have large volumes of used products potentially available, but the more expensive reverse logistics processes for passenger tire retreading further reduces the slim profit margins available.

There are a number of closed-loop supply chains operating profitably, and there are common processes required. The relative difficulty of planning and controlling these subprocesses provides insights as to the potential profitability of the particular closed-loop supply chain. We expect future research to provide frameworks for each of the processes to show the crucial activities and decision support systems to be developed that allow for the processes to be managed more effectively.

References

Guide, V.D.R., Jr. (2000). Production planning and control for remanufacturing: Industry practice and research needs. *Journal of Operations Management*, **18**, 467–483.

Guide, V.D.R., Jr. and L. N. Van Wassenhove (2001). Managing product returns for remanufacturing. *Production and Operations Management*, forthcoming.

Kodak (1999). *1999 Corporate Environmental Report*, Rochester NY: The Kodak Corporation.

Krikke, H., A. van Harten and P. Schuur (1999). Business case Océ: Reverse logistics network re-design for copiers. *OR Spektrum*, **21**, 381-409.

Thierry, M., M. Salomon, J.A.E.E. van Nunen and L. N. Van Wassenhove (1995). Strategic issues in product recovery management. *California Management Review*, **37**, 114-135.

Toktay, B., L. Wein and S. Zenios (2000). Inventory management of remanufacturable products. *Management Science*, **46**, 1412-1426.

U.S. Central Intelligence Agency (CIA) (2000). *The World Fact Book 2000*, Washington, DC: The United States Central Intelligence Agency.

Xerox, (1999). *1999 Environment, Health and Safety Progress Report*, Webster, NY: The Xerox Corporation.

Contacts:

V. Daniel R. Guide, Jr.
Department of Supply and Information Systems
509C BAB
Smeal College of Business Administration
The Pennsylvania State University
University Park, PA 16802

Email: dguide@psu.edu

Luk N. Van Wassenhove
The Henry Ford Professor of Operations Management
INSEAD
Boulevard de Constance
77305 Fontainebleau Cedex
France

Email: Luk.Van-Wassenhove@insead.edu

Retail Reverse Logistics Practice

Ronald S. Tibben-Lembke and Dale S. Rogers
University of Nevada-Reno, USA

1. Introduction

In this chapter, we will discuss commercial returns or reverse logistics (RL) practice in the U.S. retail market segment. We begin with a definition and an overview of retail reverse logistics, and discussion of important strategic considerations for retail RL. We present findings from a study regarding consumers' attitudes about retailer return policies. Finally, we present a case study of reverse logistics at Kmart Corporation, and its online arm, BlueLight.com.

To summarize the definition from the Council of Logistics Management (CLM), logistics is the process of getting products from the point of origin to the point of consumption. Reverse logistics deals with product flowing in the opposite direction. Drawing on the language of CLM's definition, we will define reverse logistics as:

> *The process of planning, implementing, and controlling the efficient, cost effective flow of raw materials, in-process inventory, finished goods and related information from the point of consumption toward the point of origin for the purpose of recapturing or creating value or proper disposal.*
> (Rogers and Tibben-Lembke, 1999, p. 2)

Material in the reverse flow is flowing toward its origin, but typically may not flow all of the way back to the point of origination, because in many cases, specialized companies can process the returning material more efficiently than the original producers can.

In many European countries, product producers are legally responsible for ensuring that a product and its packaging are recycled, and different specialized systems have been set up in various countries to deal with these flows (Rogers and Tibben-Lembke, 1999, ch. 5). We will restrict our attention to products that are returned in the retail channel.

2. Literature Review

Recently, reverse logistics has received much attention in practitioner magazines (e.g., Jedd, 1999, 2000; Ross, 1998) and in academic papers (e.g., Dowlatshahi, 2000; Fleishmann, et al., 1997) that can have implications for product returns. It is clear that reverse logistics as a field of study is unique enough to undergo specialized research.

The bulk of research in reverse logistics has focused on remanufacturing or recycling products that have reached the end of their useful lives (see Fleischmann et al., 1997 for a review). Guide et al. (2000) and Flapper (1995) consider the differences in supply chain management issues for manufacturing and remanufacturing. Also, much mathematical modeling of closed-loop supply chains has been done. See Fleischmann et al. (2001) for an overview.

Rogers and Tibben-Lembke (2001) look at the ways reverse logistics differs from forward logistics. Carter and Ellram (1998) give an overview of the literature on reverse logistics in the marketing and logistics fields. Thierry et al. (1995), Stock (1992, 1998), Kopicki et al. (1993), and Rogers and Tibben-Lembke (1999, 2001) also look at a variety of important strategic considerations for reverse logistics with implications for product returns. Other issues such as the impact of commercial returns on total cost of ownership and the relationship to the product life cycle have also been studied (Tibben-Lembke, 1998, 2001).

Although case studies have been written in the end-of- product-life decision making, (e.g., Ritchie, et al., 2000; Klausner and Hendrickson, 2000), the reverse logistics flow from retailers has been much less widely studied than other areas of reverse logistics, and will be the focus of this chapter.

3. Structure of Retail Reverse Logistics Flow

Forward and reverse logistics have many important differences in the nature of the supply of product, the demand for it, and the quality of the product itself. In forward logistics, product is ordered and its arrival is scheduled as a function of forecasts and actual demand. Truckload shipments from vendors are sent to distribution centers (DCs) designed to handle large volumes of product. At the DC, the product may be stored before being sent via truckload to stores, or may be directly cross-docked onto other trucks for truckload deliveries to retail stores. In catalog or Internet sales operations, large shipments are received, and the product is stored, and small shipments are sent to individual customers.

As many authors have discussed (e.g., Guide, et al., 2000; Flapper, 1995) the reverse flow of product is much more erratic and difficult to predict. The returns rate for retailers overall has been estimated at 6 percent, with a higher rate for catalog retailers. (Rogers and Tibben-Lembke, 1999). Returns of a product are likely to be seasonal, and may also change over the life cycle of a product. Although firms may make predictions about likely return rates based on past experience, it is the end customer that ultimately determines the timing of the return.

When product is returned to a retail location, it may be resold at the store as new, or may be marked down and sold as an "open box" item. The store may also donate the product to a local charity, or send the product to a landfill. However, there are many other possible ultimate destinations for the product: it may be sent back to the vendor, sold via the Internet, sent to an outlet store, or sent to a broker that will sell the product in a different market. As described in detail below in section 4.1, many firms find it beneficial to send returned merchandise headed for these destinations to a centralized returns center (CRC), instead of sending this product back to the DC. Typically, trucks will visit each retail location on a periodic basis, and pick up pallets filled with returned merchandise to take to the CRC.

3.1 Disposition Decisions

Where to send an item that has been returned, or how to "disposition" the item, is one of the most important decisions to be made in retail reverse logistics. As Rogers and Tibben-Lembke (2001) note, a company has a variety of possibilities of where to send product in the reverse flow. A returned product that cannot be sold as new will typically be sold for a fraction of its original cost. Choosing the right disposition option can mean an increase of a number of percentage points, which is a significant percentage increase in revenue, which can make a significant impact on the corporate bottom line. For example, by improving disposition decision making, some large retailers have realized savings of as much as $6 million per $1 billion in retail sales (Jedd, 2000).

45

Table 1 below lists the possibilities roughly in order of decreasing return. Selling the product again as new is the most profitable thing that the retailer could do with the product. Any repackaging and/or refurbishing costs will reduce the profitability of selling the product, both in terms of the cost of the rework, and also because the product may sell at a lower price point because it may no longer be able to be sold as new. Getting a full refund from the supplier will allow the retailer to recover the cost of the item, but not the costs incurred in processing the return. If a full refund is not available, and the product cannot be sold as new, less profitable retail channels, such as outlet stores or Internet sales, should be considered. If the company cannot sell the product itself, it may sell the product to a broker that will sell the product, perhaps overseas. Finally, if the product cannot be sold, the tax and/or public relations benefits of donating the product to charity may be preferred to recycling the product or sending it to a landfill.

Disposition Options

Sell as new
Repackage, sell as new
Return to vendor
Sell via outlet, Internet
Remanufacture / Refurbish
Sell to broker
Donate to charity
Recycle
Landfill

Table 1: Disposition Options

In some cases, the vendor may provide the retailer with a full refund for the product, and rather than instructing the retailer to send the product back to the vendor's facility, the vendor may instruct the retailer to destroy the product, or may allow the vendor to recover some processing costs by selling the product to a broker.

3.2 Customer Return Reasons

Product in the reverse flow has generally either been put into the reverse flow by retail customers, or by retail stores (Rogers and Tibben-Lembke, 2001). We will consider each separately.

Customers may decide to return product for a variety of reasons, including:
1. product didn't work properly (defective),
2. customer changed mind about wanting product,
3. customer could not understand how to properly operate the product,
4. product was recalled, and
5. proper disposal at end of life.

Even when the customer's true reason for returning the product is that the customer has changed his or her mind about wanting the product, or the customer was unable to properly operate the product, the customer may claim that the item was defective in order to return the product. Retailers typically will ask a customer why the customer wants to return an item, and many customers apparently are unwilling to say that they changed their minds, or are too embarrassed to admit that they were unable to properly operate the product (Rogers, 2000). Retailers have different names for these products, but often refer to them as "no fault found" (NFF) items, or "non-defective defectives."

Although product recalls are high-visibility events, in conversations, practitioners report that recalls are a relatively rare occurrence, and represent a very small portion of returned merchandise. However, when products are recalled, the expenses involved can be very significant (Murphy, 1986; Murphy and Poist, 1989).

In many European countries, product take-back at the end of life is mandatory for a wide range of products. However, in the United States, such requirements are very rare (Rogers and Tibben-Lembke, 1999).

3.3 Brick and Mortar vs. Internet Retailers

Catalog retailers have typically had significantly higher returns rates than brick and mortar retailers, with returns rates for clothing catalogs typically around 30 percent. Because Internet retailers may be believed to be more similar to catalog retailers than brick and mortar retailers, Internet retailers as a whole may be expected to have returns rates much closer to the rates for catalog retailers than brick and mortar retailers. However, some studies have shown Internet retailers, as a whole, to have an average return rate of 5.7 percent (Shop.org, 2000).

This finding is somewhat surprising, and in private conversations with the authors, many Internet retailers and returns processors have indicated that they believe this estimate is too low, and that future studies will find higher returns rates for Internet retailers than for brick and mortar retailers.

However, some arguments can be made in favor of lower returns rates for Internet shoppers. Studies have shown that many people use the Internet to research products before buying (Hwang, 2000). Also, many Internet shoppers may be 'multichannel' shoppers, who learn about products online, view products in person at retail stores, and then ultimately purchase products either online, or in person, depending on which is most convenient (Davis, 2000). If Internet shoppers are more educated about the products they are buying than retail shoppers are, it would not be surprising that the Internet shoppers would have lower returns rates. One example of this phenomenon is personal computers. In order for a customer to purchase a computer online, from, for example, Dell, the customer must make a number of technical decisions about the computer, including the amount of memory and hard disk space, and choose between many other options for additional equipment. Making these decisions requires a certain level of sophistication on the part of the customer. This customer is well-informed, and knows what he or she is looking for in the product, and therefore, arguably less likely to suffer from buyer's remorse and want to return the product, or to be unable to operate the product. By contrast, a person buying a computer at a retail location may choose from a relatively small number of pre-configured computers, and may be less knowledgeable, and be more likely to return the product.

3.4 Retailer Returns

Retail stores also have a number of reasons for returning product to their suppliers:
1. stock balancing returns,
2. marketing returns,
3. alleviating credit constraints,
4. end of life or season,
5. transit damage, and
6. 'lifts' or product bought out by competing vendor.

Stock balancing returns occur when one retail location has an excess of a product that may not be selling well there, and another location has a shortage. Bringing the product out of the retail store gives the retailer a chance to redeploy it to a higher-demand location. In theory, the product could be transferred from one retail location to another by direct transshipments, or the product could be sent back to the DC or the CRC. CRCs are set up to receive product coming back from the stores, and a system is in place for transporting the product to the CRC. If the items need to be distributed to other stores, it may be easiest to send them to the DC, where they can be included in regular store deliveries. However, if the destination store is close to the CRC and far from the DC, it may be cheaper to deliver to the store from the CRC. However, CRCs are often not set up to do this type of activity.

Marketing returns are products that did not sell as well as anticipated, either because a product has not sold as well as predicted, or a planned marketing promotion did not have the anticipated success. For example, some of the marketing returns may be specially packaged, seasonal combinations of items, like fragrances and bath powder packaged together in a holiday gift set. If the gift set did not sell, the items will be sent to the CRC. From there they may be sent back to the manufacturer, where the items will be repackaged with a spring theme, or separated and sold as new (Hamilton, 2001).

If a retailer has a large inventory of a product, and wants to buy more of a different product offered by the vendor, and the retailer has maximized its available credit with the vendor, the retailer may return product to the vendor, in order to buy more of another product (Reda, 1998).

End of season returns are products whose selling season has ended (e.g., winter coats and snow blowers). Some items, like snow blowers, may be held at the vendor's DC until the following selling season. Other items, like winter coats, will more likely be sold (through brokers) to retailers in the Southern Hemisphere, to be sold in that climate's coming winter. Also, such items may be purchased by "value" or "discount" retailers, who will hold the items in inventory for a full year, before selling them the following year.

End of life returns are products that have been discontinued and will no longer be sold. See Tibben-Lembke (2001) for a discussion of life cycle issues and retail reverse logistics. Transit damage returns are products that were damaged on the way to the retail location.

Lifts are when one vendor buys all of a retailer's stock of another vendor's product, and has the product removed from the store, in order that the first vendor can sell its products in the store (Ono, 1998).

With the exception of transit damage returns, all of these items are new items that can be resold. The reverse logistics network is a natural way to collect these items for resale.

3.5 Secondary Markets

The secondary market is a term describing the collection of brokers, consolidators, and other companies that buy products that for one reason or another cannot be sold as new. Because companies do not want to emphasize their failures, the secondary markets are a part of the retail world that has traditionally operated with very little visibility to the outside world. Consequently, very little research has been done about secondary markets.

Rogers and Tibben-Lembke (1999) describe seven types of firms that operate in the secondary markets.

Secondary Market Firms

Close-out liquidators
Job-out liquidators
Brokers
Insurance Claim Liquidators
Barter Companies
Gray Markets
Discount Retailers

Table 2: Secondary Market Firms

Close-out liquidators specialize in purchasing products that have reached the end of their sales lives. The product is likely to remain in the United States, and may be sold to discount or value retailers, such as "dollar" type stores. Job-out liquidators purchase seasonal products at the end of the selling season. They will typically negotiate directly with a retailer while the product is still being sold, to buy whatever the retailer has left over at the end of the selling season. This product is likely to be sold to similar retailers as the product purchased by close-out liquidators. Both close-out and job-out liquidators may not take physical possession of the goods, but arrange to buy the product, find a buyer for the product, and have it shipped directly from the retailer to the buyer.

Brokers may buy new product, but they also are the largest buyers of used or damaged products. Unlike close-out and job-out liquidators, brokers typically take possession of the product. Because the product is often returned merchandise, the broker may get very few identical items. Some brokers will buy mixed pallet loads of returns, by the pound. The broker then has to determine exactly what product has been purchased, what condition it is in, and determine where it should be sold. A large amount of the product purchased by brokers is sold overseas.

Insurance claim liquidators purchase product that has been claimed as destroyed for insurance purposes, but which may, in fact, still be in salable condition. Barter companies help companies with excess inventories get rid of unwanted assets and trade them for assets from other companies, without having to write down the value of their assets.

Gray market items are new products that are sold outside of the factory-authorized sales channel. Product can reach the gray market when an authorized reseller needs to raise capital and sells product to a nonauthorized reseller. Gray market items typically do not carry a manufacturer's warranty. Gray market consumers purchase new, genuine product without a warranty. Because the unauthorized resellers purchase the product at prices below the original reseller's cost, they are able to sell at prices lower than retail.

Finally, discount retailers often operate like job-out or close-out liquidators, buying large lots of product from retailers at the end of a selling season, or from a manufacturer, perhaps when large overruns occur. For example, some discount retailers will purchase another retailer's supply of Valentine's Day cards shortly after the holiday. Because the discounter pays much less than the retailer paid, the discounter can afford to keep the items in inventory until the following year's selling period.

When selecting where to sell unwanted product, retailers must consider a number of factors. First and foremost, the retailer must abide by any conditions placed by the manufacturer. Companies have invested large sums of money in developing new products, and they do not want to see the value of that investment in "brand equity" damaged by having their products appear in places that will damage the product image that the companies have worked so hard to create. For that reason, vendors may place restrictions on where the product may be sold, and to whom. Vendors are also concerned that secondary market sales not cannibalize demand from the primary sales channel.

In addition to purchasing unsold merchandise from retailers, job-out and close-out liquidators and discount retailers may also purchase new, unsold product directly from manufacturers. In addition to trusting the secondary market firm, manufacturers may place an importance on finding a single company that will be able to buy and disposition all of the product in one transaction.

4. Strategic Reverse Logistics Decisions

Given the differences between forward and reverse logistics networks, a number of important areas have been identified that help retail reverse logistics operate efficiently and effectively.

4.1 Centralized Return Centers

CRC personnel receive more extensive training about how to disposition returned merchandise than in-store processing returns personnel would typically receive. Also, because CRCs process the returned merchandise for perhaps hundreds of stores, employees at CRCs can gain much greater familiarity with individual products. This allows them to better diagnose what is wrong with the products. If the product has been partially assembled, or comes with any accessories, the personnel will have a better idea of what parts must be looked for, and if any are missing. A prediction must be made about how this will affect the item's value on the secondary market. This knowledge allows them to better diagnose what is wrong with the products, and also better able to determine the best disposition option for each product (Rogers and Tibben-Lembke, 2001), which should increase the return the company is able to realize for the merchandise.

Using a CRC should also reduce the time it takes to disposition an item. CRC personnel have greater experience deciding what to do with a particular type of product, and should be able to classify the quality of the product more quickly. If returns are processed in a retail store, it may be done by personnel who are not devoted to returns processing full-time. Processing returns may often be viewed as a difficult and unpleasant task, and product may not be dispositioned very quickly. Because a CRC is devoted exclusively to processing returns, it avoids this difficulty.

Unlike new product, returned product arrives to a store in very small quantities, with each customer returning a small number of items. If the retailer were to send the product directly to its ultimate destination (vendor, broker, etc.) from the store, the shipments would be sent by small parcel carrier, a much more expensive option than sending full or partial truckloads. Collecting returned merchandise at a CRC before sending it to its ultimate destination significantly reduces the cost of shipping the product. Product typically arrives at a CRC via a truck that has collected one or more pallets of returns from a number of stores. Scheduling the arrivals of these trucks makes worker scheduling easier at the CRCs because the CRC can control the timing of the inbound supply, which it could not do if products arrived via small parcel carriers.

Using the CRC also increases the revenues for the merchandise because the larger volumes of product available at a CRC are more attractive to brokers than the small quantities available at each retail store. Also, brokers do not incur the cost of collecting the products.

Finally, Rogers and Tibben-Lembke (1999) indicate that many practitioners believe that returns should not be processed at a DC. If forward and reverse logistics are in the same facility, there is a danger that forward logistics will be seen as more important, and the resources dedicated to reverse logistics will frequently be commandeered to help the forward logistics function every time an emergency arises.

Because personnel at a CRC are focused on reverse logistics (RL) full time, any products that enter the CRC are dealt with promptly, and sent on to their ultimate destinations. By contrast, when disposition decisions are made at the retail store level, there is the possibility that the unpleasant task of sorting and sending on returns will be only carried out periodically.

Benefits of Using CRCs
Workers gain better knowledge, specialization
Higher prices in secondary market
Faster processing of returns
Lower transportation costs to vendors
Larger volumes increase broker interest
No problem of "serving two masters"

Table 3: Benefits of Using CRCs

4.2 Faster Disposition Cycle Times

As one executive observed, returned merchandise is not like fine wine. It does not get better with age. Letting returned product sit for long periods of time can have several disadvantages. Unlike new product, which arrives at the store in new condition, in identical packaging, returned merchandise may or may not be in the original packaging, and may or may not have been properly put back into the packaging. As returned product sits around waiting to be sorted, it may be stacked up in piles and moved around several times. The longer the product sits around, the more likely it may be to suffer damage. Also, for seasonal products, or products with short product life cycles, the more time that passes, the more the potential value of the product to brokers is likely to decline (Tibben-Lembke, 2001).

In addition to processing the product quickly, companies need to process the customer's refund quickly. For example, if a customer returns an online purchase to a Kmart store, the customer's credit card will be credited the next day. If a customer returns an online purchase to a J.Crew store, the store simply mails the item to a CRC in Virginia, which will then issue a credit (Malone, 2000).

4.3 Gatekeeping

As soon as product enters the reverse stream, it begins to incur costs. In order to keep costs low, "gatekeeping" is the process of preventing product from entering the reverse flow that should not be there. One approach is that product that is destined to be landfilled should be landfilled as early as possible, to avoid unnecessary transportation costs. Kmart uses this strategy, as described below.

Another consideration is to prevent unauthorized returns, or "returns abuse," as it is called by some retailers. Most retailers require a receipt in order to be able to return an item. The receipt proves that the item was purchased at that particular retailer, it indicates the price paid, and it shows how recently the item was purchased. Many retailers have fixed periods (for example 90 days) in which customers are allowed to return items for a refund or an exchange. However, many retailers give returns personnel authority to accept returns even if these conditions are not met. If a customer complains loudly enough and long enough, they may be able to return an item. Other retailers, like Nordstrom, take a different approach, allowing customers to return items with very few questions asked.

Nintendo Corporation faced a particular returns abuse situation when it introduced its new 16-bit system in 1991. Many customers returned 8-bit systems purchased earlier, and exchanged them for new 16-bit systems. The retailers sent the machines back to Nintendo, which incurred tens of millions of dollars in returns costs that year. In 1993, Nintendo implemented a system in which retail sales personnel removed a registration card from the box and mailed it to Nintendo. The card contained the serial number of the unit sold, which allowed Nintendo to learn when a particular unit was sold, and at what chain the unit was sold. Unfortunately, registration never exceeded 75 percent (Hoffman, 1998b).

In 1994 Nintendo implemented a new computerized system in which a bar code bearing the serial number is on the bottom of the unit, and the bar code is visible through the unopened package. At the point of sale, the bar code is scanned in, and the information forwarded to Nintendo. In order to increase compliance, Nintendo pays the retailer 50 cents for every product registered. Now when a unit is returned, Nintendo knows exactly when it was purchased, to know if it was eligible for return or not. The retailer also benefits, because when a customer tries to return an item, the return desk personnel call an 800 number, and can find out when the product was purchased, and if the product was purchased from one of the retailer's stores. This way, the retailer does not issue a refund, only to find out later that Nintendo will not credit it for the item (Rogers and Tibben-Lembke, 1999; Hoffman, 1998b; Reda, 1998).

4.4 Use of the Internet

Retailers can use the Internet in a variety of ways to improve returns processing. As described below, the Kmart Corporation chose to outsource its returns processing to a company called Genco. Genco founded a subsidiary division, eGenco, to focus on opportunities for utilizing the Internet to improve returns processing.

According to Pete Rector, head of eGenco, eGenco believes there are two important ways that the Internet can improve returns processes. First, the Internet can be used to sell returned merchandise, and secondly, the Internet can be used to educate consumers about products and help prevent returns from occurring. When companies sell products to brokers, they often receive a small fraction of the product's original cost. For many consumer products, the price is on the order of one tenth of the product's cost. If the retailer can sell the product via an outlet store, the revenue may be much closer to the product's cost. Many retailers are beginning to use the Internet as a giant outlet store (Rector, 2001).

Instead of offering this product directly from the retailer's Website (and hence risking demand cannibalization), many companies sell this product more quietly through other channels. For example, many companies sell a considerable amount of excess product through online auction sites like eBay, Yahoo! and Amazon. Products sold in such auctions sell for considerably more than would have been received from secondary market firms. There are limits to how much these options can be used, however. If a retailer places a large number of the same item for sale at the same time, the price per unit will fall greatly. When large volumes of product need to be sold, secondary market firms still must be used (Wingfield, 2001).

Preventing returns is another important way for the Internet to help lower returns costs. Most manufacturers now post FAQ (frequently asked question) bulletins on their websites, and allow customers to download product manuals and talk to customer service personnel via email or discussion groups. The more information that the customer can be provided with, the better the chances that the customer will be able to satisfactorily use the product, and will not seek to return it.

If the customer ultimately decides to return the item, many companies allow customers to receive return material authorizations (RMAs) online, print out shipping labels, and track the status of their returned merchandise online. Anything that reduces the customer's need for interaction with an employee should lead to lower costs for the retailer or vendor.

5. Kmart Corporation

The Kmart Corporation is the third-largest retailer in the United States behind Wal-Mart and Sears, with over 2,113 stores in North America. In 2000, Kmart Corporation had over $800 million worth of returns on $40 billion in sales (Winter, 2001). Since 1997, sales have grown from $32 billion to the current $40 billion, but the amount of returns to be processed has not increased, a sign that Kmart's efforts to control returns are working (*Vision*, 1999).

In 1995, Kmart examined costs with merchandise returns and the disposition of outdated and obsolete product, and decided to outsource these functions to Genco (Hoffman, 1998). Before outsourcing returns processing, all returned items would be stored in the back of the store, and an employee would periodically sort through the items and send the items directly to the vendors. The process was time-consuming, expensive, and uneven. It depended heavily on the store employees' knowledge of the many vendors' returns policies and the employees' ability to predict which brokers would pay the highest price for each item.

Genco operates four returns centers, called returned goods centers (RGCs), for Kmart. As an example of the volume handled by these facilities, the Atlanta facility typically processes 30,000 items per day. After Christmas, the volume will increase to 40,000 items per day (Hamilton, 2001).

5.1 Flow of Returned Product

When products are returned to a Kmart store, if the customer has a receipt from the purchase of the product, and the product was purchased within the allowable returns period (90 days), the product is eligible for return. The returns desk personnel will look inside the packaging to verify that all accessories are present and that the product is in new condition. If all is in order, the return is accepted, and the customer's payment is refunded, or the customer's credit card is credited. As described in detail below, Kmart stores also accept returns for BlueLight.com, Kmart's online retail arm.

The item is scanned into the computer system so the returns processing center will know what items will be arriving. A paper note is attached to the product, indicating what is wrong with it, and the product is put in a tote. The totes are carried back to the store's returns processing area. There, products are sorted according to the reason they were returned. Depending on Kmart's agreement with the vendor, the product will either be destroyed on site, or sent to the RGC. If there is a high likelihood that the item will be landfilled at the RGC, the item will be thrown away at the store to save the costs of sending it to the RGC.

If the product is to go to the RGC and is not in its original packaging, its UPC (universal product code) must be found from corporate databases, or from looking at similar products on store shelves. The collected merchandise is palletized and sent by truck to the RGCs at regular intervals, generally every one or two weeks. Because stores do not have scales to weigh the pallets of outgoing material, the pallets are weighed when they arrive at the RGC, and transportation costs are based on weight (Bearth, 1999).

In addition to processing customer returns, the RGCs are also used to process leftover inventory (marketing returns, stock balancing returns, etc.). Roughly 85 percent of the items flowing into an RGC are customer returns, and the rest is new product sent back by the store (Hamilton, 2001). Although customer returns have not increased for Kmart in recent years, the company has made increasing use of the RGCs as a means to rotate product out of the store, to keep the merchandise "fresh" (Winter, 2001).

From Kmart's information system, the RGC knows what products should be arriving from each store. When the merchandise arrives, each product is scanned to verify that it matches the data provided by the store. The condition of each item is assessed, and a database is consulted to determine whether a refund is available from the vendor, and where and how Kmart may sell the product. Given these parameters, software finds the disposition option that will maximize return on the item (Hoffman, 1998; Davis, 1997).

5.2 Dispositioning

There are many possible disposition options for a product. Products can be sold as new, sold "as is" to brokers, remanufactured or refurbished and resold, while other products may be disassembled for components, and materials may be recycled or landfilled. In deciding about reconditioning a product, Genco carefully considers how much it will cost to recondition the product, (based on the cost of reconditioning items in the past), and the likely increase in value for the reconditioned item, given current market conditions.

For example, when gifts are returned after the Christmas sales season, roughly 65 percent of the items that arrive at the Atlanta RGC will be returned to the vendors, and 20 percent will be sold on the secondary market. Nonperishable food items will be donated to charity (Hamilton, 2001).

Kmart also uses Genco's Value Inspection Process (VIP), in which electronic products are tested at the RGC, to see if products labeled "defective" are truly defective. If not, the product will be worth considerably more in the secondary market. If it is defective, the item may be disposed of immediately, depending on the value of the item, and the cost of the necessary repairs (Reda, 1998).

If the product is going to be resold, the vendor may require that the brand name be removed from the product. This helps protect the vendor's brand name, and prevents people from buying a product on the secondary market and returning it for a full price refund at a Kmart store (called a "re-return"). To remove the brand logos, special machinery is used to "demark" products, and price tags are instantly removed with electric sanding machines (Ono, 1998).

5.3 Benefits of Outsourcing

Many benefits of using centralized returns centers have been described above. In theory, the benefits of using a CRC can be gained by performing the CRC activities in-house, using the retailer's own personnel. However, Kmart has chosen to outsource this function to Genco. By outsourcing returns processing, Kmart says it has received several benefits:

- reduced costs,
- higher revenues when selling product on the secondary market,
- greater employee productivity,
- better visibility and control of returned inventory,
- ability to reposition inventory economically,
- environmental compliance on product disposal,
- quicker payment (crediting) for returns from vendors, and
- improved vendor relations.

In short, the main reason Kmart has outsourced its reverse logistics is that it saves them money. Genco specializes in returns processing, processing over $6 billion worth of returns every year for Kmart, Target, Sears, 3M, and other companies. Because they specialize in returns processing, they have developed specialized software that helps track and manage returns. They can transport and process returns more cheaply than Kmart could when it processed returns in-house, and they can receive higher prices for Kmart when selling its merchandise on the secondary market (Winter, 2001; *Vision*, 1999).

According to Ed Winter, Director of Return Logistics for Kmart, one of the biggest benefits to Kmart is that salespeople can focus on doing "the job they're hired to do, which is to sell more products" (Winter, 2001). Kmart's returns totaled $800 million a year, but according to Winter, "This is not a huge amount to our logistics group, so we are not going to spend much time on it." Using a third party to process returns allows Kmart employees to "focus on running our business. There are bigger dollars in other areas" (*Vision,* 1999).

Genco's software provides Kmart employees with much better visibility of all returned product than would otherwise be available, if returns were not outsourced. This information allows Kmart's merchandising/buyer groups to know the cost of product returns, which helps them estimate the company's true cost of selling a product. This information has been helpful in negotiations between Kmart and its vendors regarding how much product Kmart will be allowed to return to the vendors, the payment Kmart will receive for those items, and the conditions on those returns.

This data visibility also helps Kmart spot trends and problems in product returns before they escalate. For example, when Kmart began selling bread makers, Genco personnel noticed a high return rate for one particular model. The packaging showed rectangular loaves of bread, but the machine made round loaves. The vendor was notified, and the packaging was changed (Hoffman, 2000). Another RGC noticed unusually high returns rates for dehumidifiers. Kmart contacted the vendor, which sent an engineer to look at the defective units. Studying a number of them, it was discovered that a plastic pan was melting. The problem was fixed through a design change, and the returns rate fell dramatically (Rogers and Tibben-Lembke, 1999).

As described, Kmart also uses its RGCs to move products from one store to another. If gloves are not selling one place, they can be repositioned through the returns center. The visibility allowed by the system lets Kmart see how much product arrives at each RGC. If Kmart did not have a low-cost way of pulling those products out of the stores and consolidating them, Kmart would not be able to reposition this inventory.

Because much of the product disposal is done at the RGCs, all products with environmental or hazardous materials considerations can be safely disposed of by specialists following all relevant legal restrictions. Rather than expecting personnel at all 2,113 stores to remain current on the proper way to dispose of beauty products, fragrances, household chemicals, and pest control products, the disposal can be performed centrally at the RGCs.

When Kmart recovers the cost of an item from the vendor, the payment is in the form of a "chargeback," or a "deduction," where Kmart reduces the size of a payment by the value of the returned goods. Dealing with these can be a difficult and time-consuming job. Kmart has a group of individuals who work on these full time. Using Genco's software, the data available for this task has become more thorough and more readily available, which makes their work easier (*Vision,* 1999).

6. BlueLight.com History

Between 1998 and 2000, Kmart made two attempts to create a retail Website at Kmart.com (Bott, 2000). Survey research found that only 10 percent of Kmart customers had been to the Website (Davis, 2001). Clearly, offline shoppers were not shopping at the Website. The company decided to pursue aggressively a "bricks and clicks" strategy, trying to coordinate its online and offline retail arms, referring to their efforts as "sticky bricks." To overcome any negative associations with their previous efforts, the company decided to draw on the well-known symbol of its "blue light specials" for the name of its new online offering, BlueLight.com.

Following the lead of many other brick and mortar retailers like Nordstrom and Wal-Mart, Kmart decided to spin their web operations off into a completely separate operation. BlueLight.com was 60 percent owned by Kmart, with Softbank Venture Capital being the other co-founder, and key vendor Martha Stewart Living Omnimedia being the other major investor, with 5 percent (Landy, 2000).

The company was located in the San Francisco Bay area, to make it easier to hire talented professionals already living in the area. It also followed the dot-com practice of enticing workers with stock options, the separateness of the company making a big IPO payout more likely (Bott, 2000). Unfortunately, following the crash of the NASDAQ, the hopes of a big payout from a BlueLight IPO faded. In June 2001, Dave Karraker, Vice President of Corporate Communications at BlueLight.com said "No IPOs will be happening anytime soon" (Davis 2001).

Kmart wanted to attract people to the Website by offering free, unlimited Internet access, in part because of a belief that many of their store customers were not using the Internet, but that if Kmart could help enable them to use the Internet, they would shop with Kmart online. The free Internet access was very successful, making Kmart one of the fastest growing Internet service providers (ISPs) in the country (Bott, 2000). The free ISP service proved to be expensive, and restrictions were put in place on the free service before it was dropped altogether in July 2001, for a fee-based service (*Denver Post,* 2001).

Although there seemed to be important reasons for BlueLight.com being separate, shoppers prefer multichannel retailers. An important mission of BlueLight.com now is to drive online shoppers into Kmart stores (Davis, 2001), and to sell items to customers while they are in the physical stores. As of January 2001, Kmart had placed 3,500 Internet kiosks in 1,100 stores (eRetailNews, 2001). Shoppers can use the kiosks to buy anything on the BlueLight.com Website, but the kiosks are expected to be especially important for items that are not in-stock in the store, for ordering gifts, or for ordering large, hard-to-carry items, such as big-screen televisions, which can be shipped directly to the customer's house.

BlueLight.com would not remain separate for long. In June 2001, Kmart announced that BlueLight.com would start relying more on Kmart for merchandising, marketing and procurement functions (Wagner, 2001a). Several other companies, including NBCi, Disney, and Staples have moved their Web spinoffs inside the parent company, recognizing that Internet sales, rather than being a new core business, are another channel of distribution for their core businesses (InfoWorld, 2001). In June 2001, one analyst predicted that "a few years from now we won't see any stand-alone dot-com units of brick-and-mortar merchants" (Wagner, 2001b). In July 2001, Kmart bought out its investment partners for an undisclosed sum (Sanchanta, 2001), absorbing BlueLight.com fully into Kmart.

7. BlueLight.com Fulfillment and Returns

Because of the great difficulties of using a retail distribution center (DC) for fulfilling Web orders, BlueLight.com decided not to try to use Kmart's existing network of DCs to fulfill Web orders. Rather than building its own fulfillment centers, BlueLight.com chose to drop-ship many orders directly from the vendors, or by third-party distributors (Bott, 2000; Merritt, 2001). BlueLight.com also chose SubmitOrder.com to run its fulfillment operations for items not drop-shipped, and acquired an equity stake in the company (InternetNews.com, 2000). SubmitOrder.com managed fulfillment and mail-in return services from fulfillment centers in Columbus, Ohio and Memphis (InternetNews.com, 2000; James, 2001).

Kmart has since ended its relationship with SubmitOrder, and has hired Global Sports Inc., the largest operator of online sporting goods stores, to manage some of its electronic commerce services (*New York Times,* 2001). BlueLight.com returns are also now completely handled by Kmart's existing returns processing network (Winter, 2001).

BlueLight.com had 250,000 items for sale on its Website in time for the holiday shopping season of 2000 (Sullivan, 2000). Compared to the roughly 1,000 items carried by Kmart.com in 1999, this was a tremendous increase (Sullivan 2000). This is more than double the approximately 100,000 items carried by a typical physical store (Kiosk, 2001). To avoid customer complaints about out-of-stock merchandise, as soon as an item is sold out, it is removed from the Website (Bott, 2000).

One of customers' biggest complaints about shopping online is the difficulty of returning items (Rogers, 2000). A Jupiter Media Matrix study found that 42 percent of online shoppers said they would buy more on the Internet if the returns process were easier (Rosen, 2001). Many customers prefer to return items directly to a retail store, instead of mailing the item back to a return center. Returning an item directly to a retail store allows a customer to receive a refund or a credit immediately. Returns are accepted at retail stores even for items not carried by the physical stores (Smith, 2000). If the item is carried at the retail store, the customer will be able to receive a replacement without having to wait for the replacement to arrive.

According to BlueLight.com, 85 percent of Americans live within six miles of a Kmart store (VanScoy, 2000). Having stores close to so much of the population should make it convenient for consumers to return items. The convenience of returning items to brick-and-mortar stores should therefore help online shoppers buy more items.

Returning online purchases to brick-and-mortar stores should also help Kmart in another way. When customers go to the store to return items, they may also decide to buy some additional items, especially when the customers are exchanging items, and need to go into the store to retrieve the replacement item.

When a customer returns an item at a store, the retail store's service personnel use a Web-based interface that lets them connect into the Oracle Financials application that manages orders for BlueLight.com (Smith, 2000). This lets store employees check on the status of the Web order, as well as access data about returns (Frook, 1998). Although customers can return online purchases at retail stores, the online and retail operations maintain separate databases on returns, because from a corporate point of view, the merchandise is owned by BlueLight.com, not by the retail store. Once a day, data on returns is batch processed and entered into the order-management system. Then, returns data is matched up against original sales data, and credits or checks are sent to online customers who returned items to the store (online customers cannot receive cash back for returning items to stores) (Rosen, 2001).

Despite the claims by some e-tailers that customers don't really mind returning items by mail, customers are returning items to stores instead of by mail by a ratio of about three to one (Rosen, 2001). When customers do want to return items by mail, they are mailed to a central returns processing facility and processed by the Kmart returns facilities (Hamilton, 2001).

8. Future Research

Managing returns quickly and efficiently is an important concern for any retailer, whether in the physical world, or on the Internet. This chapter has shown some of the methods used by a number of retailers and manufacturers. Although companies have made many discoveries about how to manage returns well through trial and error, there are ways that theoretical research may make a contribution to improving retail reverse logistics.

Unfortunately, one of the biggest hurdles to implementing theoretical results is that reverse logistics has long been a low priority for many companies. As a result, reverse logistics processes have not been measured and tracked nearly as well as production and forward distribution processes. Therefore, many companies are not yet ready to think in terms of making optimal decisions, because they are not even sure of what options may exist, much less how much those options would cost.

Disposition decision making is an area where companies could be helped considerably. How can companies maximize their income from secondary market sales? Again, optimization is difficult because the prices that a broker will pay at any time are a function of the broker's perception of demand for the product, the product's stage in the life cycle, and most importantly, the supply of the product. Gaining the information about how much the broker would pay is not without cost. If a broker is repeatedly asked for quotes for product, but is rarely given the business, the broker will lose interest in making bids. What strategies should companies follow to maximize revenues in the face of this uncertainty?

Some of the research needed in this area is aligned with marketing: how much risk of demand cannibalization exists? How can revenue be maximized, while minimizing this risk?

When selling product through Internet auctions, the prices received will obviously be a function of the supply. How many products should be offered how often? What times of day should be chosen for ending auctions? (Some times are better than others.) If a lot of product is to be sold, some must be sold (at a lower price) to brokers. Depending on how quickly the company wants its revenue, how much should be sold to brokers, and how much should be sold online? Some products sell better in different auction sites. What strategies should companies follow to maximize the total return from these sales?

Rogers (2000) has begun an interesting area of research, studying how consumers perceive returns policies, and how these policies affect their behavior. In general, vendors would like retailers to accept fewer products for return (to keep the vendors' costs low), and retailers would like to accept more returns, to keep the customers happy. Both retailers and manufacturers would like to better understand how these policies affect consumer behavior, to develop better policies that keep customers satisfied, but help reduce the cost of processing returns.

Finally, both manufacturers and retailers alike are always looking for better ways to keep customers from wanting to return an item. A customer that returned an item is a customer that was not happy with the performance of a product. Anything a company can do to prevent or reduce that customer's frustration will have benefits in the immediate term, and potentially, far into the future.

References

Bearth, D.P. (1999). Shifting logistics into reverse. *Transport Topics*. (January 18) 1, 10-12.

Bott, J. (2000). Kmart with a kick: Its BlueLight.com rockets to no. 1: free internet service gives it an edge on rivals. *Detroit Free Press*. (August 21).

Bowman, R.J. (2001). E-tail distribution: making it a two-way street. *Global Logistics & Supply Chain Strategies*. (February).

Carter, C.R. and L.M. Ellram (1998). Reverse logistics: a review of the literature and framework for future investigation. *J. Business Logistics,* 19(1), 85-102.

Davis, G. (1997). The best return-reverse logistics management is fast becoming a competitive necessity. *Consumer Electronics.* (September).

Davis, J. (2000). Catalog Distribution may signal e-tailers are getting with the program. *InfoWorld.* (November 13) 114.

Davis, J. (2001). BlueLight special lesson: Kmart's unsuccessful spin-off, BlueLight.com, taught the retail giant an important lesson about b-to-c commerce. *Infoworld.* (June 6) 48.

Denver Post (2001). Bluelight.com cuts free service. (July 31). C-02.

Dowlatshahi, S. (2000). Developing a theory of reverse logistics. *Interfaces,* 30(3), 143-155.

eRetailNews.com (2001). NewsSnippet: BlueLight.com and Kmart complete phase one of country's largest in-store internet shopping kiosk program, retrieved June 7, 2001.

Flapper, S.D.P. (1995). On the operational logistic aspects of reuse. *Proceedings, Second International Symposium on Logistics.*

Fleischmann, M., J. Bloemhof-Ruwaard, R. Dekker, E. van der Laan, J.A.E.E. van Nunen, L.N. Van Wassenhove (1997). Quantitative models for reverse logistics: a review. *European J. Oper. Res.,* 103(1), 1-17.

Fleischann, M., H.R. Krikke, R. Dekker, S.D.P. Flapper (2000). A characterization of logistics networks for product recovery. *Omega,* 28(6), 653-666.

Frook, J.E. (1998). Kmart: A blue light web site. *InternetWeek.* (December 14).

Guide, V.D.R. Jr., V. Jayaraman, R. Srivastava, W.C. Benton (2000). Supply-chain management for recoverable manufacturing systems. *Interfaces,* 30(3), 125-142.

Hamilton, M.M. (2001). A firm that wants what no one else did; Genco reroutes, recycles returned gifts. *Washington Post.* (January 6) E1.

Hoffman, K. (1998). Kmart smooths the kinks from snarled reverse pipeline. *Global Logistics and Supply Chain Strategies Magazine.* (November 1998).

Hoffman, K. (1998). Nintendo reins in returns. *Global Logistics and Supply Chain Strategies Magazine.* (November 1998).

Hwang, S.L. (2000). Revamping the model: clicks and bricks. *Wall Street Journal.* (April 17) R8.

InfoWorld (2001). BlueLight.com cuts back. (June 4) 35.

InternetNews.com (2000). "BlueLight.com Selects SubmitOrder.com for Fulfillment," April 11.

James, S. (2001). Indepth distribution & logistics: specialized systems designed to deliver. *Memphis Business Journal,* (January 5).

Jedd, M. (2000). Returns happen: reverse logistics online. *Inbound Logistics,* (February) 22-28.

Kiosk Magazine (2001). BlueLight.com and Kmart launch largest in-store internet shopping kiosk program in U.S. history, (January).

Klausner, M. and C.T. Hendrickson (2000). Reverse-logistics strategy for product take-back. *Interfaces.* 30 (3) 156-165.

Kopicki, R., M.J. Berg, L. Legg, V. Dasappa and C. Maggioni (1993). *Reuse and Recycling—Reverse Logistics Opportunities.* Council of Logistics Management, Oak Brook, IL.

Landy, H. (2000). Kmart venture buys part of packer, shipper. *Detroit News.* (April 4).

Malone, H. (2000). Check Out Return Policies Before Buying. *Charlotte Observer.* (December 3).

Merritt, K. (2001). BlueLight.com is green to go. *Frontline Solutions.* (August) 50.

Murphy, P.R. (1986). A preliminary study of transportation and warehousing aspects of reverse distribution. *Transportation Journal.* 35 (4) 12-21.

Murphy, P.R., R.P. Poist (1989). Management of logistical retromovements: an empirical analysis of literature suggestions. *Transportation Research Forum.* 177-84.

New York Times (2001). Business/Financial Desk. (August 22) C4.

Ono, Y. (1998). Inventory switch: where are the gloves? They were stocklifted by a rival producer. *Wall Street Journal.* (May 15).

Rector, P. (2001). Vice-President, eGenco, Telephone interview. May 25.
Reda, S. (1998), Getting a Handle on Returns. *Stores.* (December).

Ritchie, L., B. Burnes, P. Whittle, and R. Hey (1999). The benefits of reverse logistics: the case of the Manchester Royal Infirmary Pharmacy. *Supply Chain Management: An Internat. J.* 5 (5) 226-331.

Rogers, D. (2000). Return policies from the consumers' point of view. Reverse Logistics Conference, Lake Tahoe, CA. (September 14).

Rogers, D. and R.S. Tibben-Lembke (1999). *Going Backwards: Reverse Logistics Trends and Practice.* Reverse Logistics Executive Council, Pittsburgh, PA.

Rogers, D. and R.S. Tibben-Lembke (2001). An examination of reverse logistics practices. To appear *J. of Business Logistics*.

Rosen, C. (2000). Federal Express shifts gears. *InformationWeek*. (November 13) 225.

Rosen, C. (2001). Ready for returns? *InformationWeek*. (January 8).

Ross, J.R. (1998). Returns gatekeeping seen as key to efficient reverse logistics. *Stores*. (February) 49-50.

Sanchanta, M. (2001). Kmart blames loss on charges. *The Financial Times (London)*. (August 24) 22.

Shop.Org (2000). The state of online retailing 3.0. (April).

Stock, J.R. (1992). *Reverse Logistics* (white paper), Council of Logistics Management, Oak Brook, IL.

Stock, J.R. (1998). *Development and implementation of reverse logistics programs,* Council of Logistics Management, Oak Brook, IL.

Ruda, M. (2001). Four lease deals wrapped up in Bensenville industrial park. *GlobeSt.com*. (March 8).

Smith, T. (2000). Kmart's plan to light up the web: upgrades bode well for renewed online effort. *InternetWeek*. (July 17).

Sullivan, B. (2000). Brick-and-mortars, brand names boost '00 online sales. ComputerWorld. (Dec. 26).

Thierry, M. M. Salomon, J. van Nunen, and L. Van Wassenhove (1995). Strategic issues in product recovery management. *California Management Review*. 37 (6) 114-135.

Tibben-Lembke, R.S. (1998). Reverse logistics and total cost of ownership. *J. Marketing Theory and Practice*. (Winter).

Tibben-Lembke, R.S. (2001). Life after death: reverse logistics and the product life cycle. Working Paper.

Tibben-Lembke, R.S. and D.S. Rogers (2001). Differences between forward and reverse logistics in a retail environment. Working Paper.

VanScoy, K. (2000). New Money Models. *Smart Business*. (July 17).

Vision: Genco Distribution System News (1999). Kmart turns to Genco to lift burden of Returns. (February). reprinted from *Chargeback Solutions Monitor*.

Vision: Genco Distribution System News (2001). Kmart award. 1.
Wagner, J. (2001a). Buyers beware: bluelight.com announces staff layoffs.

internet.com. (May 24) accessed June 20 2001.

Wagner, J. (2001b). BlueLight.com CEO resigns. internet.com. (May 25) accessed June 20, 2001.

Wingfield, N. (2001). Ebay watch: corporate sellers put the online auctioneer on even faster track. Wall Street Journal. (June 1).

Winter, E. (2001). Director of Return Operations, Kmart Corporation. Telephone interviews. June 22, September 2.

Contact:

Ronald S. Tibben-Lembke
Department of Managerial Sciences
College of Business Administration
University of Nevada - Reno
Mail Stop 028
Reno, NV 89557

Email: rtl@unr.edu

Product Recovery Strategies

*Simme Douwe P. Flapper, Technische Universiteit Eindhoven,
The Netherlands*

1. Introduction

During the last decade, many publications describing what companies are doing in the field of product recovery have appeared, including (Kopicki et al., 1993), (Kostecki, 1998) and (Rogers and Tibben-Lembke, 1998). However, it is rarely explained how the underlying strategy has been determined. The aim of this chapter is to provide more insight into the main factors to be taken into account when defining a recovery strategy for a certain group of products during certain periods of time.

In many respects, defining a strategy for product recovery does not differ from defining a strategy for "usual" production, distribution, and service activities. Also, in case of product recovery, supply, processing, and distribution are the three main issues. At first sight, defining a strategy for product recovery seems to have a lot in common with defining a strategy to introduce and include a new product in an existing product assortment. However, there are a number of important detail differences on which this chapter focuses.

The structure of this chapter is as follows. Starting point for the design of a product recovery strategy are the reasons why a company should define such a strategy. These reasons are the topic of Section 2. Although the reasons for having a recovery strategy strongly influence the strategy, usually there are still a number of choices left. To be concrete: having agreed to allow certain types of commercial returns, it still has to be decided how to collect them and what to do with them; or knowing the types of recovered products certain customers are interested in, it still has to be decided which products to collect and how to process them in order to fulfil the demand. In Section 3, attention is paid to the inputs and outputs that might be related to a recovery strategy. Once these inputs and outputs are known, it has to be decided which partners to involve in which activities, and how to ensure that these partners behave as required. These topics are dealt with respectively in Section 4 and Section 5. There are a lot of companies for which product recovery is only one out of a number of activities. For these companies, the product recovery strategy should fit the overall strategy and vice versa. In Section 6 attention is paid to the interaction between the two strategies, where special attention is paid to the consequences for a company's relationships with external partners in non-recovery activities and the internal organisation of the company. Finally, in Section 7, a brief summary of the chapter is given and topics for further research are indicated.

2. Reasons for product recovery

There are a lot of different reasons for defining a product recovery strategy, which in general strongly influence the strategy to be defined. Hereafter, an overview is given, starting with the production of an item and ending with the final disposal of the item.

2.1 Purchase related reasons

Dependence on suppliers
During the last decade, a lot of companies decided to reduce the number of their suppliers. One potential drawback of such a strategy is an increased dependence on these suppliers. Product recovery may limit this dependence. On the one hand, product recovery may result in better contracts with the above-mentioned suppliers. On the other hand, product recovery may act as an extra source when available suppliers are not able to fulfill demand in a timely manner due to capacity limitations.

Only possibility to get items
Sometimes, certain items can only, or can only in an economically viable way, be obtained via product recovery. This holds, for instance, for functional components that are no longer produced, but are still required to fulfill warranty responsibilities.

2.2 Production related reasons

Forced use of used materials in production
In The Netherlands, producers of paper for daily newspapers are legally required to have a certain percentage of fibres from used paper in the paper they produce.

Production scrap
For all kinds of reasons, things may go wrong during production resulting in in-process or finished products that have to be rejected at the production site. Moreover, apart from the materials making up part of the products, there are usually also auxiliary materials and production scrap (e.g., trim losses).

2.3 Distribution related reasons

Wrong deliveries
For all kinds of reasons, products are delivered at the wrong time, in the wrong quantity, or wrongly packed. Many of these products have to be taken back and something has to be done with them.

Distribution scrap
For all kinds of reasons, the storage or transport of products may result in products, distribution items, or package materials that are damaged. Also, something has to be done with these products, distribution items, and package materials.

Sales with a return option
Still, more customers want their suppliers to allow them to make wrong purchase decisions. The number of sales with a take back clause when a product does not satisfy a customer (which among others holds for most sales via Internet), or in the case of obsolete stocks (e.g., related to the introduction of a new product) is rapidly increasing. Recently, companies selling in Germany via Internet only are legally forced to give their customers a certain preset number of days to return the products they ordered.

Returns in the context of warranties or recalls
Once in use, and sometimes before, it turns out that there are or may be problems with products that have (or even have not) been distributed.

Service to customers
Also, without being legally forced, companies may take back packaging, distribution items, undesired parts from maintenance/repair/replacements activities at the customers, as a service (as well as for market protection, a cheap source for pallets, reusable parts, etc.). (See also Rathband and Anderson, 1999). Some companies, including Mercedes-Benz, offer their customers the

possibility to have the engine in their cars replaced by a recovered engine of the same or other type against a relatively low price and a high guarantee (Driesch et al., 1997).

Increased interest in leasing and renting
Still more companies, but also households, no longer buy products, but lease or rent them. At the end of the lease or rent period the lessor has to take back these products.

Legally forced take back and processing
In a growing number of countries, producers and distributors of products are forced to take back their products when they are no longer desired by their owners, and to ensure an environmentally conscious disposal of these products. The same holds for distribution items like crates, bottles, pallets, and the packaging materials used for distributing products.

Take back forced by customers
Customers are also confronted with disposal bans or high disposal costs. Because of this, customers increasingly force their suppliers to take back their products at their end of life, as well as the items that the suppliers use for the distribution of their products. For instance, BASF and DSM are forced by some of their big customers to take back the kegs they use for the distribution of certain chemicals, as well as to take care of an environmentally conscious treatment of these kegs after collection.

2.4 Other reasons

Market protection
By collecting, processing, or distributing products that are disposed of by distributors or users, a company can control what happens to these products. In this way it may prevent others to reuse (parts of) these products. The latter may be undesired: on the one hand, because (parts of) these products may enter the market as a substitute of the products the company is producing or distributing, on the other hand, because others may damage the reputation of the company due to bad recovery practices. The latter notably holds for branded products.

Lower costs
Product recovery may result in lower purchase, production, or distribution costs, as well as in lower disposal costs.

Shorter delivery times

Product recovery may take less time than purchasing or producing new products. This may result in shorter delivery times, as well as lower storage costs.

New markets

There are numerous examples of companies that started to offer recovered products in order to preempt certain market segments. Well-known examples are copier manufacturers and producers of big medical devices.

Green image

In many publications producers and distributors of "new" products mention offering a so-called green image as a reason for product recovery. Companies think that product recovery may attract new customers or retain present customers because of their concern for the natural environment.

Environmental report

In some countries in Europe, companies have to submit to the authorities or their customers a yearly environmental report on their behavior, with respect to the environment, including the behavior of their suppliers.

Disposal bans

There are a growing number of governments and local authorities forbidding the disposal of certain (parts of) products, like the Dutch government did for CFC and glass-made bottles.

Notably, the combination of forced take back (by customers or legislation) and disposal bans or very high disposal costs are an important reason for OEMs and distributors of products to define a recovery strategy.

3. Inputs and outputs

In the foregoing section numerous reasons for defining a product recovery strategy have been mentioned. Some of these reasons also partly or completely define the set of in- and outputs of the recovery process. Usually at least part of the inputs and outputs can be decided on freely, as well as the quantities to be recovered in a certain way.

3.1 Recovery process inputs

The inputs for recovery processes are usually the undesired results of production, distribution, use, and end-of-life activities. They can be subdivided into production-related vs. distribution-related.

Examples of production-related inputs are: production rejects, i.e., products that were not produced according to preset specifications; production scrap, i.e., the materials that are not part of the products produced, but are required for making the production of these products possible; and obsolete stocks of unused materials.

Examples of distribution-related inputs are: defective products, returned in the context of warranties or recalls; wrong deliveries; unused products, returned unsold by dealers due to inventory realignments, as well as commercial returns; leased or rented items, returned at the end of a lease or rent period; distribution items like pallets, bottles, and crates; and used products or obsolete stocks from (in)direct customers or others.

With respect to the inputs of recovery activities that can be decided upon, the following points should be taken into account. In general, more than one input can be used as a starting point for getting a certain output via recovery. This notably applies to functional components or materials that, due to globalisation and standardisation, are contained in different products. In this context it generally is important to distinguish between unused and used copies of products. The configuration and condition of different used copies of the same product may differ, some copies requiring a lot of effort to obtain certain parts or to recover them as a product as a whole, other copies requiring much less effort. Sometimes there exist big differences between different geographical areas and different types of users.

There may also be legal restrictions with respect to the inputs of a recovery process. Sometimes it is not allowed to transport (parts of) used products from one (part of a) country to another (part of the) country. Sometimes some inputs are not allowed because their processing may or can result in undesirable by-products.

How much of each input is collected usually depends on the reasons for having a product recovery strategy in place. For instance, consider a company defining a recovery strategy to fulfill a legal requirement to collect and process a certain minimum percentage of the package materials that the company uses for distributing its products. In case the collected packaging materials cannot be sold with a profit, the company will only collect the minimum quantity required, thereby focusing on customers to whom a lot of packaging materials are sent, in order to keep costs as low as possible.

3.2 Recovery process outputs

In general, products can be reused as a whole, via their functional components or via their building materials. Thereby a distinction should be made between reuse as such, i.e., as a product, functional component or material, or as an energy carrier like wooden pallets that are burned in order to generate heat. Usually complete reuse (reuse as a whole) is limited to products that have not been used and to distribution items like pallets, crates, and containers. In case of assembled products, made up of a number of different parts, often one or a number of functional components have to be replaced in order to fulfil quality requirements, or in order to allow for reuse via upgrading.

Aside from the parts of a product that can be reused by a company or sold with profit to others, product recovery always results in items that are no longer desired but have to be taken care of nonetheless.

Demand and technical possibilities to transform the inputs into the outputs, and costs and benefits, are not the only factors that determine the outputs of product recovery. Legislation also may prescribe which outputs are or are not allowed. Some governments require that certain materials always be removed from products, after which these materials have to be supplied to specific companies, as, for example, holds in The Netherlands for CFCs from refrigerators. Moreover, some governments do not allow the disposal or export of certain (parts of) products.

3.3 Technical aspects

Deciding on the inputs and outputs of a product recovery strategy necessitates insights into the technical possibilities to transform inputs into outputs. This requires the technical specifications of outputs and inputs in terms of configuration and condition, where the configuration describes the elements (functional components, materials), as well as how many of each of these elements a product contains and how these elements are assembled; whereas the condition of a product describes how, how much, and how long a product has been used and how it has been maintained.

Based on the above information, the actual processes for transforming inputs into outputs can be determined. It is outside the scope of this chapter to discuss in detail the different technical processes that might be used for different types of recovery for different types of products. For a discussion of some, see the chapter on design engineering. Below, attention is paid only briefly to two important, often forgotten points.

Disassembly: separation at the source
In many situations it is impossible or very costly to separate certain items, such as holds for glass of different colors. Therefore, in a number of countries, glass is collected via containers with separate compartments for white, green, and brown glass.

Reassembly: limitations on combining used-used / used-new (the "gear-wheel-chain problem")
As an example, consider the problem that occurs when the chain of a bike with gears needs to be replaced. If we would only replace the chain, it would hardly improve riding the bike because due to wear and tear, the new chain and used gear wheel do not fit well. So replacing the chain entails the replacement of the gear-wheel combination as well. This "gear-wheel-chain problem" occurs for many mechanical parts.

Thus far, the products have been assumed to be given. However, it is possible to take into account recovery when designing a product. Even when a company is not interested in engaging in recovery operations itself, this may be worthwhile because it is expected that in the future, buyers of new products will have to pay a fee for the environmentally friendly recovery of the product they buy. This fee may depend on the recovery costs which are influenced by the design of the product.

Depending on the desired (level of) recovery, attention should be paid to
- (re)design for collection (like pallets that can easily be broken down),
- (re)design for disassembly (like pallets that easily be cleaned),
- (re)design for maintenance and repair, and
- (re)design for reassembly.

Companies have to be very careful when designing their products for recovery, especially if they are interested in recovering (some parts of) their products themselves. Making disassembly, repair, and reassembly of their products easier for themselves, often also means the same for others, which might be undesirable.

3.4 Business economical aspects

In the end, business economic considerations determine, within the earlier mentioned set of restrictions, which recovery strategy is chosen.

With respect to costs, a distinction should be made between costs that are directly related to recovery activities (including the price that might have to be paid for an item to be recovered), costs related to the (re)design of products in the context of recovery, and other costs, such as lost sales of new products due to the introduction of recovered products in the market.

With respect to potential benefits, a distinction should be made between benefits directly related to the product recovery process, including lower purchase, production and disposal costs, stocks (which especially holds for the so-called "last series" stock, i.e., the last quantity of a product that is produced or that can be bought before its production or distribution is ended), fees received for the delivery of items for recovery, and indirect benefits, such as sales of new products due to shorter delivery times, or to offering new services like product recovery.

Very important in this context are the remaining technical life (cycle) and the remaining business economical life (cycle) of an item, both from the point of view of the company interested in recovery and from the point of view of the present owner. See also (Geyer and Van Wassenhove, 2000) and (Ferrer, 1997). In general, the business economic life cycle of materials is much longer than that of functional components, which in turn is usually longer than the products they are part of. Related to this, product prices decrease more rapidly than prices for functional components, which in, turn decrease more rapidly than prices for materials. One of the consequences of the above is that the higher the level of reuse, the more important it is that products are returned quickly.

4. Partners

Once the inputs and outputs have been decided upon, the next question is who to involve in the actual product recovery process. Decisions have to be made with respect to the customers for the different flows resulting from the product recovery activities; the suppliers of items for recovery, including collectors; the processors of these items; and the distributors of the different recovered parts, including the undesired parts, i.e., the partners in our product recovery network. Thereby, a distinction should be made between partners outside and inside a company involved in product recovery.

4.1 A common network for product recovery?

With respect to external partners, the first thing a company has to decide is: should we set up our own recovery network or should we collaborate with others?

Examples of companies that have set up their own recovery network for some of their products are Rank Xerox for their copiers (Kostecki, 1998), Mercedes-Benz for many functional components including engines and waterpumps (Driesch et al., 1997), and Kodak for their "single-use" cameras (Kostecki, 1998). The reasons a company decides to have its own product recovery network are essentially the same as for deciding to set up its own network for production and distribution of products in general: no possibilities for sharing resources, to distinguish oneself from competitors, and difficulties in agreeing upon the allocation of costs and benefits related to a common network. The reasons for setting up a product recovery network with others also does not deviate from the arguments used for setting up a shared production or distribution network with others: economics of scale combined with no competition issues related to a combined recovery effort. A somewhat different reason is the increased ability to obtain the support of governments and local authorities, not only to allow the crossing of borders, but also for the introduction of a uniform fee to finance the collection and processing of products at the end of their life.

Among the companies that have decided to set up a network with others are the producers and importers of cars in The Netherlands, who set up a nationwide system for the recycling of car wrecks (Groeneveld and De Hond, 1993). The same holds for the producers and importers of white and brown goods (Dillon, 1994), and the producers and importers of batteries with weights up to one kilogram.

Note that companies may set up different networks for different recovery activities with completely different partners. For instance, for the reasons mentioned above in, The Netherlands, Rank Xerox participates in the Dutch nationwide network for the end-of-life recovery of white and brown goods for their smaller products like printers; Mercedes-Benz participates in the Dutch network for the recovery of car wrecks; and Kodak, Rank Xerox, and Mercedes-Benz participate in the Dutch battery recovery network.

4.2 Outsourcing

Once a company has decided to set up a recovery network, alone or in collaboration with others, the next question to be answered is: which activities should the company or group of companies take care of and which activities should be outsourced, and to whom? With respect to the latter, it does not suffice to mention companies, organisations, and households as is done in most publications dealing with partners in the context of product recovery. The actual partners within these companies, organisations and households (i.e., the people involved in the recovery process within these companies, organisations, and households) have to be defined.

4.2.1 Supply

All flows of items to be recovered start with the last owner or user of the item. With respect to disposal, two extreme types of persons can be distinguished: those who want to get rid of an item as soon as they do not need it anymore (as can been seen at many beaches during summer), and those who are inclined to keep items very long because they wonder whether they might use the item again somewhere in the future. So far, only a few publications on disposal behavior of people have appeared in literature. For an overview, see (Tucker et al., 2000).

In companies, an important group of persons that should be included are environmental officers, whose core business it is to ensure that a company acts in an environmentally conscious way. They may play an important role in stimulating the supply of items for recovery from a company, as well as in stimulating the sales of recovered items.

Purchasers also play a crucial role. Their key task is to realise the timely supply of items required for production, distribution, or service activities at the lowest price. Increasingly, this includes consideration of the costs for disposing packaging materials and containers used for the distribution of these products to the company.

A central question with respect to collection is: should we use a bring or a pickup system, where, in the case of a bring system, the product users return their product at some collection point, whereas in a pickup system, products to be recovered are picked up from the users. See also (Kopicki et al., 1993). Both the bring and the pickup systems present pros and cons for both the disposer and the collector.

In case of a bring system, the present owner or user of an item has to spend time and money to bring it to a collection point; whereas in case the of a pickup system, the owner or user should make pick up of the item possible.

At first sight, pickup systems seem more convenient for the suppliers, especially in the case of big and heavy products. However, pickup systems may be less suited because they may require someone to be present at the moment of collection, because if not, others may collect the products. For instance, some collectors of used cloths no longer visit households, but place containers at points where people can drop their used cloths, day and night, thereby risking that things other than cloths are disposed of in the container, or that the cloths in the container are set on fire.

In practice, often a combined bring-pickup system is used to bring the products to be recovered to the location where they are further processed or disposed. For instance, in The Netherlands, glass from households is disposed in glass containers by the households. The containers are emptied by a company that brings the glass either directly to a glass recycler or to intermediate storage.

Apart from companies specialised in the collection of certain items for recovery, also companies involved in the distribution of new products or companies involved in the collections of other items to be recovered may be involved in the collection. For instance, supermarkets are quite often involved in the initial collection of beer bottles and bottles for softdrinks for which the consumer of the beer or softdrinks pays a deposit fee.

4.2.2 Processing

As far as the actual processing of collected items is concerned, the initial suppliers of these items may take care of some of the sorting and separation activities. For instance, in a number of countries, households are willing and able to assist in sorting and separating glass with different colors and in removing metal or plastic caps from glass bottles.

4.2.3 Distribution

Although there are examples of distribution networks for new products that also are used for the distribution of recovered (parts of) products (e.g., for toner cartridges, copiers, and car engines), there are many examples for which this does not hold. Among the reasons for this are: image and geographically separated markets for new and recovered (parts of) products.

There is no recovery without disposal! Even if a company can completely determine the inputs and outputs of a recovery network, there will be parts that cannot be used. It is essential to have partners who are willing and able to take care of these unusable parts. For instance, in the case of glass bottles that are collected in order to be refilled, there should be contracts with glass recyclers or companies collecting glass to remove bottles that cannot be safely refilled.

4.3 Often forgotten potential partners

We end this section by paying attention to four often forgotten potential partners.

Governments
Governments can be asked to introduce legislation that makes certain types of recovery easier or cheaper to realise. For instance, the Dutch government has forbidden glass to be put in garbage containers, leaving only the disposal via glass containers, which helps glass recycling companies, keeping the costs for the initial collection relatively low. As mentioned before, governments may have to be involved in order to cross borders between countries, and may be required to introduce nationwide fees for financing part of the recovery of products at the end of their useful life.

Municipalities
Municipalities can play a role in collecting, storing, and processing (sorting, separating) parts of products, as they do in The Netherlands for the recovery of end-of-life white and brown goods (Dillon, 1994). See also Lund, 2001.

Competitors "new"
As mentioned before, there are a number of examples in The Netherlands and in other countries, where competitors collaborate in the recovery of the materials in their products. Another area for collaboration may be obsolete stocks. For instance, a number of airlines have set up a Website to inform each other about the possibilities for buying each other's osbolete service parts.

Competitors with respect to used or obsolete unused items
Temporary shortages for one seller may be satisfied temporarily by a supply of another seller, who at that moment, does not need the required items. For instance, Mercedes-Benz sells obsolete parts to brokers and recyclers, and buys parts from them at times as well (Driesch et al., 1997).

5. Tools to stimulate desired behavior of partners

Defining tools to stimulate the desired behavior of partners both outside and inside a company requires insight into the product recovery alternatives for these partners and the costs (time, money, space) and benefits related to each of these alternatives. A well functioning product recovery network requires relevance for all partners, where creating a win-win situation for all might not be enough.

The tools described below can be subdivided into economical and non-economical tools. These tools can be used to plan and control the supply of products to be recovered. They can be used to influence supply quantity, supply configuration, and condition of the items, as well as timing. For each tool, the main pros and cons for both the company using the tool and the potential suppliers of items for recovery are indicated.

5.1 Economical tools to stimulate the timely supply of products for recovery

- *Deposit fee*. This fee may concern the product itself or the item used for its distribution. It has to be paid by the buyer to the seller. The fee is reimbursed when the item is returned according to certain preset requirements, with respect to configuration and condition. Via a deposit fee, a company tries to build a longer-term relation with its customers. Moreover, in case an item sold with a deposit fee gets lost, the company is at least partly compensated for the loss. A disadvantage of a deposit fee is that it makes buying the product somewhat more expensive, and that the items for which a deposit fee has been paid, have to be taken back when they fulfill the preset requirements, even if the company is no longer interested in them. Deposit fees usually have no advantage for the buyer.

- *Buyback option.* At the moment a product is sold, the buyer is offered the possibility to return the product to the seller for a preset price, provided the product fulfills some preset requirements, such as the use of the product, distance driven, or timing of returns. A company interested in the recovery of a product that it sells should be very careful when using this option. From examples in practice, buyers use this option only when they cannot sell their product to someone else for a higher price, which usually means that the original seller will have problems making a profit from recovering the product. The buyback option offers the buyer a guaranteed minimum price.

- *Reduced price "new."* When delivering a used copy of a prodcut fulfilling certain preset specifications, buyers of a new copy of the same or another product get a reduction on the sales price of the latter during certain periods of time. An advantage of this tool is that a company can use it only when necessary and during certain limited periods of time. This tool also stimulates buyers to buy a new product earlier.

- *Fee.* This fee is paid when a person delivers a product for recovery. Usually the fee depends upon the condition and configuration of the product delivered, but sometimes upon timing since this may determine the possibilities to reuse (parts of) it. A company using a fee to attract products for recovery can use this tool only when truly required. An advantage for the buyer is that (s)he does not need to buy a (similar) product from the seller in order to get the fee.

- *Take back with or without costs for supplier.* A person who wants to dispose of a product can do this for free or for a lower price than he would have to pay elsewhere.

- *Gift.* For each product received for recovery, a nonprofit organisation receives an amount of money. Hewlett Packard used this tool in order to collect toner cartridges (McGavis, 1994). It may result in problems, because other organisations may also ask for a gift. Generally, it is very hard for the buyer to find out whether the company that promises to give the gift really does so.

Note the first two, and sometimes also the third economic tools imply a longer and different relation between seller and buyer. In these cases, the relation between seller and buyer changes due to product recovery.

One of the main problems with each of the above tools is how to estimate quickly the configuration and condition of the item supplied. The use of chips, on which data on the use of products are stored, seems to be a step forward. See also the chapter on Design Engineering.

5.2 Noneconomical tools to stimulate the timely supply of products for recovery

- *"New for old."* One can get a new copy of a product only if another copy is returned. An advantage of this tool is that it is simple to use. However, there are also a number of disadvantages related to the use of this tool. First, it should be possible to buy a product without a return the first time. Second, the tool is not suited for situations with seasonal sales, because it is not always possible to buy the same quantity as at the start of the season. On the other hand, products left after a peak in sales cannot be returned before the next peak. If a customer decides not to buy the product again, there is no stimulus to return the products he still has. Less strict applications use registration of the number of copies sold and returned over time.

- *Lease or rent contracts.* Products are not sold, but leased or rented. Usually the configuration and condition of products that are leased are quite well known. Via the duration of the contract, both the moment that the products are returned and their condition can be influenced. Moreover, the user is known, and can be contacted directly, when for some reason, the product in the field must be recovered earlier than originally expected.

- *Easy and simple method of supply.* Some suppliers for toner cartridges, both OEMs and third parties, deliver their cartridge in a box that can be returned for free either by post or by another third-party logistics service provider. The same strategy is followed by some manufacturers of batteries (Yender, 1998).

- *Timely and clear information.* The importance of this tool is illustrated by a pilot system for the collection of different types of batteries in Denmark and Germany, which showed that it was too difficult for consumers to figure out which type of battery they had (Faria de Almeida and Robertson, 1995).

- *Appeal to the environmental consciousness of people.* This tool usually requires a lot of advertising, and is, in general, not very reliable.

- *Legislation.* Disposal bans and high disposal costs may help realise a cheap supply of products for recovery, as discussed earlier for the collection of glass from households in The Netherlands.

The first two noneconomic tools may result in changed relations between producers, distributors, and their customers. This especially holds when companies no longer sell products but lease them. Note that the number of leased products is rapidly increasing (which, among other results, made many car importers in The Netherlands set up their own lease company).

When deciding which tool to use, insights into the alternatives options for all parties involved should be researched. To be concrete: if the only thing a company can do with an item is to dispose of it at high costs at an incineration site, this company should not be paid for supplying this item, but should perhaps be asked to pay for this service.

Using each of the above tools requires that many issues be specified, including the period of time during which a certain tool will be applied, how the configuration and condition of what is supplied can (quickly) be estimated, the height of a fee, and so on. At the moment, only very limited insight into the functioning of many of the above-mentioned tools is available. No mathematical models supporting the decision which tool to use under which conditions are available at this time.

5.3 Performance measurement

In principle, performance measures defined for regular production-distribution situations can also be used to evaluate the functioning of the product recovery network. More specific performance measures include the percentage of products in the field that is collected by the network, and the percentage of reusable products or functional components among the collected products.

A major issue concerns the controllability of collectors and processors. Both may be very hard to control: collectors, with respect to quantity and quality collected, and processors, with respect to the outputs of their processes. For example, if a company involves a third party to take care of collection, without further information from the initial suppliers, it is hardly possible to determine whether or not this partner has removed interesting products and sold them to others. The same applies for processors.

6. Recovery strategy as part of the overall strategy of a company

In the event that product recovery is only one of the activities a company is involved in, which holds for OEMs, distributors and service companies, the product recovery strategy should fit with the overall strategy of the company. Below, attention is paid to the consequences product recovery may have for the relations with present customers, as well as what the consequences may be for the organisation of the company.

6.1 Consequencesfor existing relations with suppliers and customers

Suppliers
Important reasons for considering product recovery are reduced purchase costs, due to less buying, or price reductions, due to the supply of clean production scrap materials. Whereas the latter option might result in a win-win situation for both parties, buying less from existing suppliers may have undesirable consequences for them. It may mean the end of the relationship, result in much higher prices for the product they deliver, or worse delivery conditions.

Customers

Clearly, product recovery strategies, where lessee-lessor relations replace buyer-seller relationships, result in quite different interfaces with customers. This also holds when a company wants to set up a common pool of distribution items with some or all of their customers or suppliers. But also when a company wants its customers to store and return products with a certain configuration and condition in a certain way, and even doing some disassembly like removing metal caps from glass-made bottles.

Another important issue are the consequences of offering recovered products. Part of an existing customer base may no longer buy new products, but, rather, recovered products, or may no longer buy, but lease. Some customers may find it unacceptable that a company is offering recovered products and these customers may be lost.

6.2 Consequences for the company's own organisation

Above, attention was paid to some of the consequences a product recovery strategy may have for the relations between a company and existing external suppliers and customers. Usually product recovery also has consequences for the company's own organisation, especially when product recovery is only one of the activities of the company. For instance, salesmen have to decide which tools to use to stimulate the supply of items the company wants to recover, or may have to define lease contracts, involving new service activities. Designers may have to include issues related to product recovery. Purchasers may have to work on timely supply of recovery items. Production people may have to be involved in sorting, disassembly, repair activities, which quite often differ from what they are used to, not only from a technical point of view, but also from a mental focus point of view. For instance, regular production may require people to be precise, whereas recovery may require people to be fast and cheap.

Truck drivers (as far as belonging to the company) may have to do a first quality check when they collect products for recovery, as in the case of reusable pallets, and register the results. Servicemen may have to take back undesired parts, distribution items and packaging materials, and may have to separate and sort recoverable from nonrecoverable items.

The questions to be answered in this context are similar to the questions that have to be answered when a company wants to extend its product assortment or activities: Should we have a separate business unit for product recovery, or should the different activities and decisions with respect to product recovery be allocated to one or more existing departments? Should we create new functions, or should we allocate the new activities to existing functions?

7. Summary and conclusions

This chapter presented a number of important issues when defining a recovery strategy: the reasons for having a product recovery strategy; the inputs and outputs of the recovery process, including legal, technical, and business economics issues; which partners to choose; and which tools to use to guarantee a well functioning product recovery network. Although the same issues play a role in defining a strategy in general, it was shown that the options and details differ.

A lot of questions remain to be answered, including: Which tool to use and when? What should be the values of the different parameters related to a tool? What are the consequences of a recovery strategy in terms of overall profits? Answering these questions may require new quantitative models.

We hope that this chapter will stimulate research on these and other important issues in the context of defining a product recovery strategy.

References

Dillon, P.S. Salvageability by design. *IEEE Spectrum*, August 1994, 18-21.

Driesch, H.-M., J.E. van Oyen and S.D.P. Flapper. Control of the Daimler-Benz MTR product recovery operation. *Proceedings 3. Magdeburger Logistik-Tagung*, Magdeburg, Germany, 20-21 November 1997, 157-165.

Faria de Almeida, A. and A. Robertson. Domestic Batteries and the Environment: A Life-Cycle Approach to Consumer Electronic Products. *Concept Proceedings International Conference Clean Electronics Products & Technology*, Edinburgh, Scotland, 9-11 October 1995, 162-167.

Ferrer, G. The Economics of Tire Remanufacturing. *Resources, Conservation and Recycling* 19, 1997, 221-225.

Geyer, R. and L.N. van Wassenhove. Component Reuse and the Product Life Cycle. Working Paper, INSEAD, Fontainebleau Cedex, France, 2000.

Groenewegen, P. and F. den Hond. Product waste in the automotive industry: technology and environmental management. *Business Strategy and the Environment* 2(1), Spring 1993, 1-12.

Guide, Jr, V.D.R. and L.N. van Wassenhove. Managing Product Returns for Remanufacturing, *Production and Operations Management* 10(2), 2001, 142-155.

Kopicki, R., M.J. Berg, L. Legg, V. Dasappa. and C. Maggioni. Reuse and Recycling -Reverse Logistics Opportunities. Council of Logistics Management, Oak Brook, IL USA, 1993.

Kostecki, M., ed. *The Durable Use of Consumer Products: New Options for Business and Competition*, Kluwer Academic Publishers, 1998.

Lund, H.F. *The McGraw-Hill Material Recycling Handbook*, McGraw-Hill, 2001.

McGavis, D. The Energy Bucket and a Not-So-Drop-In-The-Bucket Portion of the Waste Stream, Consumables. Proceedings 1994 IEEE International Symposium on Electronics & the Environment, San Francisco, California, May 2-4, 1994, 267-272.

Rathband, P. and R. Anderson. A case study of refurbishment and re-sale of automatic teller machines. *Proceedings 1999 IEEE International Symposium on Electronics and the Environment*, Danvers, MA, USA, May 11-13, 1999, 303-307.

Rogers, D.S. and R. Tibben-Lembke. *Going Backwards: Reverse Logistics Trends and Practices*, Reverse Logistics Executive Council, University of Reno, Center for Logistics Management, 1998.

Tucker, P., D. Speirs and Duncan Smith. The impact of a change in collection frequency on kerbside recycling behavior. *Journal of Environmental Planning and Management* 43(3), 2000, 335-350.

Yender, G.L. Battery recycling technology & collection processes. *Proceedings 1998 IEEE International Symposium on Electronics and the Environment*, Oak Brook, IL, USA, May 4-6, 1998, 30-35.

Contact:

Simme Douwe P. Flapper
Faculty of Technology Management
Technische Universiteit Eindhoven
BDK, Paviljoen
P.O. Box 513
5600 MB Eindhoven
The Netherlands

Email: s.d.p.flapper@tm.tue.nl

Contracting and Coordination in Closed-loop Supply Chains

Charles J. Corbett, University of California at Los Angeles, USA
R. Canan Savaskan, Northwestern University, USA

1. Introduction

"Coordination" has become a key concept in much of the modern literature on supply-chain management. The notion of a "supply chain" inherently involves multiple independent decision makers. These decision makers can be a single company's geographically dispersed warehouse managers; a company's different departmental managers; or different firms, vertically aligned to form a supply chain or competing horizontally, each within their own respective supply chain. In such a context of decentralized and independent decision making, outcomes will rarely be "optimal" for the entire supply chain unless there is some degree of coordination between the decision makers' actions. In general, the starting point for much of what happens in supply chain management, whether in academia or in practice, is the objective of achieving greater coordination between parties. This can be done in several ways, including formal contracts or informal mechanisms to realign incentives or to encourage more information sharing, or by changing the physical or economic nature of the product or the system.

It is also clear, though, that there are many reasons why such coordination may be difficult or impossible to implement. Parties may have fundamentally conflicting incentives, or no party may be large or powerful enough to impose a coordinated outcome, and some parties may hold private information that they are unwilling to share but that could help others make better decisions. Many such problems have recently been studied for unidirectional or "forward" supply chains, and several general lessons about design and operation of such supply chains can be drawn.

With the recent emergence of product take-back laws in Europe and the ever-increasing tendency of customers worldwide to return products for whatever reason, many supply chains are becoming inherently bidirectional. Ideally, many (though not all) of these returns can be fed into a supply chain again, either back into the original supply chain from which they originated (such as when products are reused or remanufactured), or into another supply chain (such as when they are recycled to a lower-grade product). The ideal notion often espoused by some is that of a "closed-loop supply chain." Though clearly some chains are not and will never be truly "closed-loop," we will use that terminology to refer to any supply chain that encompasses flows of products that have been surrendered by the original customer.

The presence of such additional flows, whether they feed back into the original supply chain or are recycled or disposed of separately, further complicates the already tough challenge of achieving coordination in supply chains. In this chapter, we review what is known about coordination and contracting in forward supply chains, extrapolate these learnings to managing reverse flows, and then examine how these lessons may be affected by the presence of reverse flows. Our objective is obviously not to provide a full review of the supply-chain management literature (for that, see Tayur, Ganeshan, and Magazine, 1999), but rather to examine the ways in which forward and reverse flows interact.

In this chapter, we first identify several key reasons why closed-loop supply chains are emerging worldwide, as these will directly affect the coordination challenges faced and remedies available. Then we review various aspects of supply chains that could, in principle, be coordinated upon. After that, we review existing literature on (forward or unidirectional) supply chains to see what can be learned about designing and managing such supply chains. In each case, we extrapolate these lessons to reverse flows, and also examine how these lessons change in the presence of a reverse supply chain.

2. Many reasons to think about Reverse Logistics

Supply chains come in many shapes and sizes, each with their own specific requirements. A company's *supply chain strategy* defines the set of customer needs that it seeks to satisfy through its products and services. By ranking the customer's top priorities with respect to product price, quality, variety, and time to market, a company defines its strategic position relative to the competitors. For example, Walmart's supply chain operations emphasize low cost and high variety in the grocery business, while Dell aims to provide high product customization and responsiveness to its customers at reasonable prices. For any company to be successful, there needs to be consistency between the customer's priorities which the firm chooses to emphasize, on the one hand, and the type of capabilities designed into a product/service supply chain and its operating principles, on the other. In other words, there should be a *strategic fit* between what the supply chain operations are designed to be good at and how the firm wants to compete with its products in the market (Porter, 1996). In this respect, decisions regarding the design and the operating principles of reverse logistics channels should also be coordinated with the existing capabilities of forward supply chain structures.

The concept of *strategic fit* can be formulated in a general framework, which links the reverse logistics channel decisions to the overall business plan of a company and to existing forward supply chain capabilities. The linkage can be established based on the answers to the following three sets of questions:

- What is the firm's desired strategic positioning for its reverse logistics operations?
- Given the positioning of the reverse logistics operations, what capabilities are required from reverse logistics processes in terms of cost, flexibility, quality, and time? Do the present capabilities in the forward supply process complement the desired capabilities from reverse logistics operations?
- Given the positioning of the forward supply chain and its present capabilities and the desired capabilities from reverse logistics processes, how should the reverse supply chain be structured, and the product and pricing decisions in the reverse flows be coordinated with the forward supply system?

The current practice shows that a company can use its reverse logistics capabilities to increase its cost efficiency in manufacturing and in supplying products to the market, and also to enhance the value of its product to customers. We use these two dimensions to classify different types of product returns as they relate to the overall supply chain strategy of the firm. The extent of interaction between decisions on the forward and the reverse logistics channels highlights areas where coordination challenges may arise.

Reverse logistics capabilities can lead to more cost-efficient operations either by reducing the life cycle costs of a product or by providing a means to make better decisions on the forward supply chains. Here are some examples of how reverse logistics can reduce costs. Table 1 summarizes the cost and value implications of reverse logistics activities and highlights areas for better supply chain integration. Below, a detailed discussion of each type of reverse logistics activity is given.

	Types of Reverse Logistics Activities	Decisions Involved
COST REDUCTION	•Environmental Product Take-Back •Buybacks for Short Life Cycle Products	•Capacity Choice •Product Pricing •Information Sharing •Product Introduction Timing
PRODUCT VALUE CREATION	•Return Allowances •Trade-In Offers •Warrenty Claims	•Used-Product Pricing •Information Acquisition and Sharing •Quality Choice

Table 1: Supply Chain Implications of Reverse Logistics Activities

2.1 Environmental Product Returns

Political concerns for the environment in Europe, in the United States, and in Japan have resulted in legislation dictating recycling of materials (e.g., chemical products, glass, paper, plastics, aluminum, lead) up to a certain percentage, as they are disposed of by the end-consumers either directly, e.g., in the case of packaging, or indirectly, in the case of various products such as computers, TVs, automobiles, home appliances, cartridges, and cameras (Krikke, 1998).

For material suppliers, the strategic priority in managing the return flows evolves around cost-efficient collection and recycling of materials and the attainment of scale economies. Some of the supply decisions, which require coordination with the reverse flows, are: capacity choices of virgin and recycled materials, degree of material recyclability, and the pricing of the recycled and virgin materials (Martin, 1982).

Cost-efficient reverse logistics is a strategic priority for product manufacturers, in particular, for products that cannot be recovered in other forms of reuse. For instance, several car manufacturers have recently set up joint ventures with dismantlers to recycle the end-of-life cars in the most cost-efficient way (*Automotive News,* 2000). Since the cost efficiency of the recovery operations depends on the scale of the return flows, an important decision has been finding the right incentive schemes to stimulate the reverse flows from the end users. In this respect, the manufacturer faces the challenge of setting the *right salvage value* for used products, which reveals the consumer's valuations in a costless manner, and avoids products ending up in other distribution channels (Purohit and Staelin, 1994). The pricing decision of the salvage products also has implications for pricing decisions in forward channel. Several marketing papers have addressed this issue in the context of used cars (Levinthal and Purohit, 1989).

2.2 Retailer Returns of Short Life-Cycle Products (Retailers/Distributors to Manufacturers)

For seasonal products with uncertain demand, allowances for product returns from retailers/distributors to manufacturers have been a popular means of improving coordination in forward supply chains. Research shows that return policies can improve supply chain efficiency by freeing the channel of obsolescent products, by reducing the cost of lost sales due to under stocking decisions by the retailers, and by increasing the competitive strategic interaction at the retail level (Padmanabhan and Png, 1997). The type of contracts is called *buyback contracts.* The manufacturer has to determine the buyback price of a leftover unit as a fraction of the purchase price of the product (Pasternack, 1985). The buyback contracts in the reverse channels lead to more cost-efficient operations by reducing the risks for retailers associated with short life cycle (fashion) products.

Reverse logistics activities can also be a means to improve competitiveness of the product in the market by enhancing its value to consumers. Rather than being a means to reduce supply chain costs, reverse flows can lead to increases in demand as well. Here are some examples of such value creation.

2.3 Retail Return Allowances (Consumer to Retailer)

Most manufacturers and retailers have liberalized their return policies from consumers due to competitive pressure. The main drive has been to provide higher product value and to increase switching cost of consumers between suppliers. For several products, retailers can agree to take back merchandise at no cost to the consumers with or without replacement of a new product. One of the difficulties of managing this type of returns is the difference between the objectives of the manufacturers and the retailers. When the retailer wants to return an item, the two parties can disagree on the condition of the item, value of the item, and the timeliness of the response. In most cases, the manufacturer or the distributor does not allow the retailers to return items, and, instead, they give the retailer or the downstream partner a certain amount of *return allowance credit* and guidelines for proper disposal of the product. The main benefit of such a contract is that the manufacturer does not incur the handling costs of the returns. On the other hand, a disadvantage associated with this approach is that the products can end up in other distribution channels, which cannibalize the original product. The return allowance credits are sometimes subject to ex-post renegotiation of the contract if the retailer has sufficient channel power and the returns exceed the cap suggested by the manufacturer in the ex-ante contract.

2.4 Trade-In Offers and Product Acquisition (Consumer to Distributor/ Manufacturer)

Manufacturers such as Dell, Xerox, HP or Compaq frequently use trade-in programs to stimulate new product sales by providing cost-effective replacement options for their customers. Trade-in offers are also popular for white goods and automobiles. A trade-in offer includes a rebate for the old product, and in some, cases an upgrade price for the new product. The customer can trade in either the manufacturer's own product or a product of a different manufacturer, as long as it is in sufficiently good condition. The used product that is returned to the manufacturer can be disposed, recycled, or remanufactured depending on the product's condition. Research in economics looks into how trade-in offers can be used as a price discrimination mechanism for first and repeat buyers (Van Ackere and Reyniers, 1993, 1995). Fudenberg and Tirole (1998) present a detailed analysis of trade-in offers in a monopoly market with and without second-hand markets. The paper shows that the rental outcome can be replicated with a trade-in offer. Several issues associated with this type of product returns remain open for study, such as: Who in the channel should set the trade-in offer? How should the trade-in offer account for uncertainty in the product's condition? How do trade-ins affect the competition in the market?

3. Aspects of Supply Chains, which Require Coordination in Closed-Loop Supply Chains

We have seen that reverse logistics can occur both for cost-efficiency reasons and to increase the product's value to customers. To analyze the role of contracting and coordination in managing such reverse flows, we now turn to several key lessons, which have emerged from existing supply chain literature. The basic premise is, in many cases, that coordination is beneficial for the entire supply chain. Ideally, coordination should occur for all activities throughout the supply chain, from product design through manufacturing, logistics, marketing, managing return flows, and recycling or disposal. In this section, we review the various aspects of supply chains, which require coordination, and the lessons that emerge from existing literature in each of these areas.

The literature on supply chain management frequently emphasizes the existence of three key flows, each of which can occur in forward and reverse directions:

- flows of physical goods, typically from upstream to downstream, but increasingly including reverse flows;
- flows of information about inventories, demands, forecasts, etc.;
- flows of money, representing purchase or lease payments, buyback agreements, etc.

Understanding and managing each of these flows is important to supply chain success. Clearly, there are interactions between them, and the notion of "coordination" of supply chains typically requires managing all three flows at once; for instance, changing the financial flow in order to accelerate the information flow in order to improve the physical flow.

In this section, we identify the various aspects of each of these flows that require coordination and the types of contracts that are or could be used to enhance that coordination. In the next section we discuss learnings from the supply chain management literature on each of these coordination issues.

3.1 Physical flows

Broadly speaking, coordination of physical flows requires agreeing on quantities, timing, and place of product deliveries. In closed-loop supply chains, forward physical flows now generally induce future reverse physical flows, for which the same coordination issues arise. In both cases, availability of appropriate capacity levels for manufacturing, disassembly, remanufacturing, transportation, collection, etc., also need to be coordinated. Several aspects of product design itself can also require coordination between parties in the system; for instance, the number of reuse cycles for which the product is designed (Geyer and Van Wassenhove, 2000), or when product design affects ease of remanufacturing.

3.2 Information flows

The information flows required in supply chains are manifold, including short-term and long-term demand forecasts, actual orders, inventory availability throughout the system, etc. In closed-loop supply chains, information about quantities, timing, and quality of returns is also useful in coordinating. Increasingly, as a result of producer responsibility laws and product stewardship actions, information about use and disposal of products also needs to flow between all parties in the system, and even to external parties such as consumer groups and regulatory agencies.

3.3 Financial flows

Financial flows consist of purchase price, lease payments, service payments, etc., but, in the case of closed-loop supply chains, also include buyback clauses, disposal costs, and other end-of-use costs. While pricing for the original product is relatively straightforward, designing contracts specifying conditions under which the product will be taken back after use is more challenging, as the quality of the product is unknown and often difficult to observe. Yet, as Guide and Van Wassenhove (2001) argue, appropriate financial incentives are an important way of managing the physical return flow.

4. Lessons from Literature on Forward Supply Chains and Interaction with Reverse Supply Chains

Perhaps the most important general lesson that can be drawn from the supply chain management literature is that all three flows (physical, information, and financial) must be managed in conjunction with one another to obtain the desired performance. In this section, we examine some specific instances of such interaction between these three flows: we summarize prescriptions from existing literature on how contracts can be used to improve the interaction between the three flows, how these lessons can be extrapolated to reverse flows, and how the combined presence of forward and reverse flows affects the received wisdom in the field. It is obviously not our intention to provide a complete review of the literature on supply chain contracting; for that, see, for instance, Tsay, Nahmias, and Agrawal (1999).

The basic premise in most cases is that coordination is beneficial for the entire supply chain. However, there are many reasons in practice why such coordination may be hard to achieve. In this section, we review the obstacles standing in the way of achieving coordination, and the recommendations that have been made to overcome these obstacles.

4.1 Aligning incentives

Incentive conflicts can take many forms. Below we review some of the most common occurrences: pricing, inventory decisions, capacity planning, investments in process improvement, and the effects of competition.

Pricing: Perhaps the most common incentive problem in supply chains is that known as "double marginalization" (Tirole, 1988), referring to the situation where a manufacturer sells a product to a retailer, who then sells to a final market. Both manufacturer and retailer add a markup to their sales price (the double margin), causing the final price to be higher and final demand to be lower than would be the case if both firms were vertically integrated. A simple solution to the double marginalization problem is to allow two-part pricing. If the manufacturer can charge a fixed fee (such as a franchise fee), he will set his wholesale price equal to his marginal cost, hence increasing demand, and will set the franchise fee high enough to recoup his profits. Corbett and Tang (1999) show how such more flexible contracts can indeed lead to better coordination, even when the manufacturer does not know the retailer's cost structure.

Many other incentive problems are similar in nature. Cachon and Larivière (2000) study reusable products, such as videotapes for rental, and show how reducing the price at which the tape is sold to the rental store will induce the rental store to stock more tapes, hence increasing rental income for both parties.

A recurrent pricing issue in reverse flows is the use of buyback contracts, as discussed earlier. One consequence of the double marginalization effect is that retailers will hold less safety stock than optimal (assuming that stockout penalties exceed holding costs) when demand is uncertain; to overcome this, Pasternack (1985) and others have shown how buyback contracts can help retailers overcome their fear of over ordering.

Closed-loop supply chains often consist of even more parties, hence further increasing the scope for double marginalization or related effects. However, it also introduces mechanisms for more flexible pricing without having to resort to two-part or more complex pricing schemes. For instance, Savaskan (2000) shows that the presence of a reverse channel can in fact eliminate the double marginalization problem in the forward channel. In a related study, Savaskan (2000) also shows that a manufacturer can use the payments in the reverse flows to price discriminate between retail outlets with different market sizes.

Inventory control: Incentive problems also occur in inventory management, such as lot sizing or safety stock decisions. Cachon and Zipkin (1999) show how a manufacturer and a retailer setting inventory levels independently will generally not achieve the system optimal outcome. They also show that tracking inventory in a more appropriate way (using echelon inventory rather than local inventory) brings them closer to the system optimal outcome, and that simple linear transfer payments can lead to full coordination. Corbett and de Groote (2000) and Corbett (2001) show how lot sizing and safety stock decisions can be suboptimal if the party making the decision does not internalize all associated costs; they also conclude that appropriate assignments of ownership and corresponding costs of inventory (e.g., implementing consignment stock or not) can improve coordination.

Capacity planning: Similar problems arise here as for inventory control, but with potentially even more serious consequences given the strategic nature of capacity decisions. Capacity is often built on the basis of long-term demand forecasts; these forecasts however are often generated for other reasons and need not be realistic, especially when the forecasters are not penalized for inaccurate (overoptimistic) forecasts. Porteus and Whang (1991) show how contracts can be used to provide marketing managers with the incentive to forecast accurately and to exert the right amount of sales effort, and to provide manufacturing managers with the incentive to build the right amount of capacity.

However, they also show that no "budget-neutral" scheme exists.[1]

The existing capacity planning models focus on conventional supply chain settings on the basis of long-term demand forecasts. In product markets where commercial returns are a large percentage of sales, capacity planning models should include not only the forecasts of sales but also of return flows.

Process improvement: All parties can exert effort to improve the system, but, as before, generally do not internalize the full benefits of such improvements. A familiar problem in the economics literature is the "moral hazard" problem (see e.g., Holmström, 1979), in which a principal obtains value from an agent's efforts, but cannot observe that agent's efforts directly, and hence can only reward the agent based on indirect measures such as output. If the agent is risk-averse, the system optimal outcome can be achieved simply by "selling the firm" to the agent, i.e., letting the agent incur all variable costs and benefits resulting from his effort, in exchange for a fixed fee paid to (or by) the principal.

What happens, though, if both supplier and customer can exert effort to achieve such improvements? Corbett and DeCroix (2001) study the case of suppliers of indirect materials such as solvents or other chemicals used in customers' processes, but which do not become part of the final product. The customer wants to minimize usage of such chemicals, which is also desirable from a system-wide perspective, but the supplier will obviously not cooperate with such efforts as long as his profits depend on the volume of chemicals sold. Again, moving to a two-part contract (with a fixed component and a component that depends on volume) can improve coordination within the system, but can never lead to the system-wide optimal outcome. This is known as the double moral hazard problem (see Bhattacharyya and Lafontaine, 1995, Kim and Wang, 1998), and it has been shown that a contract, which is linear in consumption, is optimal for the supplier (Corbett, DeCroix, and Ha, 2001).

Competition: The role of competition in increasing efficiency of transactions is often ambiguous. On the one hand, allowing multiple suppliers to compete will generally lower the procurement price for the buyer. On the other hand,

---

[1] Budget neutral means that the principal (i.e., the owner of the firm) can implement the policy without spending extra money, i.e., the bonuses and penalties exactly cancel out, so the owner's budget is not affected.

the literature has also frequently pointed out the importance of building more stable supply chain relationships. Long-term relationships can approximate the vertically integrated outcome, which may yield larger benefits than the short-term benefits of allowing competition (Corbett and Karmarkar, 2001).

In the reverse logistics context, Savaskan (2000) shows that when the retail outlets perform product take back, the buyback payments from the manufacturers to the retailers can induce more intense competitive interaction between the retail outlets. Majumder and Groenevelt (2000) examine how third-party remanufacturing can induce competitive behavior when the recycled products can cannibalize the demand for the original product.

Conclusion: The well-established general recommendation in designing supply chain incentive mechanisms is to attempt to make all parties internalize the full system-wide costs and benefits associated with their decisions. This requires the ability to offer more complex contracts than pure spot-market volume-based agreements. This could include two-part tariffs instead of simple linear prices, or even more complicated "menus" of contracts from which the other party can choose the most appropriate. The presence of multiple flows of goods, for instance a forward and a reverse flow, can in itself be used as a way to implement more sophisticated contracts.

Perfect coordination through contracting is rarely possible in practice. Several common conditions will immediately lead to the coordinated outcomes being suboptimal from a system-wide perspective:

- if the party designing the contract (the principal) does not have full information about the other party (the agent),
- if the same contract must be offered to different agents without being able to perfectly price-discriminate between them,
- if the agent is risk-averse, and
- if effort exerted by both parties (principal and agent) can influence the outcome.

Whenever any of these conditions are present, it may still be possible to implement the system-wide optimum, but the contracts required to achieve that would not be optimal from the principal's perspective.

4.2 Information sharing

The notion that sharing information can lead to more efficient outcomes for an entire supply chain is intuitively clear. However, there are often many obstacles to full sharing of information. The technological hurdles are increasingly being overcome, but for many parties, information (for example, about final market demand) still conveys power. Below we identify several different types of information and the ways in which sharing them can improve coordination within a supply chain.

Demand information: The distortion of final market demand as one moves further upstream is well documented, and often referred to as the "bullwhip effect." The central notion is that in any system where variability (or uncertainty) is combined with delayed response, amplification will occur. In the context of supply chains, this means that demand uncertainty coupled with a positive lead time to respond to changes in demand will cause those changes to be amplified further upstream. Lee, Padmanabhan and Whang (1997ab) identify several main causes of this bullwhip effect, including:

- updating of forecasts based on customer orders rather than final market information;
- batching of orders, for instance, due to transportation economies or fixed order costs;
- pricing variability, for example, that caused by periodic promotions; and
- shortage gaming, for instance, when limited capacity is allocated based on customer orders rather than true final market demand.

Another cause of amplification was identified in Corbett, Blackburn and Van Wassenhove (1999), who observed how total weekly order quantities were allocated in a seemingly random fashion between multiple suppliers, who therefore perceive much higher demand variability than is actually present in the final downstream market. Chen et al. (2000) demonstrate that centralizing all demand information does indeed reduce the severity of the bullwhip effect. Lee, So, and Tang (2000) find similar results, especially when demands over time display significant positive correlation. By contrast, Cachon and Fisher (2000) find that the value of sharing demand information can be quite small, and that the main benefit from using information technology lies in accelerating physical flows rather than expanding information flows.

Sharing information about longer-term demand forecasts is also important. Porteus and Whang (1991) study the case where marketing and manufacturing managers need to coordinate capacity plans based on demand forecasts. Without putting the appropriate contracts in place, the marketing managers will have an incentive to exaggerate demand forecasts in order to avoid stockouts, potentially saddling the manufacturing managers with excess capacity. Porteus and Whang (1991) show that the owner of the firm can induce the marketing and manufacturing managers to make the optimal decisions, but that the owner cannot do so in a budget-neutral way. Cachon and Larivière (1999) examine the case of a supplier building capacity based on a customer's demand forecasts. They study a range of different supply contracts, and analyze which ones will lead the customer to forecast accurately. In their setting, firm commitments are not desirable for aligning incentives, but do convey information about the customer's demand expectations.

Inventory information: Several authors have identified the importance of allocating inventory holding costs appropriately to all parties in a multi-echelon system. Clark and Scarf's (1960) original decomposition scheme for a two-echelon system already relied on making each party bear the holding costs associated with his "echelon" inventory, i.e., the inventory at that party's level and all levels downstream from there, where the holding cost rate is the value-added at that party's level. Cachon and Zipkin (1999), Lee and Whang (1999) and Chen (1998, 1999) provide further analyses of systems based on echelon inventories rather than physical (or "installation") inventory levels. Most of these policies therefore require each party to have full visibility of inventories at all levels in the system; Lee and Whang (1999) propose a system which can be operated with only locally available information (but which requires a central planner to design it), and Chen (1999) suggests a scheme based on "accounting inventory levels" which also allows decentralized control of the system, even when there are information delays. Chen (1998) finds that the optimal inventory policy based on installation inventory levels (hence using local information only) performs only slightly worse (between 0% to 9%) than the optimal policy based on echelon inventory levels.

Manufacturing systems with product returns have several unique operational characteristics, which make existing models of inventory control insufficient for these environments. These characteristics are: two exogenous supply sources, time-dependent availability of the remanufacturing source, and stochastic manufacturing lead times. Van der Laan et al. (1998) develop both continuous and discrete time models of inventory control for hybrid systems with and without disposal of returned units. They model the uncertainy using a Coxian – 2 arrival process for used products and correlation between return and demand patterns. The information structure in this case is exogeneous to their model. Scenario analyses are provided to determine the effect of system parameters on the optimal inventory control policy. At a supply chain level, Toktay et al. (2001) develop joint forecasting and inventory control to determine the optimal procurement policy of a remanufacturable product. In their analysis the information structure is made endogenous to the problem formulation and is updated during the planning horizon.

As highlighted in the current research, most of the complexity in reverse logistics comes from the inability to forecast product return patterns. In an exploratory study Kokkinaki et al. (2001) discuss the use of electronic marketplaces, which facilitate returns from end users and reduce the uncertainty in the timing and the quality of the product returns. Pooling and transaction cost benefits arise from using electronic markets for reverse logistics. There is a need to understand the exact benefits and the pricing mechanisms in these market environments for used products. The findings would certainly be useful to address issues related to design of reverse logistics systems.

Other information: Many of the types of contracts discussed earlier ideally require one party to have full information about all relevant parameters, such as both parties' cost structure. For instance, in Porteus and Whang (1991), marketing managers have private information about demand, so the owner of the firm must give them an appropriate incentive in order to reveal that information truthfully. Corbett (2001) examines cases where one party has private information about stock out costs or holding costs. Both papers conclude that such private information leads to inefficiencies in the system. A central planner with full information would be able to avoid such inefficiencies. In the absence of such a central planner, it is clear why many parties in practice are extremely reluctant to share certain types of information, especially related to cost structures.

Such information asymmetries immediately arise in the case of closed-loop supply chains too. If collection and remanufacturing activities are outsourced to a third party, the original manufacturer will generally not know what the true costs are. A third-party subcontractor for remanufacturing has an incentive to overstate those costs, which would lead the original manufacturer to reduce the quantity of material remanufactured. Though arguments exist in favor of separating remanufacturing from the original manufacturer, the resulting information asymmetries will generally lead to efficiency losses in the reverse supply chain.

4.3 Supply chain structure

Supply chains are designed to meet various goals, depending on the product and market characteristics. Fisher (1997) characterizes two general types of products (functional vs. innovative), and two general types of supply chain (focused on cost and efficiency vs. focused on responsiveness). He argues that the supply chain structure should be aligned with the product/market characteristics. Intuitively, similar advice should carry over to the reverse side of a closed-loop supply chain. Virtually all supply chain design decisions come down to that basic distinction: how many layers should the supply chain have, who should the players be, what modes of transportation should they use, how should the network be designed and activities be allocated.

4.4 Interaction between product design and (reverse) logistics

Not only supply-chain design, but also product design, will affect the performance of a supply chain. This is well known, through examples such as the HP DeskJet (Lee et al., 1993). Once the printer was redesigned to allow localization (ie., adding the country-specific power supply) at the local warehouse rather than in the central factory, inventories were reduced and logistics simplified. This same principle has been applied in many instances, under names such as "design for logistics," "postponement," "delayed differentiation," etc. Similarly, the notion of "design for disassembly" or "design for remanufacturing" or "design for environment" is increasingly well established in the design world. For true closed-loop supply chains, one might expect both of these design concepts simultaneously to be important, which clearly requires coordination between the design teams, logistics parties (both forward and reverse), remanufacturers, etc.

5. Conclusions

Based on the current state of the literature on reverse logistics, we believe that there are two fundamental research questions that should constitute the basis of future research in this area.

- How can we use our learnings to date and the existing theory in forward supply chains to address issues faced in reverse logistics?
- How can the theory of reverse logistics help us improve our understanding of forward supply chain issues?

Because the forward supply chain literature is more developed, we expect that many lessons from this area can be of value for closed-loop supply chains too, but the exact nature of the relationships between forward (or open-loop) and reverse (or closed-loop) supply chains still needs to be examined. For instance, with respect to pricing and demand management, we still need to understand better how lease terms and prices should be adapted for remanufacturable products such as copiers, taking into consideration the life cycle effects. What can economic theory tell us about the quality of remanufacturable goods, and how can we use this knowledge to improve the product acquisition process? Similarly, on the operational side, what can we say about the impact of uncertainty on a production line for recoverable products based on our understanding with JIT systems? How can we coordinate maintenance and remanufacturing decisions, in particular for high value products like medical systems? How do we decide on make/buy decisions in a reverse logistics context? What trade-offs exist if we allow third-party remanufacturing? What can transaction cost economics, agency theory, or cooperative game theory tell us about the incentive issues in the reverse logistics channels?

The list of such research questions can easily be extended through critical thinking about reverse logistics as it relates to the overall supply chain strategy of a company. It is our hope that this chapter will provide some food for thought in that direction.

References

Automotive News 2000, Ford Finding Treasure in Trash.

Bhattacharyya, S. and F. Lafontaine 1995, Double-sided Moral Hazard and the Nature of Share Contracts. *Rand Journal of Economics.* 26 (2) 761-781.

Cachon, G. and M. Fisher 2000, Supply chain inventory management and the value of shared information. *Management Science.* 46 (8) 1032-1048.

Cachon, G. and M. Lariviere 1999, Capacity Choice and Allocation: Strategic Behavior and Supply Chain Performance. *Management Science.* 45 (8) 1091-1108.

Cachon, G. and M. Larivière 2000, Supply Chain Coordination with Revenue Sharing Contracts: Strengths and Limitations. Manuscript.

Cachon, G.P. and P.H. Zipkin 1999, Competitive and Cooperative Inventory Policies in a Two-Stage Supply Chain. *Management Science.* 45 (7) 936-953.

Chen, F. 1998, Echelon reorder points, installation reorder points, and the value of centralized demand information. *Management Science.* 44 (12) 221-234.

Chen, F. 1999, Decentralized supply chains subject to information delays. *Management Science.* 45 (8) 1076-1090.

Chen, F., Z. Drezner, J. Ryan and D. Simchi-Levi 2000, Quantifying the bullwhip effect in a simple supply chain: the impact of forecasting, lead times and information. *Management Science.* 46 (3) 436-443.

Corbett, C.J. 2001, Stochastic Inventory Systems in a Supply Chain With Asymmetric Information (Cycle Stocks, Safety Stocks, and Consignment Stock). *Operations Research*, 49(4), 487-500.

Corbett, C.J., J.D. Blackburn and L.N. Van Wassenhove 1999, Partnerships to Improve Supply Chains. *Sloan Management Review.* 40 (4) 71-82.

Corbett, C.J. and X. de Groote 2000, A Supplier's Optimal Quantity Discount Policy Under Asymmetric Information. *Management Science.* 46 (3) 444-450.

Corbett, C.J. and G.A. DeCroix 2001, Shared Savings Contracts for Indirect Materials in Supply Chains: Channel Profits and Environmental Impacts. *Management Science.* 47 (7) 881-893.

Corbett, C.J. and U.S. Karmarkar 2001, Competition and Structure in Serial Supply Chains. *Management Science.* 47 (7) 966-978.

Corbett C.J. and C.S. Tang Designing Supply Contracts: Contract Type and Information Asymmetry. Chapter 9 in *Quantitative Models for Supply Chain Management*, S. Tayur, R. Ganeshan and M. Magazine (eds.), Kluwer Academic Publishers, Boston, 1999, pp. 270-297.

Fisher, M.L. 1997, What is the Right Supply Chain for Your Product? *Harvard Business Review.* (March-April) 105-116.

Geyer, R. and L.N. Van Wassenhove 2000, Product Take-back and Component Reuse. INSEAD Working Paper 2000/34/TM/CIMSO 12.

Guide, Jr., V.D.R. and L.N. Van Wassenhove 2001, Managing Product Returns for Remanufacturing. *Production and Operations Management,* forthcoming.

Holmström, B. 1979, Moral Hazard and Observability. *The Bell Journal of Economics.* 10 74-91.

Kim, S.K. and S. Wang 1998, Linear Contracts and the Double Moral hazard. *Journal of Economic Theory.* 82 (5) 342-378.

Krikke, H. 1998, Recovery Strategies and Reverse Logistics Network Design. *PhD Thesis, University of Twente, Netherlands.*

Lee, H.L., C. Billington and B. Carter 1993, Hewlett-Packard Gains Control of Inventory and Service through Design for Localization. *Interfaces.* 23 (4) 1-11.

Lee, H.L., V. Padmanabhan and S. Whang 1997a, Information Distortion in a Supply Chain: The Bullwhip Effect. *Management Science.* 43 (4) 546-558.

Lee, H.L., V. Padmanabhan and S. Whang 1997b, The Bullwhip Effect in Supply Chains. *Sloan Management Review.* 20 (3) 93-102.

Lee, H.L., K.C. So and C.S. Tang 2000, The Value of Information Sharing in a two-level Supply Chain. *Management Science.* 46 (5) 626-643.

Lee, H.L. and S. Whang 1999, Decentralized Multi-echelon Supply Chains: Incentives and Information. *Management Science.* 45 (5) 633-640.

Levinthal, D. and D. Purohit 1989, Durable Goods and Product Obsolescence. *Marketing Science.* 8 35-56.

Martin, R.E. 1982, Monopoly Power and the Recycling of Raw Materials *The Journal of Industrial Economics*, 30 (4) 405-420.

Padmanabhan, V. and I. P. Png 1997, Manufacturer's Return Policies and Retail Competition. *Marketing Science.* 16 (1) 81-94.

Pasternack, B.A. 1985, Optimal Pricing and Return Policies for Perishable Commodities. *Marketing Science.* 4 (2) 166-176.

Porteus, E. and S. Whang 1991, On Manufacturing/Marketing Incentives. *Management Science*. 37 (9) 1166-1181.

Purohit, D. and R. Staelin 1994, Rentals, Sales, and Buyback: Managing Secondary Distribution Channels. *Journal of Marketing Research*. 31 325-338.

Savaskan, R.C., S. Bhattacharya, L.N. Van Wassenhove, (2000 a) Channel Choice and Coordination in a Remanufacturing Environment. INSEAD *Working Paper Series, 99/14/TM.*

Savaskan, R.C. and L.N. Van Wassenhove (2000 b), Strategic Decentralization of Reverse Channels and Price Discrimination thorough Buyback Payments. Kellogg School of Management, *Working Paper Series.*

Tayur, S., R. Ganeshan and M. Magazine (eds.) 1999, *Quantitative Models for Supply Chain Management*, Kluwer Academic Publishers.

Tirole, J., *The Theory of Industrial Organization*, The MIT Press, Cambridge, MA, 1988.

Toktay, B., L.Wein and S. Zenios 2001, Inventory Management of Remanufacturable Products. *Management Science*. 46 (11) 1412-1426.

Tsay, A.A., S. Nahmias and N. Agrawal 1999, Modeling Supply Chain Contracts: A Review. Chapter 10 in *Quantitative Models for Supply Chain Management*, S. Tayur, R. Ganeshan and M. Magazine (eds.), Kluwer Academic Publishers.

Van Ackere, A. and D. J. Reyniers 1993, A Rational for Trade-ins. *Journal of Economics and Business*. 45 1-16.

Van Ackere, A. and D. J. Reyniers 1995, Trade-Ins and Introductory Offers in a Monopoly. *Rand Journal of Economics*. 26 58-74.

Van der Laan, E., Salomon M., Dekker R. and L.N. Van Wassenhove 1999, Inventory Control in Hybrid Systems with Remanufacturing. *Management Science*. 45 (5) 772-748.

Contacts:

Charles Corbett
Decisions, Operations and Technology Management
Anderson Graduate School of Management
University of California at Los Angeles
110 Westwood Plaza
Box 951481
Los Angeles, CA 90095-1481

Email: charles.corbett@anderson.ucla.edu

Canan Savaskan
Kellogg Graduate School of Management
Northwestern University
2001 Sheridan Road
Leverone Hall
Evanston, IL 60208-2001

Email: r-savaskan@kellogg.nwu.edu

Reverse Logistics Network Structures and Design

Moritz Fleischmann, Erasmus University Rotterdam, The Netherlands

1. Introduction

In the preceding chapters examples of closed-loop supply chains have been presented, encompassing a variety of products, actors, drivers and business processes. One of the common elements across all of these cases concerns the need for an appropriate logistics infrastructure. Just as in traditional supply chains, the various business processes need to be embedded in a corresponding logistics network. In conventional supply chains, logistics network design is commonly recognized as a strategic issue of prime importance. The location of production facilities, storage concepts and transportation strategies are major determinants of supply chain performance. Analogously, setting up an appropriate logistics network has a fundamental impact on the economic viability of a closed-loop supply chain. In order to exploit successfully the opportunities of recovering value from used products, companies need to design a logistics structure that facilitates the arising goods flows in an optimal way. To this end, decisions need to be made about where to locate the various processes of the reverse supply chain and how to design the corresponding transportation links. Specifically, companies need to consider how to collect recoverable products from the former user; where to grade collected products in order to separate recoverable resources from scrap; where to reprocess collected products to make them fit for reuse; and how to distribute recovered products to future customers.

In this chapter, we take a detailed look at logistics network design for closed-loop supply chains. We highlight key issues that companies face as they decide upon the logistics implementation of a product recovery initiative. In particular, we point out differences and analogies with logistics network design for traditional 'forward' supply chains. Moreover, we discuss the strategic fit between the specific context of a closed-loop chain and the logistics network structure.

To illustrate the scope and variety of these issues we complement the business cases presented in the previous chapters by some additional examples.

- IBM's business activities involve several closed-loop chains, concerning end-of-lease product returns, buyback offers, environmental take back and production scrap. The total annual volume of these flows amounts to several ten thousand metric tons worldwide. In order to recover a maximum of value from the various sorts of 'reverse' goods flows, IBM considers a hierarchy of reuse options on a product, part and material level. In this way, product recovery accounts for an annual financial benefit of several hundred US$, and at the same time, reduces landfilling and incineration to less than 4 percent of the volume processed (see IBM, 2000).

- In The Netherlands, manufacturers and importers of electric and electronic equipment are legally obliged since 1999 to take back and recover their products after use. In response, manufacturers have set up a joint collection and recycling network managed by the branch organization NVMP. The system includes a network of regional storage centers where products that are collected via municipalities and retailers are sorted and consolidated and then shipped to some recycling subcontractors. The system is financed by a fixed recycling charge added to the sales price of the products (NVMP, 2001).

- Dupont operates several facilities for recycling nylon from used carpeting material. A large-scale plant in Tennessee (United States) processes carpet waste collected from carpet dealerships in major United States metropolitan areas. Reusable content is separated from waste and is recycled for several applications, including new carpet fibers and automotive parts. In 2001 a pilot project for additional recycling operations was implemented in Ontario, Canada (Dupont, 2001).

In what follows, we consider management issues arising in these and other examples as companies' design and implement reverse logistics networks. The material is organized as follows. The next section links logistics network design to the framework laid out in Chapter 1. We discuss the impact of the various reverse channel functions from a network design perspective and highlight the main business decisions involved. Section 3 takes a more detailed look at different types of closed-loop supply chains and discusses specific requirements for each of them. Section 4 then presents a quantitative modeling framework for addressing the key issues identified. In particular, the impact of several context parameters on reverse logistics network design and related costs is illustrated. Finally, Section 5 summarizes our conclusions and indicates further research needs.

2. Issues in Reverse Logistics Network Design

In Chapter 1 the channel functions closing the supply chain loop have been structured in a generic set of activities, namely acquisition and collection, testing and grading, reprocessing, and redistribution. While the specific implementation of these tasks differs per example, the overall scheme is reflected in all of the various cases presented in the preceding chapters. At the same time, this set of activities naturally delineates the scope of the logistics network we are considering here. Specifically, an appropriate logistics structure is sought for bridging the gap between two market interfaces, namely acquisition of used products on the one hand, and sales of reusable products and materials on the other hand. Figure 1 illustrates the typical structure of such a network (compare Fleischmann et al., 2000).

The figure suggests a subdivision of the network in two main parts. First, a convergent part accumulates used products from individual sources and conveys them to some recovery facility. Second, a divergent network part links recovery facilities to individual customers purchasing reusable products. Between these two parts the network hosts the actual transformation process of turning used products into reusable ones, in other words, the test and grade and the reprocessing stages.

It is worth indicating that only the first, convergent network part is actually 'reversed', in the sense that it concerns goods flows from the user back to a producer, thereby reversing some previous steps of the original value chain. In contrast, the outbound network part very much resembles a traditional distribution network. Furthermore, it should be noted that a company may not necessarily be responsible for the entire network as sketched in Figure 1. Depending on the role of various channel members, the selected scope may extend across the boundaries of several parties. However, in line with supply chain management philosophy, it seems wise to consider the presented network in its entirety, in order to correctly understand the relevant issues in reverse logistics network design. As the different network stages have a significant impact on

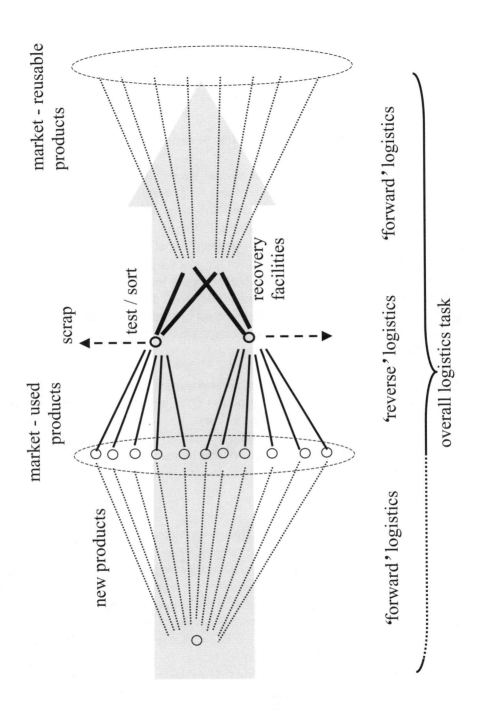

Figure 1: Reverse Logistics Network Structure

each other, considering a single one in isolation reflects a distorted picture and may entail suboptimal decisions. In fact, one may argue that even more supply chain stages should be taken into account, namely the distribution of the original 'virgin' product, as sketched in Figure 1. We return to this point in our analysis below. In the next step, let us consider specific issues for each of the aforementioned channel functions.

2.1 Acquisition / Collection

Collection of used products potentially accounts for a significant part of the total costs of any closed-loop supply chain. Analogous with the 'last mile' issue in distribution, transportation of a large number of low volume flows tends to render collection an expensive operation. While this issue is particularly apparent for the case of acquisition from a consumer market, transportation cost for the 'first mile' may be a significant burden even for business products. In addition, it should be noted that transportation is a key factor in the overall environmental performance of any closed-loop chain. Hence, avoiding conflicts with 'green' arguments that play an important role – at least for marketing in many product recovery initiatives – may be another reason for avoiding excessive transportation.

Companies have explored several options for reducing transportation costs of the 'first mile'. First, analogous with distribution, some of the most expensive tasks may partly be shifted onto the customers. Rather than actively collecting goods, a company may install some drop-points where customers can hand in used products. In this way, a first consolidation step is achieved. For example, consider public glass or paper collection boxes and of consumer electronics handed in at retail outlets. While this strategy reduces transportation, additional storage space is required. Moreover, this approach may be limited to relatively small, low-value consumer products.

Another route to consolidation is in combining collection with other transportation flows. In particular, there may be synergies in combining distribution and collection. Typical examples include refillable soft drink bottles and various 'old for new' programs. This integration of 'forward' and 'reverse' goods flows is facilitated by the fact that the reverse channel may involve less time pressure. Hence, flows may be planned forward-driven, with collection being added afterwards. On the other hand, efficiently integrating distribution and collection requires both flows to follow the same route, which may not always be optimal. The transportation of empty toner cartridges and reusable cameras by express mail, as discussed in previous chapters, illustrates examples where bypassing some network stages 'on the way back' appears to be a better choice. The same holds for cases where speed does matter in the return channel, such as in electronics remanufacturing, which faces quick depreciation.

2.2 Testing / Grading

The location of the test and grade operations in the network has an important impact on the arising goods flows. It is only after this stage that individual products can be assigned to an appropriate recovery option and hence to a geographical destination. Basically, we observe a tradeoff between transportation and investment costs at this stage. Testing collected products early in the channel may minimize total transportation distance since graded products can directly be sent to the corresponding recovery operation. In particular, unnecessary transportation can be avoided by separating reusable items from unrecoverable scrap. On the other hand, expensive test equipment and the need for skilled labor may be drivers for centralizing the test and grade operations.

It is worth mentioning that this centralization may be restricted by legal constraints. Transportation of waste across borders is strictly regulated in many cases, such as between different states in the United States and between countries in Europe. Cross-border transportation is often allowed only for recoverable resources, but not for waste that is to be disposed. Centralizing the test and grade operation of a large-scale network results in a concentration of disposable waste in one country or state, which may be infeasible. On the other hand, recent developments in information and communication technologies may help reduce the cost of 'local' testing. By means of sensoring and online data exchange, test and grade operations may increasingly be carried out in a 'remote' fashion, thereby substituting information flows for physical flows. We illustrate this trend in more detail in Section 3.

Finally, one should observe a tradeoff between the effort for testing and collection strategies. While shifting part of the collection function onto the customer may help minimize transportation cost, it may be difficult in this case to keep different products separated, which tends to increase testing and sorting costs. Alternatively, individual collection may offer opportunities for separating recoverable items from scrap right at the source, thereby reducing the need for sorting later in the channel.

2.3 Reprocessing

Often the reprocessing stage requires the highest investments within the reverse logistics network. The costs for specialized remanufacturing or recycling equipment largely influence the economic viability of the entire chain. In many cases, high investment costs at the reprocessing stage call for high processing volumes to be profitable. It is worth emphasizing that the chain's throughput is dependent on both of the aforementioned market interfaces. A sufficient sales volume is required for recovered products and for a sufficient supply of recoverable resources. The latter entails the need for a collection strategy that not only minimizes transportation cost but also, or even primarily, assures a sufficient acquisition volume. Recall in this context the different incentive schemes for managing product returns, as discussed in Chapters 2 and 8.

If the closed-loop chain is managed by the original equipment manufacturer (OEM), designing the reprocessing stage may involve a tradeoff between integration and dedication. In this case, partly integrating product recovery operations with the original manufacturing process may offer economies of scale. Integration may concern shared locations, workforce, or even manufacturing lines. On the other hand, variable processing costs may benefit from two separate, dedicated systems. Similarly, transportation economics may differ for 'virgin' versus 'recovered' products. Furthermore, it should not be overlooked that integration in many cases adds significantly to organizational complexity.

2.4 Redistribution

As discussed at the beginning of this section, the design of the redistribution stage very much resembles a traditional distribution network. In particular, we find the conventional tradeoff between consolidation and responsiveness in transportation. What may add to managerial complexity in redistribution is again the issue of integration. For example, one may consider combining collection and redistribution in order to increase vehicle loading, as discussed above. OEMs may also find opportunities for integrating redistribution with the distribution of the original product.

We condense the above discussion in three main managerial issues that distinguish the design of reverse logistics networks from traditional distribution networks, namely:

- *centralization of testing and grading*

We have seen that the location of the test and grade operations has major consequences for the product flows in a closed-loop supply chain. What is special about this situation is the fact that product destinations can only be assigned after the test stage. In a traditional distribution environment, product routings are, in principal, known beforehand. While there may be exceptions, e.g., for by-products or rework, this is not a major focus of conventional production-distribution networks.

- *uncertainty and lack of supply control*

It has often been claimed that reverse logistics environments are characterized by a high level of uncertainty (see e.g., Thierry et al., 1995). While in traditional supply chains demand is typically perceived as the main unknown factor, it is the supply side that significantly contributes to additional uncertainty here. Used products are a much less homogenous input resource than conventional 'virgin' raw materials in that timing, quantity, and quality may be uncertain and difficult to influence. Effectively matching demand and supply therefore is a major challenge in closed-loop supply chains. Consequently, robustness of the logistics network design with respect to variations in flow volumes and composition appears to be particularly important in this context.

- *integration of forward and reverse flows*

As discussed above, logistics implementation of closed-loop supply chains may offer several opportunities for exploiting synergies between different product flows. While traditional distribution networks are typically perceived as 'one-way' objects, closed-loop chains naturally involve multiple inbound and outbound flows of different 'orientation'. Hence, there may be room for integration both in transportation and facilities. At the same time, these opportunities raise a compatibility issue. In many cases, reverse logistics networks are not designed 'from scratch' but are added on top of existing logistics structures. One may wonder whether this sequential approach allows for efficient solutions or whether an integral redesign of the entire closed-loop network offers tangible benefits.

Before addressing these issues in a quantitative analysis, we discuss their relative importance in different supply chain contexts in further detail. To this end, the next section takes a closer look at different types of reverse logistics networks.

3. Fitting Reverse Logistics Networks to the Supply Chain Context

The framework presented in Chapter 1 and the various cases discussed throughout this book demonstrate that closed-loop supply chains are far from homogenous. Different business environments result in different factors being dominant and hence in different forms of closed-loop chains. The disparate supply chain contexts also have a major impact on the design and operation of corresponding reverse logistics networks. We complement the general discussion developed in the previous section by a more differentiated picture.

Fleischmann et al. (2000) have distinguished three classes of reverse logistics networks based on the form of reprocessing: remanufacturing, recycling, and reuse-networks. We extend this classification by including two additional context variables, namely, the driver for product recovery (economics versus legislation) and the owner of the recovery process (OEM versus third party). In what follows, we consider reverse logistics networks for different combinations of these variables and put the issues discussed in the previous section into perspective. It should be noted that the three proposed dimensions are not independent. In particular, we do not have evidence for all possible combinations. Table 1 summarizes the cases considered in the sequel.

	Economically driven			Legislation-driven		
	Reuse	Remanu-facturing	Recycling	Reuse	Remanu-facturing	Recycling
OEM	3.5	3.2	3.4	-	-	(3.1)
3rd Party	(3.5)	3.3	(3.4)	-	-	3.1

Table 1: Supply chain context of reverse logistics networks

3.1 Networks for Mandated Product Take-Back

A first important group of reverse logistics networks concerns supply chains established in response to environmental product take back legislation. For a typical example recall the national electronics-recycling network in the Netherlands from Section 1. Similar systems have been implemented or are underway in Scandinavia and in several countries in Asia, and are discussed on a European scale. Furthermore, consider the well-known German 'green dot' system for packaging recycling (Duales System, 2001). Scrap cars form another important product group targeted by legislation. In all of these cases OEMs are held responsible for keeping their (mostly consumer) products out of the waste stream at the end of the life cycle. As the opportunities for recapturing value from end-of-life products are small in most of these cases, we see companies opting for a fairly conservative approach, focusing on cost minimization. Material recycling is the typical form of recovery. Costs are charged to the customers either directly or via the price of new products.

While OEMs are legally and financially responsible for product take back and recovery, the execution is typically outsourced to logistics service providers and specialized recycling companies. Moreover, in many cases we see systems established in industry-wide cooperation. The corresponding reverse logistics network design very much focuses on low-cost collection. Typically, we find solutions involving drop-locations, possibly in cooperation with municipal waste collection, where customers can hand in their products, which are then stored and shipped for further processing once a certain volume has accumulated. In contrast, the test and grade operation does not appear to play a prominent role in these systems. Products may be roughly sorted by product category at the collection side, partly for administrative reasons. Further separation of material fractions occurs during the recycling process.

3.2 OEM Networks for Value Added Recovery

Another important class of reverse logistics networks concerns closed-loop supply chains managed by OEMs with the goal of recapturing value added from used products. The case of IBM sketched in the introduction to this chapter is one of the typical examples. Other cases have been discussed in the previous chapters, e.g., copier and automotive parts remanufacturing.

Typically, OEM-managed closed-loop chains encompass multiple sorts of used product flows, from different sources and with different motivations, such as end-of-lease returns, and 'old-for-new' buybacks and take back as elements of customer service. However, the focus in all of these cases tends to be on the business market, due to higher product values and closer customer relations, which facilitate product monitoring during the entire life cycle. At the same time, OEM-managed systems often include a scale of alternative, quality-dependent recovery options on a product, component, and material level.

In view of these heterogeneous product flows, the test and grade operations play an important role in order to maximize the value recovered. Currently, we see a tendency towards a centralized test operation in many cases. Analogous with the development of supranational distribution structures in the past decade, economies of scale appear largely to outweigh transportation costs. Rather than cost considerations, it may be legal constraints to cross-border transportation that form a barrier to further geographical concentration of return flow management (see Section 2). As discussed in the previous section, advances in IT may be a factor that reverses the balance in this cost tradeoff. For example, electronic sensors already allow copiers to be closely monitored during the entire life cycle. Extensive data collected in this way may support the assignment of returned machines to appropriate recovery options without detailed physical inspection. In addition, remote monitoring may even provide a basis for a proactive take back policy instead of purely reactive recovery decisions. Similar technological developments can easily be imagined for other product categories.

Finally, it should be noted that coordination issues are particularly important in these OEM-managed networks. As indicated in the previous section, not only inbound and outbound flows of used products need to be coordinated, but also recovery and original manufacturing, which may partly substitute each other. Hence, reverse logistics networks typically need to be embedded in a larger overall solution. While this close interrelation may allow for exploiting synergies, it also adds to the complexity of logistics decision making.

3.3 Dedicated Remanufacturing Networks

In addition to OEM-managed product recovery programs, specialized remanufacturing companies have been around for a long while. Recall, for example, the case of ReCellular, Inc. discussed in detail in Chapter 1. Automotive remanufacturers, industrial equipment remanufacturers, and tire retreaders are some of the numerous other examples (Guide, 2000). Comparing these types of closed-loop chains with the OEM-systems sketched above, we observe a much more prominent trading and brokerage function. The business is strongly opportunity-driven, seeking an optimal match of supply and demand.

The brokerage character of dedicated remanufacturing chains is also reflected in the corresponding logistics networks. Rather than adding some collection infrastructure to an existing logistics network, remanufacturing companies need to design an integral network spanning all the way from supply to demand. In particular, the location of the actual remanufacturing site naturally relies on both the supply sources and customer locations. Furthermore, it is worth emphasizing that profit maximization rather than cost minimization is the dominant decision criterion.

At the same time, the fact that specialized remanufacturers cannot rely on established relations in the original 'virgin' product business makes acquisition a key activity in these cases. Careful management of the supply side is vital to ensure availability of the right recoverable products (see also Chapter 8). In order to support this task optimally, the corresponding inbound network requires a high degree of flexibility and responsiveness. In the same vein, the test and grade operation plays an important role. As remanufacturers, in general, have little means to monitor products during the initial part of the life cycle, the state of an incoming product is only known after inspection. Consequently, location of this operation is an important element of the logistics network design.

3.4 Recycling Networks for Material Recovery

Systems driven by the recovery of material value through recycling form another class of closed-loop supply chains with distinctive characteristics. For a typical example, we refer to the case of carpeting recycling by DuPont outlined in the introduction. Material recycling chains are characterized by fairly low profit margins, and in view of low raw material prices, opportunities for cost advantages through recycling are limited. Therefore, it is not surprising that the number of successful recycling chains based on purely economic drivers – as opposed to the legislation-driven chains addressed in Section 3.1 – is rather small.

Another important characteristic of commercial recycling chains concerns the need for high investments for specialized recycling installations and equipment. The combination of high investment costs and low margins obviously calls for high processing volumes. Aggressively exploiting economies of scale is indispensable for achieving economic viability in this context. This reasoning is directly reflected in the structure of the corresponding logistics networks. Typically, one observes a highly centralized network relying on one, large-scale recycling facility.

As indicated in Section 3.1, testing and grading in a strict sense appear not to be very relevant for material recycling. Instead, we often find some preprocessing operation to enhance transportation efficiency. Shredding and combustion may substantially reduce transportation costs for the bulk of collected used products. Benefits are more significant in view of the large distances implied by the centralized network structure.

3.5 Networks for Refillable Containers

We conclude this section by looking at the class of closed-loop supply chains that has been presented in Chapter 1 under the header of 'refillable containers'. Many examples of this class concern reusable packaging, such as refillable beer or soft drink bottles, crates, pallets, and reusable boxes. However, recall from Chapter 1 that 'containers' may also take more sophisticated forms, such as reusable cameras (serving as 'packaging' of the film) or toner cartridges. All of these examples have in common that the various 'containers' may be reused almost instantaneously. The reprocessing stage of the corresponding supply chains is typically limited to cleaning and possibly some minor repair or replacement operations. Similarly, the main function of the test and grade stage is to filter out damaged or obsolete containers. In view of this ease of reusability, a company's pool of containers may be characterized as an asset rather than a set of consumables. Determining an appropriate pool size is one of the main issues in this context.

Assuring availability becomes the main task of the corresponding logistics networks. This concerns the collection strategy, which ought to minimize leakage from the system due to limited customer responsiveness, damage, or acquisition by competitors. Several instruments have been used to keep the supply chain closed, including deposit schemes, rebates or direct old-for-new exchange. In addition, the routing of the empty containers also influences availability. In view of the close correspondence between inbound and outbound flows, companies often use the same network structure in both directions. In addition to limiting transportation, cost this strategy facilitates organization and planning. Typically, management may concentrate on 'forward' flows, while taking returns into account via some simple cost surcharge. Yet, in some cases, considering returns more explicitly may be beneficial, as illustrated in the aforementioned example of reusable cameras. By bypassing some stages of the 'forward' distribution network, the throughput-time of the reverse flows, and hence the pipeline inventory, may be reduced, which eventually allows for a smaller pool size.

4. Quantitative Models for Reverse Logistics Network Design

Having highlighted the distinctive characteristics of Reverse Logistics networks, we now address some of the main issues in a quantitative analysis. We start by taking a look at related literature in Section 4.1. It turns out that most of the currently available models rely on mixed-integer linear programming (MILP). While this approach allows for large-scale mathematical optimization, deriving general insights as to the impact of various parameters is difficult. Therefore, we pursue another road and follow the so-called 'continuous approximation' methodology (Daganzo, 1999). In Section 4.2 we use this approach to develop a cost model for reverse logistics network design. Analyzing this model, we highlight the impact of several context variables in Section 4.3 and derive tentative answers to the issues formulated in Section 2.

4.1 Reverse Logistics Network Design Models in Literature

Logistics network design is one of the areas within the field of reverse logistics for which evidence is available from a relatively wide collection of case studies. In the past few years a considerable number of detailed business cases on this issue have been presented in literature (see Fleischmann et al., 2000). In several of these studies, dedicated optimization models have been developed that rely on extensions and modifications of traditional facility location models. Table 2 summarizes examples for the different supply chain contexts distinguished in Section 3. In addition to the specific applications, some major modeling elements are listed. We briefly consider each of these cases below before commenting on general lessons learned. For a more comprehensive literature review and discussion of mathematical details we refer to Fleischmann (2001).

		Spengler et al. (1997)	Fleischmann et al. (2001)	Jayaraman et al. (1999)	Barros et al. (1998)	Kroon and Vrijens (1995)
Application	Case	Steel by-products recycling	Electronics remanufacturing and paper recycling	Cellular telephone remanufacturing	Sand recycling	Reusable packaging
	Supply chain context (ß3)	3.1	3.2/3.4	3.3	3.4	3.5
Model	# network levels	N+2 (N)	5(3)	3(1)	4(2)	3(1)
	# dispositions	N	2	1	3	1
	dispositioning	Upper bounds	Upper bounds	-	Fixed fraction	-
	# inbound commodities	N	1	N	1	1
	# periods	1	1	1	1	1

Table 2: Characterization of Reverse Logistics Network Design Models

Spengler et al. (1997) have examined recycling networks for industrial by-products in the German steel industry. Steel production gives rise to a substantial volume of residuals that have to be recycled in order to comply with environmental regulation and to reduce disposal costs. For this purpose, different processing technologies are available. The authors analyze which recycling processes or process chains to install at which locations at which capacity level, in order to minimize overall costs. To this end, they propose a modified MILP warehouse location model. The model formulation allows for an arbitrary number of network levels, corresponding to individual processing steps, and an arbitrary number of end products, linked to alternative processing options. Analyzing multiple scenarios, the authors emphasize the need for industry-wide co-operation to achieve sufficient capacity utilizations. Moreover, they conclude that recycling targets and disposal bans may entail severe investment burdens for the industry and should therefore be handled with care.

Fleischmann et al. (2001) focus on the consequences for OEMs of adding product recovery operations to an existing production-distribution network. A fairly general MILP facility location model is presented that corresponds with the network structure in Figure 1 and encompasses both 'forward' and 'reverse' product flows. Based on a numerical study, the authors conclude that the overall network structure is fairly robust with respect to variations in the recovery volume, and that reverse logistics networks can efficiently be integrated in existing logistics structures in many cases. This situation is illustrated for the example of OEM copier remanufacturing. A second numerical example, referring to the pulp and paper industry, shows that one must be careful, if 'virgin' and recovered products rely on fundamentally different cost drivers. In that example, an increasing recycling volume literally pulls the network away from distant raw material sources and closer to the users. We reconsider these findings in Section 4.2 below.

Jayaraman et al. (1999) have analyzed the logistics network of an electronic equipment remanufacturing company in the United States. The activities considered include core collection, remanufacturing, and distribution of remanufactured products, where delivery and demand customers do not necessarily coincide. In this setting, the optimal number and locations of remanufacturing facilities and the number of cores collected are sought, considering investment, transportation, processing, and storage costs. The authors show that this network design problem can be modeled as a standard multiproduct capacitated warehouse location MILP. In this formulation, limited core supply acts as a capacity restriction to the overall level of operation. The authors highlight that managing this 'capacity', which is crucial for the system's performance, requires different approaches than in a traditional production-distribution network. Rather than considering technical capacity extension options, appropriate marketing instruments are needed to assure a sufficient core supply.

Barros et al. (1998) provide an example of a material recycling network, namely sand recycling from construction waste. In view of a substantial annual volume of sand landfilled, on the one hand, and the need for sand in large infrastructure projects, such as road construction on, the other hand, a consortium of waste processing companies in The Netherlands is investigating opportunities for a nationwide sand recycling network. Pollution is a major issue in this context. This means that sand needs to be analyzed and possibly cleaned before being reused. Cleaning polluted sand requires the installation of fairly expensive treatment facilities. In addition, regional depots need to be set up for inspection and storage. The authors develop a tailored multilevel, capacitated, facility location model for this network design problem. In their analysis they emphasize the need for a robust network structure since both supply and demand involve significant uncertainties. Therefore, multiple scenarios are evaluated, of which the solution with the best worst-case behavior is selected. Listes and Dekker (2001) revisit this case and explicitly take the uncertainty issue into account in their modeling approach. They propose a multistage stochastic programming model where location decisions need to be taken on the basis of imperfect information on supply and demand, while subsequent processing and transportation decisions are based on the actual volumes. The model maximizes the expected performance for a set of scenarios with given probabilities. The authors emphasize that the solution does not need to be optimal for any individual scenario, and this approach is more powerful than simple scenario analyses.

To conclude these examples from literature, we mention a study on reusable packaging (Kroon and Vrijens, 1995). More specifically, this case concerns the design of a closed-loop deposit-based system for collapsible plastic containers that can be rented as secondary packaging material. The system involves multiple actors, including a central agency that owns a pool of reusable containers and a logistics service provider who is responsible for storing, delivering, and collecting the empty containers. For the latter operations a set of depots needs to be located. The authors document how this issue may be addressed by means of a standard warehouse location model. In addition, they emphasize that the overall network design problem is characterized by the interaction between the various parties involved and their respective roles. Depot location, pool size, and payment structures all have an important impact on the system's performance as a whole and its competitiveness with respect to traditional 'one-way' packaging.

Considering the overall state of the literature on reverse logistics network design, as illustrated by the above examples, one observes close analogies with conventional production-distribution networks. From a mathematical perspective, the models that have been proposed in a reverse logistics context differ fairly little from traditional MILP facility location models. Some special features reflect the particular role of testing and grading and alternative market conditions on the demand and supply side. One aspect that is worth considering concerns the issue of supply uncertainty. In line with the discussion in Section 2, many authors name this issue as one of the distinguishing characteristics of a reverse logistics environment. At first glance, it may therefore be surprising that few models explicitly incorporate uncertainty other than by means of scenario analyses. Besides the aforementioned stochastic programming model (Listes and Dekker, 2001) one of the few exceptions concerns a robust network design model for carpet recycling (Newton et al., 1999). Howver, while these approaches may indeed result in different network structures than a simple scenario analysis, the corresponding cost advantages turn out to be fairly limited in many cases. Therefore, it may be debatable whether the significant additional computational effort of stochastic or robust programming pays off in this context.

What may be more important is an analysis of long-term market developments. Almost all of the reverse logistics network design models to date take a stationary, single-period perspective. However, closed-loop supply chains are in an emerging state where we see companies gradually extending their operations from moderate pilots to full-scale business processes. To support this strategic transition, multiperiod network design models may be helpful. Realff et al. (1999) provide a first step in this direction.

We note that the above type of location models have some drawbacks when it comes to establishing general insights. Sensitivity analyses in MILP models have rather severe limitations, and the interrelation between various parameters is not made explicit. Consequently, conclusions often rely on extensive numerical experiments rather than on analytic arguments. In the following section, we explore a different strategy and complement preceding studies by a continuous cost model for reverse logistics network design.

4.2 A Continuous Network Design Model

In order to investigate logistics costs and to optimize the design of corresponding logistics systems, Daganzo (1999) introduced what has become known as the 'continuous approximation methodology'. A key element of this approach is the modeling of demand as a continuous geographic density function, as opposed to the discrete demand locations assumed by traditional MILP approaches (see Section 4.1). Assuming the demand density and other system parameters to be varying slowly across the given service region, logistics costs can be approximated by geographical averages, which result in fairly simple expressions in a limited number of parameters. In this way, the cost impact of critical system parameters can be revealed and guidelines for setting up appropriate logistics structures can be derived.

We apply this approach to the analysis of reverse logistics systems. To this end, let us return to the general setup presented in Figure 1. Specifically, we start by considering the reverse logistics network in a strict sense, i.e., the logistics structure conveying used products from a collection point to some given recovery facilities. In line with the discussion in Section 2, assume that used products are collected via some collection tours, and that collected products need to be tested and sorted, after which a certain unreusable portion is scrapped, while the remainder is shipped to a recovery facility to be redistributed eventually.

Following the 'continuous approximation' approach, assume that the collection volume per time is given by a location-dependent continuous density function, denoted by $\rho(x)$, which is slowly varying in x within some overall service area A. Our goal is to approximate the total logistics costs for serving A, and eventually to minimize these costs by choosing an appropriate reverse logistics network design. To this end, it is useful to consider the costs per unit collected. The idea of the 'continuous approximation' approach is to express these costs in 'local' problem parameters only, and then to approximate the overall costs by integrating over the service area. In this light, let $C_R(r, \rho)$ denote the reverse logistics costs per unit for an (imaginary) subarea with constant collection density ρ at a distance r from the corresponding recovery facility. To assess $C_R(.)$ it is useful to distinguish two cases, depending on whether the testing and sorting is carried out at the recovery facility or at some distinct location. In what follows, we refer to them as 'central' and 'local' testing, respectively, and denote the corresponding unit cost functions by $CR_1(.)$ and $CR_2(.)$. For both cases one may consider a number of cost components, namely, inbound transportation costs to the test and sort process, outbound transportation costs after sorting, variable sorting and handling costs, and fixed installation costs for the test facility. Let us look at each of these components in some more detail.

The inbound transportation costs to the test and sort process concern the collection tours within the corresponding service area. These can be approximated, based on a probabilistic analysis of the standard vehicle routing problem by the sum of a line-haul distance from and to the test and sort installation and the distance between two consecutive collection stops (see, e.g., Daganzo, 1999).

$$\text{unit inbound transportation cost} \approx 2\frac{c_d}{v}r + 0.57 \cdot c_d\, \rho^{-1/2}, \tag{1}$$

where c_d denotes the transportation cost per distance and v the capacity of the collection vehicles. In the case of local testing and sorting, the line-haul distance depends on the surface I_R of the area covered by the test facility:

$$\text{unit inbound transportation cost} \approx \frac{4}{3\sqrt{\pi}} \frac{c_d}{v} \sqrt{I_R} + 0.57 \cdot c_d \, \rho^{-1/2} \qquad (1')$$

In the case of central testing, the only relevant outbound costs concern scrapping of rejected products, which are of the form $c_s \gamma$, where γ denotes the disposal fraction and c_s the unit scrap costs. For local testing one also needs to consider the flow of accepted products to a recovery facility. Assuming those shipments to be carried out as line-hauls rather than in tours, we can express the corresponding costs in the form

$$\text{unit inbound transportation cost} \approx 2\frac{\widetilde{c}_d}{\widetilde{v}} \, r\,(1-\gamma) + c_s \, \gamma \qquad (2)$$

where $\widetilde{c}_d$ and $\widetilde{v}$ are the appropriate transportation cost and vehicle capacity analogous with (1). Finally, an (annualized) fixed cost c_f for a local test and sort installation can be expressed on a per product basis as

$$\text{fixed installation cost per product} \approx \frac{c_f}{I_R \, \rho} \qquad (3)$$

and any variable handling and processing costs can be aggregated into a term c_h. Summing up, one obtains the following expression for the unit reverse logistics costs in the case of central testing and sorting

$$(4)$$

$$C_{R1}(r,\rho) = 2\frac{c_d}{v} r + 0.57 \cdot c_d \, \rho^{-1/2} + c_s \gamma + c_h$$

For the 'local testing' case, one can estimate the optimal size of the service area I_R from (2) and (3). First order conditions yield

$$I_R^* = \left(\frac{3\sqrt{\pi} \cdot c_f \, v}{2 \cdot c_d \rho} \right)^{2/3} \approx 1.92 \left(\frac{c_f \, v}{c_d \rho} \right)^{2/3} \qquad (5)$$

Inserting this expression for I_R and summing up the different cost components, then leads to the following cost function

$$C_{R2}(r,\rho) = 2\frac{\tilde{c}_d r}{\tilde{v}}(1-\gamma) + c_s\gamma + 0.57 \cdot c_d\rho^{-1/2} + c_h + 1.56\left(\frac{c_d^2\,c_f}{v^2\rho}\right)^{1/3} \qquad (6)$$

By comparing $C_{R1}(r,\rho)$ and $C_{R2}(r,\rho)$ one can now derive an appropriate service area for the central test and sort operation. Specifically, (4) and (6) define a critical distance $r_R{}^*$ from the recovery facility up to which central testing is preferable over local testing. Equating the cost functions yields

$$r_R^* = 0.78\left(\frac{c_f v}{c_d\rho}\right)^{1/3}\left(1 - \frac{\tilde{c}_d}{\tilde{v}}\frac{v}{c_d}(1-\gamma)\right)^{-1} \text{ optimally.} \qquad (7)$$

From the above analysis one finally obtains the overall reverse logistics unit cost function $C_R(.)$ which can be written as $C_R(r,\rho) = \min\{C_{R1}(r,\rho), C_{R2}(r,\rho)\}$ and the total reverse logistics cost which, as discussed above, is approximated by

$$\int_A \rho\,C_R(r,\rho)dx.$$

Analogously, one can derive cost expressions for the 'forward' parts of logistics networks (see Figure 1). Assuming that items are shipped via some distribution center, one obtains the same formulas as above, where ρ is replaced by an appropriate demand density δ and γ equals zero. In fact, in this way one obtains the original formulas discussed by Daganzo (1999). Let us denote the 'forward' logistics costs by $C_F(.)$ in what follows.

In the next section we exploit the above cost expressions for analyzing in more detail the reverse logistics issues highlighted in Section 2. Before doing so, however, some remarks may be in order. First, it should be clear that the above discussion provides a very basic cost model that can be extended in manifold ways. In particular, we have not included any inventory considerations and we have assumed all vehicles to operate at full capacity. While it is easy to relax these assumptions and to include additional aspects such as lot sizing and dispatching frequencies, these refinements do not change the core of our argumentation, and are omitted for sake of simplicity. The reader is referred to Daganzo (1999) for more detailed modeling using the 'continuous approximation' technique. Second, we have assumed collection and disposal volumes to be given and therefore have not included any revenues in the analysis. However, it should be noted that the above cost expressions can also be used to assess profitability of a recovery operation. In particular, the tradeoff between reverse logistics costs and production cost savings or additional revenues can be made explicit. Finally, it is worth mentioning that the above cost model is a ontinuous analogue to the MILP model presented in Fleischmann et al. (2001).

More specifically, the expression $\int_A [\rho\, C_R^*(r,\rho) + \delta\, C_F^*(r,\delta)]dx$ provides a continuous approximation of the cost function of the latter. In this light, we revisit the conclusions of that paper in the next section.

4.3 Analysis of Reverse Logistics Network Design Issues

In Section 2 three major issues in reverse logistics network design have been highlighted, namely, the degree of centralization of the test and grade operation, supply uncertainty, and integration of 'forward' and reverse logistics. Let us examine how the cost expressions formulated in the previous section can help in analyzing these issues.

The centralization issue is reflected in the size of the service areas of the different test locations, which is captured in the parameters r^* and I_R^*. Expressions (7) and (5) show the impact of the various context parameters on these two design variables. Not surprisingly, the range of central testing r^* depends on the tradeoffs between fixed installation costs and variable collection costs and between short- and long-distance transportation costs. In fact, these are the usual tradeoffs concerning the use of transshipment points in distribution. What may be more interesting is the impact of the parameters, ρ and γ, that characterize the supply of used products. Their influence on the optimal distance for switching from central to local testing is depicted in Figure 2. Table 3 lists the parameter settings for this example, which are used throughout this section unless stated otherwise.

Parameter	Value
$\sim c_d$	0.9
c_d	0.4
$\sim v$	100.0
v	20.0
r	500.0
c_f	500000.0
c_h	3.0
δ	0.4
ρ	0.2
γ	0.5

Table 3: Parameter Settings for the Numerical Example

As expected, the critical distance r^* from the recovery facility is decreasing in the supply density ρ . The more products to be shipped, the sooner an investment in local test installations separating scrap and consolidating transportation volumes pays off. Moreover, it should be noted that the impact of ρ is quickly decreasing. Unless supply volumes are very low, the boundary beween central and local testing shifts fairly little. This is an important observation for understanding the impact of supply uncertainty, which is addressed in more detail below. It should be noted that this relation is analogous with what we know from conventional 'forward' distribution. Furthermore, Figure 2 illustrates r^* to be decreasing in γ; in other words, a higher scrap rate calls for a more decentralized network design. Equation (7) shows that the importance of this shift towards decentralization depends on the relation between long- and short-distance transportation costs. If both cost rates differ markedly, the need for consolidation requires a decentralized network structure, independent of γ. Only if both shipment rates (per product) are fairly close, the scrap rate becomes a more crucial factor, which acts as a reduction of the long-distance transportation costs.

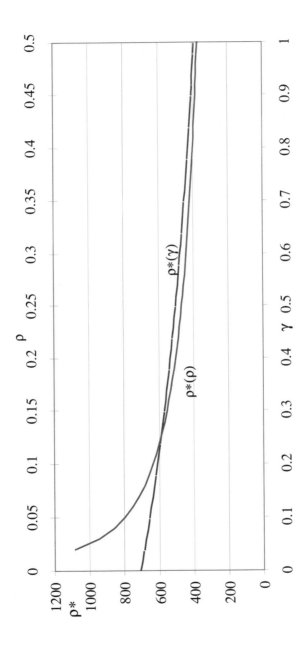

Figure 2: Dependence of Optimal Service Area on Collection Density and Scrap Rate

The surface of the area covered by a local test installation I_R^* is another facet of the centralization issue. Equation (5) documents that the optimal size of this service area depends on ρ in much the same way as the area for central testing. Note that I_R^* denotes a surface area, whereas r^* is expressed as a distance, which explains the difference by a power of two. In contrast, I_R^* does not depend on γ. This can be explained by the fact that the average line-haul distance to the recovery facility is fairly independent of the size of the individual collection areas.

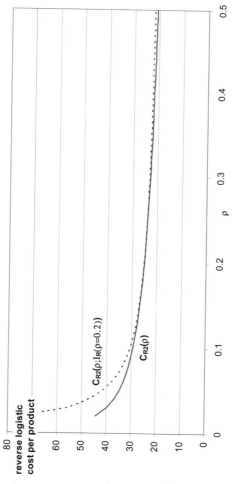

Figure 3: Dependence of Reverse Logistic Costs on Collection Density

Having analyzed these relations, we can now take a closer look at the conse-quences of supply uncertainty, another important characteristic of reverse lo-gistics networks. In the model, the supply characteristics are expressed in terms of the parameters ρ, reflecting the supply volume, and γ, capturing supply qual-ity. In this setting, supply uncertainty concerns variations in both of these pa-rameters. Figure 3 illustrates the reverse logistics costs per unit as a function of the supply density. Specifically, the solid graph depicts $C_{R2}(\rho)$, i.e., the unit cost function in case of local testing (see Equation (6)). As expected, one observes economies of scale since more concentrated supply allows for more efficient transportation and processing. In order to illustrate the impact of uncertainty in the supply volume, the dashed graph in Figure 3 displays the corresponding costs for a fixed network structure with $I_R = I_R^*(\rho=0.2)$. The figure shows that the cost penalty for deviating from the optimal network design is very small in this example. We only find a significant difference between both cost functions in case of very low supply volumes.

This observation can be generalized as follows. From (1) and (3) we see that unit costs as a function of I_R have the form $c + \alpha \sqrt{I_R} + \beta / I_R$. As in the case of the EOQ-formula, this function turns out to be extremely 'flat' around its mini-mum. Specifically, one can show that a deviation by a factor $1+\varepsilon$ from the optimum entails a relative cost penalty of less than $\varepsilon^2 / 3(1+\varepsilon)$. In addition, Equa-tion (5) shows that a relative error ε in ρ leads to a relative error of at most ε 2/3 in I_R. Putting both of these relations together, one finds, for example, that an error of 50 percent in ρ entails an eventual cost penalty of less than 3 percent. This documents that the reverse logistics network design is fairly ro-bust and may be based on rough supply estimates. Supply uncertainty has little effect in this context. It should be noted, though, that the *level* of the reverse logistics costs does depend on the supply volume (see Figure 3) and that uncer-tainty does play a role in the decision of whether or not to set up a recovery process at all.

While the analysis concerns only one of the parameters and one of the cost functions, the other cases exhibit a fairly similar behavior. I_R^* is independent of γ and there is no cost penalty in $C_{R2}(.)$ for a misjudgment of this parameter. With respect to the area assigned to central testing and grading, Equation (7) shows that error propagation, both with respect to ρ and γ is limited. One should note that choosing a critical distance r' different from r^* only affects the reverse logistics costs for supply locations at a distance between r^* and r' from the recovery facility. The average cost penalty across the entire service region is again small for moderate deviations from the optimal network design. This confirms earlier results based on MILP models (see Fleischmann et al., 2001).

This robustness of reverse logistics networks also has important implications for the potential integration of 'forward' and 'reverse' logistics operations. It can be expected to leave a fair amount of flexibility for using joint locations, such as colocating test and grade operations with distribution centers, which may allow for exploiting economies of scale (see also Section 2).

Another aspect of the 'integration' issue concerns the compatibility of reverse logistics networks with logistics structures already in place. We may extend the above cost model to include both 'forward' and 'reverse' network parts (see also Figure 1). We can then determine the optimal size of the service area covered by a single recovery facility. If demand and collection densities are roughly proportional, the resulting area is characterized by an expression analogous with (5) where ρ is replaced by $\delta + \rho (1-\gamma)$. However, this means that the impact of variations in the collection density is even smaller in this case. Therefore, one may expect little difficulties with respect to the compliance of reverse logistics with previously designed distribution structures. This is again in line with earlier findings (Fleischmann et al., 2001).

The results may be different if the densities, ρ and δ, are far from proportional. Reverse logistics programs may call for substantial changes in the overall network design if supply and demand are located in largely different areas, such as collection of used products in industrialized countries for 'secondhand' sales in developing countries. Another example reported in literature where reverse logistics has a significant impact on the overall network structure concerns the substitution of virgin raw materials that strongly influence the 'forward' network, such as in the pulp and paper industry (Fleischmann et al., 2001; see also Section 4.1). While, again, one may modify the above model for capturing these situations, we omit a detailed development here since results appear to be rather intuitive.

5. Conclusions and Outlook

In this chapter we have addressed the structure and design of reverse logistics networks. We have delineated this topic as concerning the logistics structures that link the different physical processes of a closed-loop supply chain. Numerous examples from various industries highlight the prime importance of reverse logistics networks as an issue that largely impacts the profitability of any closed-loop chain. In order to structure the discussion, we have considered specific network design issues for each of the closed-loop channel functions, namely acquisition and collection, testing and grading, reprocessing, and redistribution. Contrasting our observations with logistics network design in a more traditional context, three main issues have been highlighted that appear to be specific of reverse logistics networks.

First, the need for testing and grading entails a particular centralization-decentralization tradeoff when it comes to the network structure. What distinguishes this situation is the fact that goods flows can only be assigned to a definite destination after testing. Therefore, testing and grading close to the source may reduce transportation costs, in particular by separating scrap from valuable resources. On the other hand, investment costs for test equipment may call for a more centralized operation. In Section 4 we have captured this tradeoff in a quantitative model, illustrating the impact of several parameters, such as transportation costs, collection volume, and scrap rate. Finally, it appears interesting to see whether new advances in IT that facilitate remote testing may change the balance in this tradeoff.

Second, uncertainty on the supply side is another key feature with which reverse logistics network design is confronted. Used products form a supply source that is much more variable and difficult to control than conventional 'virgin' resources with respect to volume, timing, and quality. Consequently, reverse logistics networks need particularly to be robust with respect to variations in flow volumes and composition. Quantitative analysis confirms the robustness of this property. The relevant logistics costs turn out to be fairly stable with respect to the network design. Therefore, a moderate deviation from the 'optimal' network structure results in low cost penalties. One may conclude that rough supply estimates, as opposed to more advanced stochastic models, may be sufficient for a company's reverse logistic network design. It should be noted, though, that this does not mean that supply uncertainty is irrelevant in this context. Supply variations may have a significant impact on the overall cost level and on the profitability of the closed-loop chain as a whole.

Third, integration and coordination of different inbound and outbound flows is key to reverse logistics. The discussion unfolded in this chapter should have made clear that reverse logistics networks should not be perceived as isolated objects, but rather as a part of some larger overall logistics structure. Both at the front and the back end, the actual 'reverse' network is linked with other logistics structures that one would typically consider as 'forward' networks. Interaction, coordination, and integration of these different structures are among the key logistics issues in managing closed-loop supply chains. More specifically, there may be synergies in terms of transportation or shared facilities, e.g., between collection and distribution, or between distribution of new and recovered products. At the same time, these opportunities raise a compatibility issue since reverse logistics networks often are not designed 'from scratch' but are added to existing logistics structures. A quantitative analysis puts this issue into perspective and suggests that there is enough flexibility in the design to exploit successfully potential synergies. While this does not mean that 'forward' and 'reverse' logistics operations should always be integrated (see also Section 2), it indicates that transportation economics do not prevent potential synergies from being realized.

Given the short history of reverse logistics, there are many issues yet to be explored. More specifically, the same is true for underlying network design aspects. To conclude this chapter, we list some issues that may stimulate further developments in this field.

Perhaps the most important aspect deserving more detailed analyses concerns the multiagent character of reverse logistics network design. While different roles in reverse logistics, such as collectors, intermediaries, and processors have been identified (see, e.g., Pohlen and Farris, 1992), their impact on the logistics network structure seems to have been largely neglected. Establishing general conclusions concerning this relation would surely be valuable. Moreover, all of the network design models referred to in Section 4 follow the perspective of one central decision maker. However, as emphasized in recent supply chain management philosophy, the interaction between different players with different goals and different market power is one of the important drivers of logistics systems. Addressing reverse logistics network design from this perspective may therefore be worthwhile. Potential issues include, e.g., revealing underlying incentives for different parties and analyzing the propagation of the aforementioned supply uncertainty through the reverse network.

Another important aspect that appears not to have been addressed in much depth yet concerns the role of inventories in reverse logistics networks. All of the above models largely focus on transportation considerations. However, inventory is well known to be an important factor determining the design of distribution networks. For example, risk-pooling and postponement play a major role in this context. Consequently, the impact of inventories on the structure of the reverse network undoubtedly deserves a close analysis. This step may call for a better understanding of the role of inventories in closed-loop supply chains. In traditional 'forward' chains, the function of inventories as a buffer between two value-adding activities is, in general, well understood; the situation in the 'reverse' chain requires further research.

Finally, reverse logistics issues related to a global supply chain scope appear to be another fruitful field. Throughout the past decade, we have witnessed the development of supply chains consisting of a large number of specialized parties globally. We question whether such a globalization is equally attractive for the reverse channel. Some potential obstacles, such as tax and cross-border waste transportation, have already been briefly discussed above. However, there may be more fundamental arguments concerning the role of the individual players within the channel. A thorough analysis of these issues seems indispensable for a better understanding of the inherent differences between forward and reverse channels and related business implications.

We conclude by noting that all of the above aspects underline once more the nature of reverse logistics as a novel element within an evolving integral logistics concept, rather than as an isolated topic on its own.

Acknowledgments

The author would like to thank the participants of the working group on Reverse Logistics Networks (Markus Biehl, Rommert Dekker, Monique French, Harry Groenevelt, Terry Harrison, Rajesh Piplani) during the seminar on Business Perspectives on Closed-Loop Supply Chains (Carnegie Bosch Institute, Pittsburgh, May 30 - June 2, 2001) for their valuable input, which greatly helped to compose the material presented in this chapter.

References

Barros A.I., R. Dekker, V. Scholten. 1998. A two-level network for recycling sand: A case study. *Eur. J. Oper. Res.* **110** 199-214.

Daganzo, C.F. 1999. *Logistic Systems Analysis.* Springer-Verlag, Berlin, Germany.

Duales System Deutschland. 2001. http://www.gruener-punkt.de/en (8.15.2001).

Dupont. 2001. Press release. June 6.

Fleischmann, M. 2001. *Quantitative Models for Reverse Logistics.* Springer-Verlag, Berlin, Germany.

—, P. Beullens, J.M. Bloemhof-Ruwaard, L.N. Van Wassenhove. 2001. The impact of product recovery on logistics network design. *Prod. Oper. Management* (forthcoming).

—, H.R. Krikke, R. Dekker, S.D.P. Flapper. 2000. A characterisation of logistics networks for product recovery. *Omega* **28**(6) 653-666.

Guide, V.D.R., Jr. 2000. Production planning and control for remanufacturing: Industry practice and research needs. *J. Oper. Management* **18**(4) 467-483.
IBM. 2000. Environment & well-being progress report..

Jayaraman, V., V.D.R. Guide, Jr., R. Srivastava. 1999. A closed-loop logistics model for remanufacturing. *J. Oper. Res. Soc.* **50** 497-508.

Kroon, L., G. Vrijens. 1995. Returnable containers: An example of reverse logistics. *Int. J. Phys. Distr. Log. Management* **25**(2) 56-68.

Listes, O., R. Dekker. 2001. Stochastic approaches for product recovery network design: A case study. Working Paper, Faculty of Economics, Erasmus University Rotterdam, The Netherlands.

Newton, D.J., M.J. Realff, J.C. Ammons. 1999. Carpet recycling: The value of co-operation and a robust approach to determining the reverse production system design. In: Flapper, S.D.P., A.J. de Ron (eds.). *Proceedings of the Second International Working Seminar on Reuse*, pp. 207-216, Eindhoven, The Netherlands.

NVMP. 2001. http://www.nvmp.nl (8.15.2001).

Pohlen, T.L., M.T. Farris II. 1992. Reverse logistics in plastic recycling. *Int. J. Phys. Distr. Log. Management* **22**(7) 35-47.

Realff, M.J., J.C. Ammons, D. Newton. 1999. Carpet recycling: determining the reverse production system design. *J. of Polymer-Plastics Technology and Engr.* **38** 547-567.

Spengler, T., H. Puechert, T. Penkuhn, O. Rentz. 1997. Environmental integrated production and recycling management. *Eur. J. Oper. Res.* **97** 308-326.

Thierry, M., M. Salomon, J.A.E.E. van Nunen, L.N. Van Wassenhove. 1995. Strategic issues in product recovery management. *Calif. Management Rev.* **37**(2) 114-135.

Contact:

Moritz Fleischmann
Erasmus University Rotterdam
Faculty of Business Administration
PO Box 1738
NL-3000 DR Rotterdam
The Netherlands

Email: mfleischmann@fac.fbk.eur.nl

PRODUCTION PLANNING AND CONTROL OF CLOSED-LOOP SUPPLY CHAINS

Karl Inderfurth, Otto von Guericke University Magdeburg, Germany
Ruud H. Teunter, Erasmus University Rotterdam, The Netherlands

1. Introduction

Closed-loop supply chains are characterized by the recovery of returned products. In most of these chains (e.g., glass, metal, paper, computers, copiers), used products (also known as *cores*) are returned by or collected from customers. But returned products can also come from production facilities within the supply chain (production defectives, by-products). In cases with internal returns, recovery is often referred to as rework.

There are two main types of recovery: remanufacturing (product/part recovery) and recycling (material recovery). Energy recovery via incineration could be considered a third type. Combinations of different recovery types are also possible. It is often not easy to decide what the best product recovery strategy is. Moreover, for a number of reasons, it is difficult to plan and control operations in closed-loop supply chains.

Based on a literature review, Guide (2000) lists the following complicating characteristics for planning and controlling a supply chain with remanufacturing of external returns:
1. the requirement for a reverse logistics network
2. the uncertain timing and quality of cores
3. the disassembly of cores
4. the uncertainly in materials recovered from cores
5. the problems of stochastic routings for materials and highly variable processing times
6. the complication of material matching restrictions
7. the need to balance returns of cores with demands for remanufactured products

Many of these complicating issues also characterize the planning and control of a supply chain with remanufacturing of internal returns, though often to a lesser degree. We discuss each of the seven complicating characteristics separately, and also mention an additional one.

The first three complicating characteristics concern closed-loop supply chains with external returns in general (with remanufacturing, recycling, incineration or combinations of these recovery options). Cores have to be collected from end-users before they can be recovered. This requires decisions on the number of collection points (take-back centers), incentives for core returns, and transportation methods from the collection points to recovery facilities (characteristic 1). The timing of a return depends on the uncertain life of a product, and the quality of a return is influenced by the uncertain intensity of use. These uncertainties complicate capacity planning and inventory control for recovery operations (characteristic 2). A core can often be disassembled in many different ways. This requires decisions on the type of disassembly, e.g., partial or complete, destructive or nondestructive (characteristic 3).

The remaining characteristics only concern remanufacturing systems. Due to the uncertain quality of cores, there is uncertainty about the possibility to remanufacture parts/materials (characteristic 4). The uncertain quality of cores also causes stochastic routings for materials and highly variable processing times (characteristic 5). In some industries (e.g., aviation), it is required that a product/component is remanufactured using the original 'serial-number-specific' parts (characteristic 6). Finally, there is a need to balance core returns and demands for remanufactured products (characteristic 7). Imperfect correlation between demands and returns may lead to excess stocks of repaired/remanufactured products/components. This holds especially if there are different needs for components/parts of the same product, since those components/parts are normally disassembled at the same time.

We want to mention an additional complicating characteristic for supply chains where products are manufactured as well as remanufactured, i.e., closed-loop supply chains of original equipment manufacturers (OEMs). In such chains, the manufacturing and remanufacturing operations have to be coordinated (characteristic 8) to prevent capacity shortages and excess stocks.

The planning and control of supply chains with internal returns also suffers from many of the above mentioned characteristics (2-5,7,8). Often this is to a lesser degree, due to reduced uncertainties. But on the other hand, returns are immediate and hence jointly planning and controlling production and rework operations can be even more crucial. Moreover, production and rework operations often share the same resources and produced/reworked products compete for the same storage space.

Due to all these complicating characteristics, planning and controlling a closed-loop supply chain is a complex task. Well-known concepts and techniques for planning/controlling supply chains are not always (directly) useful for closed-loop supply chains. Researchers have therefore developed new techniques or proposed modifications of existing techniques. In this chapter, we will discuss some of their findings. We remark that only the most practical findings, in our view, will be discussed. We refer interested readers to (Gungor and Gupta, 1999) for a recent and complete overview of all the findings in this research area.

The remainder of the chapter is organized as follows. In Section 2 we restrict our focus on disassembly and recovery operations in closed-loop supply chains. We discuss methods for finding all possible disassembly/recovery strategies, for comparing those strategies, for picking the best one, and for scheduling the disassembly/recovery operations. In Sections 3 and 4 we consider the whole closed-loop supply chain, with external and internal returns. In those sections, we discuss methods for jointly planning and controlling disassembly, recovery, assembly, and (for OEMs) manufacturing operations. We end with some concluding remarks in Section 5.

2. Disassembly and recovery

Disassembly may be defined as a systematic method for separating a product into its constituent modules, parts, etc. (to be referred to as assemblies) (Gupta and Veerakamolmal, 1994). Disassembly plays an important role in product recovery (Jovane et al., 1993). Obviously, assemblies have to be disassembled before they can be recovered. But even products that are recovered as a whole, e.g., copier machines that are sold on a secondary market, often require partial or complete disassembly, followed by cleaning, testing, and possible repair/ replacement of assemblies, before they can be reassembled. Exceptions are products that can be reused directly, e.g., containers and unopened commercial returns. Many companies, e.g., Air France, Lufthansa, BMW, Volkswagen,

Daimler-Chrysler, Nissan, Océ, Xerox, and Philips, operate large-scale disassembly plants.

In many cases disassembly is not simply the reverse of assembly. The operational aspects of disassembly are quite different from those of assembly systems (Brennan et al., 1994, Lambert, 1999). Some of the key aspects of disassembly systems are the following:

- There is uncertainty about the timing and number of core returns.
- There is uncertainty about the quality of cores (and their assemblies).
- Cores may not need to be disassembled completely.
- One can choose between disassembly processes (destructive, nondestructive), depending on the type of recovery that is aimed for.
- There is a large number of demand sources (one for each assembly) and a corresponding need for multiple demand forecasts.

Due to these complicating aspects, a disassembly system is difficult to control. Below, we will present a list of steps that can be used as a guideline for the control of a disassembly system. Afterwards, these steps will be discussed in detail. Ideally, all steps should be considered in the listed order. We remark that product design issues (*design for recovery [DFR]; design for disassembly [DFD]*) are considered to be outside the scope of this chapter, and are therefore not included in the list. We refer interested readers to (Moyer and Gupta, 1997) for a review of DFR and DFD in the electronics industries. The list of steps is as follows:

1. For each type of core: Based on technical and environmental restrictions, identify all possible/efficient disassembly strategies. A disassembly strategy is characterized by the *disassembly set* (the set of assemblies that are disassembled), by the *disassembly processes*, and by the *disassembly sequence*. Note that there can be multiple disassembly strategies with the same disassembly set, but with different disassembly processes and/or a different disassembly sequence. We remark that the possibilities for disassembling a core can depend on its quality. If so, then each disassembly strategy is actually a collection of disassembly strategies for every possible state of the core. The quality can be assessed through initial testing of the core and/or testing of assemblies at a later stage.

2. For each disassembly strategy of each type of core: Identify the recovery options (e.g., remanufacturing, recycling, incineration) for each of the assemblies in the disassembly set. We remark that the availability of a recovery option for a disassembled assembly can depend on the disassembly processes. For instance, remanufacturing an assembly might be an option after carefully removing it from a core (*nondestructive disassembly*), but not after tearing it from the core by brute force (*destructive disassembly*). We further remark that the availability of a recovery option for an assembly can depend on its quality (see the first step). We will call the combination of a disassembly strategy and of a recovery option for each of the assemblies in the disassembly set a *disassembly/recovery strategy*.

3. For each disassembly/recovery strategy of each type of core: Determine the net profit of a strategy by adding the net profits associated with recovery, disassembly, and disposal. That is, add the net recovery revenues for all assemblies in the disassembly set, and subtract all disassembly costs and disposal costs.

4. For each type of core: Based on a comparison of the net profits of disassembly/recovery strategies (and possibly also based on environmental legislation and/or on a comparison of the environmental impact of strategies), choose the best disassembly/recovery strategy.

5. For all types of cores together, given the disassembly/recovery strategy for each type of core that has been chosen in the previous step: Forecast demands for all assemblies that are in the disassembly set of one or more types of cores, and use those forecasts to schedule the disassembly operations (*disassembly scheduling*). Note that an assembly might be in the disassembly set of multiple types of cores, i.e., there can be 'component commonality'. Furthermore, disassembly operations for different types of cores might share the same equipment. Hence, scheduling the disassembly operations for all types of cores together is a complex task.

To the best of our knowledge, no researchers have addressed all these steps. However, many authors discussed one or more of the steps and proposed/tested methods that can aid in performing those steps. In the remainder of this section, we will discuss and sometimes modify some of their findings. This is done for Steps 1 and 2 in Section 2.1, for Steps 3 and 4 in Section 2.2, and for Step 5 in Section 2.3.

2.1 Steps 1 and 2: Identifying/comparing all possible disassembly strategies and the associated recovery options

In identifying all possible/efficient disassembly strategies for a core, the key role is played by the geometrical structure, though mechanical factors such as force and friction are also relevant (Chen et al., 1997; Dutta and Woo, 1995). The feasibility of recovery options associated with a disassembly strategy depends on technical, commercial and ecological feasibility criteria (Krikke et al., 1998). We will not discuss these technical issues in detail here, since our focus is on the optimal control of a disassembly system. We shall simply assume that the set of possible/efficient disassembly strategies and the associated recovery options are given, and focus on comparing the strategies in that set. For ease of presentation, we first assume that there are no variations in the quality of assemblies or uncertainties about disassembly yields. At the end of this section, however, we will discuss situations where these assumptions do not hold.

The easiest way to compare disassembly strategies is by representing them in a disassembly graph/tree, based on the geometrical structure of the product (Arai et al., 1995; Chen et al., 1997; Dutta and Woo, 1995; Johnson and Wang, 1998; Krikke et al., 1998; Lambert, 1997, 1999; Penev and de Ron, 1996; Pnueli and Zussman, 1997; Spengler et al., 1997; Veerakamolmal et al., 1998a; Yan and Gu, 1994; Zussman et al., 1994). Recall from the previous section, that the availability of a recovery option for a certain assembly can depend on the processes that are used to disassemble it. This holds especially for the remanufacturing option, which is only available if an assembly is obtained via nondestructive disassembly. Hence, it seems best to compare strategies in a disassembly graph that indicates the availability of recovery options. Furthermore, this graph should allow multiple disassembly strategies with the same disassembly set, but with different disassembly operations and/or a different disassembly sequence (see also the previous section).

An example of such a disassembly graph for a product is given in Figure 1. There, we assume that there are two recovery options for assemblies: recycling and remanufacturing. Moreover, all assemblies (including the product A and module B) can be recycled, and remanufacturing is only possible after nondestructive disassembly. We remark that these assumptions are for clarity of representation only. In Section 2.2, we show how such a disassembly graph can be used to determine the optimal disassembly/recovery strategy.

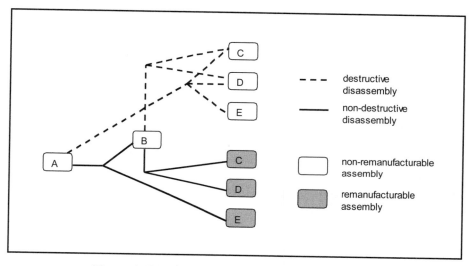

Figure 1: Disassembly graph for a 3-parts product

Variations in the quality of assemblies and uncertainties about disassembly yields can easily be incorporated in a disassembly tree. An assembly with a number of quality classes can be copied into the same number of assemblies. Uncertain disassembly yields can be modeled by splitting disassembly lines. Consider the three-part product in Figure 1, for instance, and assume that Part E is not always remanufacturable after nondestructive disassembly. Then Figure 1 can be modified accordingly, by splitting the disassembly line from the product A to a remanufacturable Part E into two lines (one to the remanufacturable Part E and the other to the nonremanufacturable Part E) and indicating the associated probabilities. See also (Krikke et al., 1998, 1999).

2.2 Steps 3 and 4: Determining the best disassembly/recovery strategy

Let us continue the example of Section 2.1 that was graphically represented in Figure 1. Assume that the net profits associated with recovery, disassembly, and disposal are as given in Table 1. Note that the net recycling profits for the product and for the module are smaller than the summed net recycling profits for their parts. This is a result of the increased material purity when recycling is preceded by disassembly.

	Product A	Module B	Part C	Part D	Part E
Disposal	-4	-3	-1	-2	-1
Recycling	4	3	2	3	2
Remanufacturing	—	—	4	4	10
Destructive disassembly	-3	-1	—	—	—
Nondestructive disassembly	-5	-5	—	—	—

Table 1: Net profits for the three-part product (see Figure 1)

Using Figure 1 and Table 1, it is easy to determine the net profit of any disassembly/recovery strategy. Consider, for instance, the following strategy: disassemble a core in a destructive way, and recycle all three parts. The net profit of this policy is $-3+2+3+2=4$. By comparing the net profits of all possible disassembly/recovery strategies, the best strategy can be determined. For this example, the optimal strategy is: disassemble a core in a nondestructive way, remanufacture Part E, disassemble module B in a destructive way, and recycle Parts C and D. The associated net profit is $-5+10-1+2+3=9$.

Of course, for products with many modules/parts, the number of possible disassembly/recovery strategies can be enormous. Fortunately, the disassembly tree-structure can be exploited to determine the best (profit-maximizing) strategy in an efficient way, using either dynamic programming (DP) (Krikke et al., 1998, 1999; Penev and de Ron, 1996) or mixed-integer linear programming (MILP) (Johnson and Wang, 1998; Lambert, 1999; Spengler et al., 1997). In our view, DP is the easiest and most insightful approach, and hence we will illustrate its use for the product depicted in Figure 1.

The DP algorithm first considers decisions for the lowest level items (Parts C, D and E in Figure 1) and then 'moves up' in the tree until it reaches the root level (the product itself). So we first consider the three parts. Based on the net profits given in Table 1, it is easy to see that (for all parts) recycling is the best available recovery option after destructive disassembly, and that remanufacturing is the best option after nondestructive disassembly. Next consider Module B. The net profits associated with destructive and nondestructive disassembly are respectively, $-1+2+3=4$ and $-5+4+4=3$. So Module B should be disassembled in a destructive way, after which Parts C and D should be recycled. Finally, consider the product A. The net profits associated with destructive and nondestructive disassembly are, respectively, $-3+2+3+2=4$ and $-5+(-1+2+3)+10=9$. So the best strategy is as mentioned before.

The DP algorithm can also be used if assemblies vary in quality and if disassembly yields are uncertain. Recall from the previous section, that the disassembly tree should be modified in those cases by introducing multiple quality copies of assemblies and by splitting disassembly lines. To illustrate that DP still works, consider the product in Figure 1 again, but assume that Part E is remanufacturable after nondestructive disassembly in only 80 percent of the cases (no quality variations or other yield uncertainties). Then the net profits associated with destructive and nondestructive disassembly of the product are, respectively, $-3+2+3+2=4$ and $-5+(-1+2+3)+(0.8*10+0.2*2)=7.4$. So the best strategy remains unchanged, though the associated net profit is lower.

We end this section with a remark on the net profits for recovery options. We assumed throughout this section that the profit for recovering an assembly is fixed and hence independent of the number of assemblies that are recovered. As a result, all assemblies of a certain type are recovered in the same (best) way. This seems reasonable for assemblies that are recycled, since demand for the resulting raw materials is (almost) unlimited. But the limited demand/need for remanufactured assemblies might make it unprofitable to remanufacture all the available assemblies. In such cases, different recovery strategies should be used for cores, depending on the demand for remanufactured assemblies in various markets. This issue of limited demand is also relevant for disassembly scheduling, which will be discussed in the next section.

2.3 Step 5: Disassembly scheduling

After completing Steps 1 to 4, the disassembly strategy for each type of core is fixed. What remains is to schedule the disassembly operations for all types of cores. This is a complex task. Compared to assembly scheduling in a traditional assembly environment, there are two important complicating factors. First, there is a separate demand source for each assembly that is in the disassembly set of one or more types of cores. Second, there is uncertainty about the timing and numbers of core returns.

Researchers (Gupta and Veerakamolmal, 1994; Veerakamolmal and Gupta, 1998b; Taleb et al., 1997ab) on disassembly scheduling have circumvented these complications. They focus on a planning horizon for which demands are fixed and known. They further assume that unlimited numbers of cores are available, and that all disassembly lead times are fixed. Under these strict assumptions, the problem of finding the best disassembly schedule is still tractable.

In fact, under the above restrictions, the optimal disassembly schedule can be determined using integer programming (IP) (Veerakamolmal and Gupta, 1998b). However, as is remarked in Taleb and Gupta (1997b), the computational complexity of IP is considerable for large systems. Alternatively, one can use a heuristic procedure to find a reasonable, though not necessarily optimal, disassembly schedule. We end this section with a summary of the heuristic approach that is proposed in Taleb and Gupta (1997b). This approach is only valid under the previously mentioned assumptions, but it does allow for the existence of common parts and/or materials in different products.

In the first step of the heuristic approach (Taleb and Gupta, 1997b), the 'core' algorithm ignores the timing of the demands for assemblies, and determines a feasible (satisfying all demands over the entire planning horizon) set of cores that have to be disassembled. In building that feasible set of cores, cores are added sequentially based on the associated profit and on the remaining demands for assemblies. After a feasible set has been determined, the 'allocation' algorithm then determines the exact times at which the disassembly of cores in the set should start.

3. Closed-loop Supply Chains with External Returns

3.1 Planning and Scheduling Issues

In Section 2, we discussed methods for comparing product disassembly and recovery strategies. In this section, we will discuss planning and scheduling issues for closed-loop supply chains with external returns if a remanufacturing strategy is chosen. So we consider cases where either whole cores or certain assemblies of cores are remanufactured. Recall from Section 1 that these are the most complicated cases from a production planning and control (PPC) point of view. Tasks like demand management, master production scheduling, capacity planning, materials requirements planning, and production scheduling have to cope with many complicating characteristics.

Demand management has to tackle the problem of balancing demands for remanufactured products with returns of remanufacturable cores. Since remanufacturing capabilities are restricted by the inflow of cores, demand planning depends on the degree of knowledge a firm has about the inflow process. Typically, this degree is low. Due to the occurrence of major uncertainties, it is very difficult to predict the number of remanufacturable products that will become available in future time intervals. Main sources of uncertainty result from limited predictability of quantity and timing of core returns, as well as of core quality and material recovery rates. Suitable forecasting procedures (e.g., Goh and Varaprasad, 1986; Krupp, 1992) and core sourcing activities (e.g., Krupp, 1993) are measures to limit major uncertainties. Thus, it is obvious that in a remanufacturing environment, an integrated demand and returns management is necessary.

Material and capacity requirements planning faces uncertain processing operations and uncertain material requirements caused by variations in the quality of used products. This requires restructuring of both the bill of material (BOM) and the bill of resources (BOR), as well as adjustments in planned lead times. Integrated disassembly and assembly BOMs and specific (quality-dependent) BOMs for different disassembly and remanufacturing options have been suggested (Krupp, 1993; Flapper, 1994). Yield and lead-time adjustments have to protect against major uncertainties in recovery rates and processing times. Material matching faces specific challenges in situations where core suppliers stay owners of the products and require that the same units be returned (Guide and Srivastava, 1998).

Uncertainties in routings and material processing times require modified BOR approaches for both rough-cut capacity planning and capacity requirements planning (Dowlatshahi, 2000). Guide and Spencer (1997a) propose to modify the BOR calculations using empirical (and regularly updated) occurrence factors for variable routings and material recovery rate factors for probabilistic recovery yields. They show that modified rough-cut capacity planning BOR techniques outperform the standard approaches (Guide et al., 1997).

For all these PPC tasks, it is most of all the high level and variety of uncertainties that require modifications in PPC systems for remanufacturing environments. In this respect, it is important to distinguish between companies that are only engaged in the remanufacturing business and those that also manufacture original products or components, i.e., OEMs.

Uncertainty in the remanufacturing environment may be smaller for OEMs. Better knowledge of original products and their markets, potential application of lease contracts, higher efforts in design for remanufacturing, and other factors allow for higher predictability of returns and more standardization and stability in the remanufacturing processes. Thus, planning and scheduling tasks are confronted with less complexity. On the other hand, for materials planning there is the additional problem of coordinating manufacturing and remanufacturing activities (see Section 1). This challenging coordination problem will be treated in more detail in the following section.

3.2 Materials Planning for OEMs

Materials planning in a hybrid manufacturing/remanufacturing environment is concerned with both disassembly and reassembly stages, in order to take the material impact from remanufacturing fully into account. Thus, a large number of different options in materials treatment, including the option to dispose of parts, components, or even cores, has to be integrated in the planning system. Even if uncertainties do not play a major role, this complex task cannot be fulfilled by simple MRP-based approaches, but has to be tackled by advanced planning methods. In Clegg et al. (1995) and Uzsoy and Venkatachalam (1998), linear programming (LP) models are suggested for optimal decision support in such difficult materials planning situations. In a more practical-oriented approach, the problem is simplified by separating the disassembly part from the combined reassembly and manufacturing part. Disassembly planning is carried out as described in Section 1 leading to standard options, which are chosen mainly depending on the quality of returned products. Thus, given or expected return volumes of remanufacturable components or products are available for coordinated materials planning for manufacturing and remanufacturing processes.

Under the separation described above, it will be shown how the standard MRP approach can be extended to incorporate return flows and availability of components or products after disassembly and remanufacturing operations in a hybrid system. We remark that there is widespread use of standard PPC systems, including MRP systems for material procurement (Panisset, 1988), in the remanufacturing business. This holds especially for firms employing a make-to-stock strategy (Guide, 2000).

As an example we use the product introduced in Figure 1 and direct our attention to joint disassembly/reassembly and regular manufacturing operations. Figure 2 shows the original manufacturing steps for producing product A, as well as additional opportunities for regaining subassembly B from a low quality core A', or regaining the entire product A from a high quality core A''.

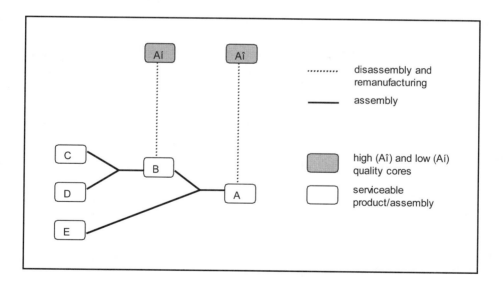

Figure 2: Assembly graph (bill of materials) for a 3-parts product

Lead times for respective operations are given in Table 2.

Operations	A from B+E	B from C+D	A from A"	B from A'	E	D	C
Lead times (weeks)	1	1	1	2	2	1	1

Table 2: Lead times for the manufacturing/remanufacturing example

As for systems without remanufacturing options, MRP can be applied in a level-by-level procedure performing the standard steps like exploding the BOM, netting gross requirements, lotsizing, and offsetting order releases. The coordination problem arises for those components that can be remanufactured as well as manufactured. In order to demonstrate the MRP extensions necessary for coping with the coordination task, we will demonstrate the respective MRP calculations for subassembly B, which can either be produced from parts C and D, or regained from used core A'.

For clarifying the specific extensions, we first present the standard MRP record (without a remanufacturing option) in Table 3. The numbers in bold are input data. Standard MRP calculations lead to the complete MRP record. Safety stocks and lot sizing are not considered in this example.

Current		Time period 1	2	3	4
Gross Requirements		**20**	**10**	**5**	**15**
Scheduled Receipts		**8**			
Projected on Hand	**14**	2	0	0	0
Net Requirements		0	8	5	15
Planned Order Receipts			8	5	15
Planned Order Releases		8	5	15	

Table 3: Standard MRP record for subassembly B

If we include the remanufacturing option, then a number of lines have to be added to the standard MRP record. These provide information on the expected number of remanufacturable core returns, projected on-hand inventory of remanufacturables as well as planned order receipts, planned order releases, and scheduled receipts concerning remanufacturing. If there is a disposal option for remanufacturables, then an additional line with information on planned order releases for disposal has to be included.

Furthermore, a priority rule for fulfilling net requirements is needed. For instance, remanufacturing could always be given priority over manufacturing (as long as remanufacturables are available). This rule is sensible if remanufacturing is less costly than manufacturing. If there is a disposal option for remanufacturables, then a disposal decision rule is also needed, for instance, limit stock of remanufacturables to a certain threshold. That threshold may be the storage capacity or may result from an economic trade-off between holding costs and remanufacturing versus manufacturing cost savings (Inderfurth and Jensen, 1999).

Table 4 gives the extended MRP record. Compared to Table 3, it includes additional input data, the expected return flows, and the current stock of remanufacturables. The 'remanufacturing first' priority rule is employed, and a disposal limit of ten items is prespecified. Table 4 shows how planned order releases for all activities (disposal, remanufacturing and manufacturing) develop over time, taking into consideration the respective lead times. As in Table 3, the numbers in bold are input data.

| | Time period | | | |
Current	1	2	3	4
Gross Requirements	**20**	**10**	**5**	**15**
Scheduled Receipts Manufacturing	**8**			
Scheduled Receipts Remanufacturing	**2**	**5**		
Projected Serviceables on Hand **14**	4	0	0	0
Net Requirements	0	1	5	15
Expected Returns Remanufacturables	**9**	**4**	**0**	**4**
Projected Remanufacturables on Hand **8**	10	4		
Planned Order Receipts Remanufacturing			5	10
Planned Order Receipts Manufacturing	1	0	5	
Planned Order Release Disposal	2	0		
Planned Order Release Remanufacturing	5	10		
Planned Order Release Manufacturing	1	0	5	

Table 4: Extended MRP record for subassembly B

We remark that alternative decision rules can also be applied. The push-rule, for instance, suggests to immediately remanufacture all units available. Of course, this will lead to order releases different from those presented in Table 3. In addition to implementing the MRP approach in a rolling horizon framework, uncertainties in returns and lead-times can be taken into account by using safety stocks and/or safety lead times as means of protection. In this situation, not only determining the size of the safety stock but also dividing it between serviceable and remanufacturable items is a relevant issue. Recent research gives some indication that compared to decision rules from stochastic inventory control, an appropriate implementation of safety stocks and – under specific conditions – of safety lead times, guarantees a high level of MRP performance even in situations with considerable uncertainties (Inderfurth, 1998; Gotzel and Inderfurth, 2001).

The cost-optimal determination of safety stocks in a hybrid manufacturing/ remanufacturing system is a very challenging problem. Helpful support for its solution can be given by stochastic inventory control models, which are addressed in another chapter of this book. Optimization models from inventory control can also contribute to provide helpful suggestions for lotsizing in the materials planning context for integrated manufacturing and remanufacturing problems.

3.3 Shop floor control

To the best of our knowledge, there is no literature on shop floor control for mixed manufacturing/remanufacturing environments, i.e., environments where the remanufacturer is also the OEM (see Section 3.1). Shop floor control for 'pure' remanufacturing environments has been studied by Guide and co-workers in a series of papers (Guide et al., 1996, 1997bcde, 1998, 1999). In these simulation studies, priority dispatching rules and reprocessing release mechanisms are evaluated. The early papers mainly focus on priority dispatching rules. The results show that simple due date (e.g., earliest due date) rules dominate other priority rules. The two most recent papers (Guide et al., 1998, 1999) concentrate on reprocessing release mechanisms. These last two papers are especially interesting, since they analyze a simulation model that is grounded in actual practice. This model captures more of the complexities of a remanufacturing environment than the models that were analyzed in earlier studies. We will describe the model below and summarize the results of Guide et al. (1998, 1999).

The simulation model of Guide et al. (1998, 1999) divides a remanufacturing facility into three shops: a Disassembly Shop, a Reprocessing Shop and a Reassembly Shop. Between these shops are the Reprocessing Buffer and the Reassembly Buffer. See Figure 3. We remark that we modified some of the shop and buffer names. If a disassembly order is released, then a product is disassembled in the Disassembly Shop. Disassembled assemblies are added to the Reprocessing Buffer, from where they are released to the Reprocessing Shop following some reprocessing release mechanism. In the Reprocessing Shop, an assembly is routed through the work centers until it is completely reprocessed. All work centers use earliest due date priority dispatching rules. Reprocessed assemblies are added to the Reassembly Buffer. As soon as a complete set of assemblies is available there, those assemblies are released to the Reassembly Shop.

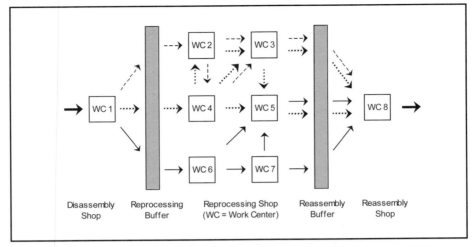

Figure 3: A typical remanufacturing facility (Guide et al., 1998; 1999)

As remarked before, the simulation model captures many of the complexities of a real remanufacturing environment. The disassembly times, reprocessing times at work centers, and reassembly times are stochastic. The routing of an assembly through the reprocessing work centers is probabilistic, and assemblies are allowed to return to previously visited work centers. A product can be composed of common assemblies, of serial number-specific assemblies (which have to be reassembled into the same product), or of a mixture of both types. However, the model does assume that the assembly recovery rates are 100 percent. This allows the restricted focus on the remanufacturing facility. In practical situations where recovery rates are less then 100 percent, procurement/manufacturing operations also have to be considered.

The main conclusions of Guide et al. (1998, 1999) are as follows:

- Most attention should be paid to operations scheduling for serial number-specific assemblies. These assemblies should spend all or most of their waiting time in the Reassembly Buffer, so these assemblies should be released directly or shortly after they enter the Reprocessing Buffer. Release mechanisms that hold serial number-specific assemblies in the Reprocessing Buffer for long time periods perform very poorly.

- For common assemblies, the choice of the reprocessing release mechanism is less important. The differences between the performances of different mechanisms are less significant. In some cases, the best mechanism

166

for common assemblies is to release them directly, as for serial number-specific assemblies. In other cases, it is better that the waiting time is divided between the two buffer locations. This can be achieved by applying a time-phased, minimum flow time reprocessing release mechanism for common assemblies. See Guide et al. (1998, 1999) for a definition of this mechanism.

- Time-phased, due date reprocessing release mechanisms (lead-time offsets as in standard materials requirements planning) perform poorly for common assemblies and very poorly for serial number-specific assemblies. The high degree of lead-time (especially disassembly time) variability makes due date mechanisms ineffective in coordinating the flow of assemblies to arrive at a common time in the Reassembly Buffer.

- Product structure complexity does not impact the performance of reprocessing release decision, but the degree of variation in the lead-times does.

4. Closed-loop Supply Chains with Internal Returns (Rework)

A specific situation in the context of closed-loop supply chains is given if returns of products do not come from external customers but from internal production facilities. This occurs when manufacturing not only results in good products, but also in reworkable production rejects. Rework is not only an issue in poor-quality manufacturing companies. In some industries, like the semiconductor or the chemical industries, production processes are simply not completely controllable. In the latter we often find production output in the form of by-products, which can be used as inputs again in the same or related production processes. Rework can be described as the set of all activities that are necessary to bring product rejects into a state that fulfills prespecified, usually as-good-as-new, qualifications. Thus, rework more or less resembles remanufacturing since it is connected with activities like testing, disassembly, cleaning, processing, and reassembly (Gupta and Chakraborty, 1984). However, systems with rework have some specific properties that have to be taken into consideration for production planning and control.

1. Production decisions immediately influence the return flow of reworkable products. Since rework operations replace future production, it is therefore essential that production and rework operations be jointly planned.

167

Inderfurth and Jensen (1999) show how the adjusted MRP approach for materials planning in hybrid manufacturing/remanufacturing systems, described in Section 3.2, can also be extended to systems with rework.

2. The inbound character of rework often is connected with a sharing of the same resources for production and rework operations. This creates a further need for integrating production planning and scheduling of both production and rework. A major task is setting up priority rules for scheduling rework operations in order to coordinate production and rework orders in a most cost- and/or time-effective way (e.g., Jewkes 1994, 1995).

3. Additional complexity in rework situations often arises from storage space and time restrictions, from perishability of reworkable products, and from the existence of preset technical lot sizes. Conditions of these kinds are typical for food and chemical production and are widespread in the process industry in general. They ask for adjusted production planning and control systems that still have to be developed in some areas (Flapper et al., 2001). The most advanced planning systems have been set up in the pharmaceutical and fine chemicals industries, where in-line rework in connection with a multistage batch production creates highly complex planning and control problems. In these cases, mixed-integer programming approaches are applied for integrated production, materials, and capacity planning (Kallrath, 1999; Teunter et al., 2000).

4. The return process usually is under closer control for rework systems. Nevertheless, product rejects or by-products normally result from unreliable production processes that are characterized by a variable and uncertain yield. Thus, uncertainty is also a major issue in production planning and control of rework, even if it may not be as dominant as in the remanufacturing environment. Although there is much research addressing production planning under stochastic yields (e.g., Yano and Lee, 1995, only few contributions consider production systems with rework options. Most consider the problem of buffer stock sizing as a means of protection against uncertainties in stochastic rework systems (e.g., Robinson et al., 1990; Denardo and Lee, 1996).

Summarizing, we can state that even though systems with rework resemble closed-loop materials supply systems with external returns in many respects, there are some differences which ask for specific production planning and control procedures. A comprehensive overview of research contributions on rework is given in Flapper and Jensen (2001).

5. Conclusions

More supply chains emerge that include a return flow of materials. Many original equipment manufacturers are nowadays engaged in the remanufacturing business. In many process industries, production defectives and by-products are reworked. These closed-loop supply chains deserve special attention. Production planning and control in such hybrid systems is a real challenge, especially due to increased uncertainties. Even companies that are engaged in remanufacturing operations only, face more complicated planning situations than traditional manufacturing companies.

We point out the main complicating characteristics in closed-loop systems with both remanufacturing and rework, and indicate the need for new or modified/extended production planning and control approaches. An overview of the existing scientific contributions is presented. But it appeared that we only stand at the beginning of this line of research, and that many more contributions are needed and expected in the future.

References

Arai, E., N. Uchiyama and M. Igoshi (1995) Disassembly path generation to verify the assemblability of mechanical products. *JSME International Journal – Series C* **38**(4): 805-810.

Brennan, L., S.M. Gupta, and K.N. Taleb (1994) Operations planning issues in an assembly/disassembly environment. *International Journal of Operations and Production Management* **14**(9): 57-67.

Chen, S.F., J.H. Oliver, S.Y. Chou, and L.L. Chen (1997) Parallel disassembly by onion peeling. *Journal of Mechanical Design* **119**(2): 267-274.

Clegg, A.J., D.J. Williams, and R. Uzsoy (1995) Production planning for companies with remanufacturing capability. Proceedings of the 1995 IEEE Symposium on Electronics and the Environment, IEEE, Orlando FL, 186-191.

Denardo, E.V. and T.Y.S. Lee (1996) Managing uncertainty in a serial production line. *Operations Research* 44: 382-392, 1996.

Dowlatshahi, S. (2000) Developing a theory of reverse logistics. *Interfaces* **30**(3): 143-155.

Dutta, D. and T.C. Woo (1995) Algorithm for multiple disassembly and parallel assemblies. *Journal of Engineering for Industry* **117**(1): 102-109.

Flapper, S.D.P. (1994) On the logistics aspects of integrating procurement, production and recycling by lean and agile-wise manufacturing companies. Proceedings 27th ISATA International Dedicated Conference on Lean/Agile Manufacturing in the Automotive Industries, Aachen, Germany, 749-756.

Flapper, S.D.P. and T. Jensen (2002) Planning and control of rework: a review. *International Journal of Production Research*, to be published in 2002.

Flapper, S.D.P., J.C. Fransoo, R.A.C.M. Broekmeulen, and K. Inderfurth (2002) Planning and control of rework in the process industries: a review. *Production Planning & Control* **13**(1): 26-34.

Gotzel, C. and K. Inderfurth (2002) Performance of MRP in product recovery systems with demand, return and leadtime uncertainties. In *Quantitative Approaches to Distribution Logistics and Supply Chain Management* (ed. by Klose, A., M.G. Speranza, and L.N. van Wassenhove), Berlin-Heidelberg, 99-114.

Guide, Jr., V.D.R. (2000) Production planning and control for remanufacturing: industry practice and research needs. *Journal of Operations Management* **18**(4): 467-483.

Guide, Jr., V.D.R. (1996) Scheduling using drum-buffer-rope in a remanufacturing environment. *International Journal of Production Research* **34**(4): 1081-1091.

Guide, Jr., V.D.R., V. Jayaraman and R. Srivastava (1999) The effect of lead time variation on the performance of reprocessing release mechanisms. *Computer & Industrial Engineering* **36**(4): 759-779.

Guide, Jr., V.D.R. and M.S. Spencer (1997a) Rough-cut capacity planning for remanufacturing firms. *Production Planning and Control* **8**(3): 237-244.

Guide, Jr., V.D.R. and R. Srivastava (1997b) An evaluation of order release strategies in a remanufacturing environment. *Computers and Operations Research* **24**(1): 37-47.
Guide, Jr., V.D.R. and R. Srivastava (1998) Inventory buffers in recoverable manufac-

turing. *Journal of Operations Management* **16**(5): 551-568.

Guide, Jr., V.D.R., R. Srivastava and M.E. Kraus (1997c) Product structure complexity and scheduling of operations in recoverable manufacturing. *International Journal of Production Research* **35**(11): 3179-3199.

Guide, Jr., V.D.R., R. Srivastava and M.E. Kraus (1997d) Scheduling policies for remanufacturing. *International Journal of Production Economics* **48**(2): 187-204.

Guide, Jr., V.D.R., R. Srivastava and M.S. Spencer (1997e) An evaluation of capacity planning techniques in a remanufacturing environment. *International Journal of Production Research* **35**(1): 67-82.

Goh, T.N. and N. Varaprasad (1986) A statistical methodology for the analysis of the life-cycle of reusable containers. *IIE Transactions* **18**(1): 42-47, 1986.

Gungor, A. and S.M. Gupta (1999) Issues in environmentally conscious manufacturing and product recovery: a survey. *Computer & Industrial Engineering* **36**(4): 811-853.

Gupta, T. and S. Chakraborty (1984) Looping in a multistage production system. *International Journal of Production Research* 22: 299-311, 1984.

Gupta, S.M. and K.N. Taleb (1994) Scheduling disassembly. *International Journal of Production Research* **32**(8): 1857-1866.

Inderfurth, K. (1998) *The performance of simple MRP driven policies for a product recovery system with lead-times.* Preprint 32/1998, Faculty of Economics and Management, University of Magdeburg, Germany.

Inderfurth, K. and T. Jensen (1999) Analysis of MRP policies with recovery options. in *Modelling and Decisions in Economics* (ed. by Leopold-Wildburger U. et al.), Heidelberg-New York, 189-228.

Jewkes, E. M. (1994) A queueing analysis of priority-based scheduling rules for a single-stage manufacturing system with repair. *IIE Transactions* 26: 80-86, 1994.

Jewkes, E. M. (1995) Optimal inspection effort and scheduling for a manufacturing process with repair. *European Journal of Operational Research* 85: 340-351, 1995.
Johnson, M.R. and M.H. Wang (1998) Economic evaluation of disassembly opera-

tions for recycling, remanufacturing and reuse. *International Journal of Production Research* **36**(12): 3227-3252.

Jovane, F., L. Alting, A. Armillotta, W. Eversheim, K. Feldmann. and G. Seliger (1993) A key issue in product life cycle: disassembly. *Annals of the CIRP* **42**(2): 640-672.

Kallrath, J. (1999) Mixed-integer nonlinear programming applications. *Operational Research in Industry* (ed. by Ciriani, S. et al.) London , 59-67, 1999.

Krikke, H.R., A. van Harten and P.C. Schuur (1998) On a medium term product recovery and disposal strategy for durable assembly products. *International Journal of Production Research* **36**(1): 111-139.

Krikke, H.R., A. van Harten and P.C. Schuur (1999) Business case Roteb: recovery strategies for monitors. *Computers & Industrial Engineering* **36**(4): 739-757.

Krupp, J.A.G. (1992) Core obsolescence forecasting in remanufacturing. *Production and Inventory Management Journal* **33**(2): 12-17.

Krupp, J.A.G. (1993) Structuring bills of material for automotive remanufacturing. *Production and Inventory Management Journal* **34**(4): 46-52.

Lambert, A.J.D. (1997) Optimal disassembly of complex products. *International Journal of Production Research* **35**(9): 2509-2523.

Lambert, A.J.D. (1999) Linear programming in disassembly/clustering sequence generation. *Computer & Industrial Engineering* **36**(4): 723-738.

Moyer, L.K. and S.M. Gupta (1997) Environmental concerns and recycling/disassembly efforts in the electronics industry. *Journal of Electronics Manufacturing* **7**(1): 1-22.

Panisset, B.D. (1988) MRP II for repair/refurbish industries. *Production and Inventory Management Journal* **29**(4): 12-15.

Penev, K.D. and A.J. de Ron (1996) Determination of a disassembly strategy. *International Journal of Production Research* **34**(2): 495-506.

Pnueli, Y. and E. Zussman (1997) 'Evaluating the end-of-life value of a product and improving it by redesign. *International Journal of Production Research* **35**(4): 921-942.
Robinson, L.W., J.O. McClain, and L.J. Thomas (1990) The good, the bad and the

ugly: quality on an assembly line. *International Journal of Production Research* 28: 963-980, 1990.

Spengler, T., H. Pueckert, T. Penkuhn and O. Rentz (1997) Environmental integrated production and recycling management. *European Journal of Operational Research* **97**(2): 308-326.

Taleb, K.N., S.M. Gupta and L. Brennan (1997a) Disassembly of complex product structures with parts and materials commonality. *Production Planning & Control* **8**(3): 255-269.

Taleb, K.N. and S.M. Gupta (1997b) Disassembly of multiple product structures. *Computer & Industrial Engineering* **32**(4): 949-961.

Teunter, R., K. Inderfurth, S. Minner, and R. Kleber (2000) *Reverse logistics in a pharmaceutical company: a case study.* Preprint 15/2000, Faculty of Management and Economics, University of Magdeburg, Germany, 2000.

Uzsoy, R. and G. Venkatachalam (1998) Supply chain management for companies with product recovery and remanufacturing capability. *International Journal of Environmentally Conscious Design & Manufacturing* **7**: 59-72.

Veerakamolmal, P. and S.M. Gupta (1998a) High-mix/low-volume batch of electronic equipment disassembly. *Computer & Industrial Engineering* **35**(1-2): 65-68.

Veerakamolmal, P. and S.M. Gupta (1998b) Optimal analysis of lot-size balancing for multiproducts selective disassembly. *International Journal of Flexible Automation and Integrated Manufacturing* **6**(3&4): 245-269.

Yan, X. and P. Gu (1994) A graph based heuristic approach to automated assembly planning. *Flexible Assembly Systems* **73**:97-106.

Zussman, E., A. Kriwet and G. Seliger (1994) Disassembly-oriented assessment methodology to support design for recycling. *Annals of the CIRP* **43**(1): 9-14.

Contacts:

Karl Inderfurth
Faculty of Economics and Management
Otto von Guericke University Magdeburg
P.O. Box 4120
D-39016 Magdeburg
Germany

Email: Karl.Inderfurth@wirtschafts-w.uni-magdeburg.de

Ruud Teunter
KNAW Research Fellow
Econometric Institute
Erasmus University Rotterdam
P.O. Box 1738
3000 DR Rotterdam
The Netherlands

Email: teuter@few.eur.nl

INVENTORY CONTROL IN REVERSE LOGISTICS

Rommert Dekker and Erwin van der Laan, Erasmus University Rotterdam, The Netherlands

1. Introduction

In this paper we give an overview of inventory control within reverse logistics. We first present a brief outline of reverse logistics and list the reasons for returns of products, as well as recovery options. Next we discuss when these situations affect inventory control. Two case are distinguished, viz., a case where returns can be re-used directly and a case in which some operations are required (value-added-recovery). For each case we classify decision problems and focus on the new aspects in inventory control caused by the product returns. Then we give an overview of the inventory control models published for these aspects. Although inventory control is very much related to production planning, the latter will be dealt with in a separate chapter, as will the collection aspect of returns.

2. Classification of Inventory Control Problems in Reverse Logistics

In this section we give a short introduction to reverse logistics and outline where and how it complicates inventory control. Reverse logistics can be defined as "the process of planning, implementing and controlling flows of raw materials, in-process inventory, and finished goods, from the point of use back to a point of recovery or point of proper disposal (RevLog, 1999). One can say that reverse logistics constitutes a reverse flow in the supply chain, although one may also say that the whole of forward and reverse flows constitutes a closed-loop supply chain. To study reverse logistics in conjunction with inventory control, we first need to identify the various reverse logistic situations.

There are many reasons for products to be returned within a supply chain. All these reasons have to do with the relations between the user/keeper of the product and the party before it in the supply chain. Sorted according to life of the product in the supply chain, we have the following return reasons:

(i)   rework,
(ii)   commercial returns and outdated products,
(iii)   product recalls,
(iv)   warranty returns,
(v)   repairs,
(vi)   end-of-use returns, and
(vii)   end-of-life returns.

Rework occurs in production when intermediate or finished products do not meet the required quality standards and are processed again. As this is very much a topic of production planning, we refer the readers to the chapter by Inderfurth and Teunter. Commercial returns are all those returns where a buyer has a contractual option to return new products to the seller. This can refer to final customers who have changed their mind about the product, or to retailers or distributors who have not been able to sell the products. Outdated products are those products whose shelf life has been too long (e.g., pharmaceuticals) and may no longer be sold. Product recalls are returns on request of the manufacturer because of potential quality, safety or health problems. As product recalls are occasional events that require case-specific decision making, no theory has been developed concerning their impact on inventory control and we will not treat them here. In case of warranty returns, customers return products because these do not (seem to) meet the promised quality standards. Sometimes these returns can be repaired, and sometimes a customer gets a new product or his/her money back, upon which the returned product needs recovery. Repairs are a related category of returning products. The main difference with warranties is that the warranty period has expired and the customer has no longer a right to get a substitute product. When successful, repaired products are returned to the original user. End-of-use returns refer to those situations where the user has a return option at a certain life stage of the product. This refers to leasing cases and reusable packaging. Although these products are not really new, they are often in a good state. Finally, end-of-life returns refers to those returns where the products are at the end of their economic or physical life, and are either returned to the Original Equipment Manufacturers (OEM) because of legal product take-back obligations or to another company for value-added recovery.

In this chapter we primarily consider those cases where the return streams mix up with standard forward flows in the supply chain, that is, after some processes the returns enter inventories in the supply chain. The reason of return is thereby not important, but the status of the returned product is, as well as the information about its return. The reason of return does, however, give some indication in this respect. For example, commercial returns are often in a good state and many of them can be reused directly. We have listed the reasons to give the reader a good idea about how these return processes originate in practice.

All returns undergo the three typical reverse logistic activities, viz., collection, inspection and sorting. The collection process is discussed in the chapter on distribution.

Depending on the outcome of the inspection companies have several recovery options, viz.,

(i)   sell in a secondary market or donate to charity,
(ii)   store and reuse after minor actions (direct reuse),
(iii)   value-added recovery,
(iv)   recycle, i.e., destroy the product structure and reuse the materials,
(v)   dispose to landfills or incinerate.

In the first case the returned products go through a separate channel and there are no specific reverse logistic aspects with respect to inventory control. Although companies like eBay are quite successful in finding new uses for old products, we do not consider them as part of a reverse logistic chain. In the second and third cases, the returns enter a supply chain and can encounter new products or parts. Here reverse logistics brings in new elements that will be treated in this paper. Direct reuse may be applied in case of commercial, warranty returns, and end-of-use returns and its relation with inventory control is discussed in section 3. The other case will be referred to as a value-added recovery as a variety of actions need to taken. It will be discussed in section 4. In case of recycling, the materials may enter the raw material inventory, but normally as a bulk product, and there are not really new aspects brought into the inventory control, so we will not discuss it specifically in this paper.

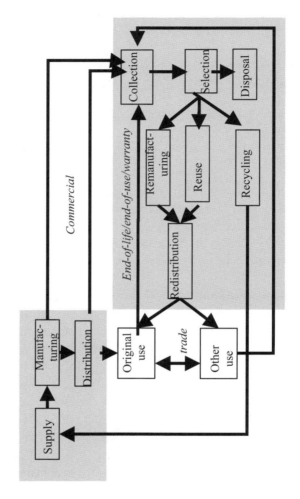

Figure 1: A schematic overview of reverse logistic situations (adapted from Kokkinaki et al. , 1999)

3. Inventory Control for Direct Reuse

3.1 Introduction

In the case of direct reuse, a product can be directly reused after its return, usually when some minor actions, like inspection and cleaning, are done which do not require decision making. In fact, the decision maker has sufficient knowledge of the average quality of the returns and plans to reuse them. In case more complex inspection or testing is needed and the decision maker has the option to delay these activities, then we are in a different situation, and, in fact, value is added, so section 4 applies.

An example of direct reuse is a mail order company selling clothes. Quite often customers order several sizes of the same type and return the nonfitting items. The mail order company collects those returns, transports them back to its warehouse, inspects and cleans the clothes, and puts them back in inventory. As quite some time may pass between the selling and the incorporation of the return into inventory, it is important for the company to predict both the return rate and the return lag. Other examples of direct reuse can be found in reusable packaging and in warehouses for spare parts. In fact, most inventory systems have returns.

From a practical point of view, one can say that return rates from customers to warehouses or to retailers are often in the range of 6 percent to 15 percent. Return rates can be quite high for mail order companies and e-tailers. For some products they can be as high as 35 percent (see Gentry, 1999), making efficient handling vital for success. Secondly, costs are likely to be high if there is no more demand for returned products, because the product has entered its final life phase or the end of its selling season. This is especially the case for fashion products sold by mail order companies. So here inventory control is of great importance. This gives some indication of the practical relevance of the inventory control models developed for these situations.

Let us next consider inventory control in more detail and discuss the mathematical models and approaches developed for the direct reuse cases. We would like to stress that although these models represent certain real cases, they may also be used in more complex cases, as they are simplifications of reality. Hence, a model for direct reuse may also be used for value-added recovery if the actual decision situation very much reflects what goes on in a direct reuse case.

Another aspect worth mentioning is that from an inventory control point of view, there is little difference between a return and a cancellation of an issue in an inventory system, or a negative adjustment of the inventory position. As a result, one could just ignore returns and apply a so-called netting procedure, i.e., cancelling out orders with their returns. This most simple policy is applied in many inventory control systems, like SAP R/3, and we will discuss it in the next subsection. When there are many returns, it becomes important to manage them and to consider separate models for the various decision problems. Several aspects can be used to classify these problems. First of all, one can discern cases with a single stocking point from ones with multiple stocking points. The latter can be either a hierarchy or a network of stocking points. In case of direct reuse we typically see a single stocking point, and in some special cases (reuse of containers), a network. The last case is also dealt with in this section. Secondly, one may distinguish between a single-period decision problem, a finite horizon multiple-period decision problem, and an infinite horizon multi-period decision problem. Thirdly, one can characterize the models by their approach, being either deterministic or stochastic. In the review we start with a single stocking point and consider the three decision situations; thereafter, we treat the network case, and finally we consider a typical aspect of inventory control in case of returns, viz., disposals.

An important aspect that comes directly forward in return situations and return models is that the inventory can reach high values. In order to avoid high inventory holding costs, one may then go over to disposal of the excess. We will treat this aspect in section 3.7.

3.2 Netting Approach

The simplest way to deal with product returns is the so-called 'netting approach'. In this approach one does not take the returns into account explicitly. Instead, one books returns as if they were negative demands. These negative demands cancel out a portion of the 'real' demand, and the remainder is treated with traditional methods for *single* source inventory control. This may be a satisfactory method when return rates are low, but may lead to unacceptable errors in case of high return rates (Van der Laan et al., 1996; Fleischmann et al., 1997). The difference lies in the variability of the real process and the process that follows from the demand netting. The net demand in a certain time interval (for instance the manufacturing lead time) is much more variable than the demand after netting. It is this excess variability that the netting approach does not take into account. If the return rate is very small, there is not much difference between total demand and net demand, so the error that one makes in applying a netting approach is also quite small.

3.3 Single-Period Inventory Decision Problems

In this section we discuss reuse cases where a single inventory decision needs to be taken. Normally this relates only to the quantity to be ordered. This problem occurs in two typical cases. First of all, in case of fashion products, one needs to determine the initial order quantity before the start of the selling season. As many fashion products are produced in Asia, they have long supply time, so it is very difficult to make resupply orders. If these goods are sold through a mail catalogue or through the Internet, then one will encounter a substantial return stream. In this case it is important to estimate the return rate and the return lag.

The second case is the final order problem, where a manufacturer makes a final production run for his parts/finished products, because he switches over to new models. The most typical model in this respect is the newsboy model. In practice it will take some time before a customer has indicated his/her wish to return the item, it is picked up, processed, and put back in to storage. In the standard newsboy problem there is typically no need for modeling of the sales pattern in a season, as only the total sales is important for the initial purchase decision. Hence, extending this model with returns would change this aspect, unless one can assume that a known percentage of returns arrives in time to be resold. This assumption was made by Vlachos and Dekker (2000) to study various return recovery options of the newsboy problem. Under this assumption, most cases can be reduced to the standard newsboy optimality equation. Finally, they show how the return rate can be approximated from sales and return patterns. It will be clear that more research is needed in this area.

3.4 Multi-period Infinite Horizon Inventory Decision Problems

In this case one considers inventory control in a usually stationary infinite horizon setting. For this case it is important to give advice both on the reorder point as well as on the order quantity. The return rate plays a less important role as all returns can be sold again. Only in case the return rate approaches the demand rate, special effects occur. The infinite horizon allows a nice mathematical analysis and is in reality applicable to stable demand and return situations. We encountered such cases in spare parts control of a refinery as well as with the warehouse operated by the nuclear laboratory CERN. Yet over longer periods of time, changes are likely as products can be phased out and replaced by others.

Several models have been formulated for these decision problems, most of them extending existing models. They can be distinguished upon assumptions they make regarding ordering and returns.

In case of zero procurement lead times and renewal demand, and return processes Heyman (1977) shows that a simple analysis can be made. He is able to show equivalence between the inventory and a queuing model. In case of Poisson distributed demands and returns, he derives an expression for the optimal disposal level and shows that a single parameter procurement policy is optimal.

Fleischmann et al. (1997) and Fleischmann (2001) study the case with independent (compound) Poisson processes for demands and returns. They show that (s,S) policies remain optimal in this situation. The main idea behind the analysis is to separate the process in two parts, represented by two buckets, one for the returns and one for the new items. The part of the new items behaves like a normal inventory process, while the other can be treated separately. They also show that the algorithm by Federgruen and Zheng (1992) can be used for optimization.

The assumption of Poisson returns is somewhat strict for reality, as De Brito and Dekker (2001) show in their analysis of returns in the CERN warehouse: they find that in many cases the return lag distribution has a somewhat stronger tail and furthermore, that most demand patterns are nonstationary. Yet the Poisson assumption represents a workable assumption as all alternatives give rise to a much more complex analysis. Yuan and Cheung (1998) assume that the return rate is a Poisson process modulated by the total number in the market. They make the rather strong assumption that for each product it is already known upon the purchase whether it will be returned.

3.5 Multi-period Finite Horizon Inventory Decision Problems

In case demand is variable, e.g., in a production situation, it is common to work with discrete time periods and a finite horizon, like in an MRP setting. Demand and returns can then be specified per period. Here one enters the domain of the standard economic lot-sizing models. The problem considered by these models is to determine when and how much to produce as both inventory holding and production set-up costs are involved. Quite some research has been done on the standard problem without returns, focusing both on deterministic and on stochastic versions. In the deterministic version, one has focused on investigating when polynomial algorithms can provide the optimal solution, with the famous Wagner-Whitin algorithm as basic example.

These cases are easily extended to reverse logistics applications by assuming returns next to demands. The returns need remanufacturing, which may take some time, in order to be used as new products. Richter and Sombrutzki (2000) made a first attempt in this direction. They study the reverse economic lot-sizing model with an unlimited quantity of returns and show that then, the zero-inventory regeneration property holds. Golany et al. (2001) show that this property is lost in the more general case with a limited quantity of returns. The limited availability of returns then introduces a capacity restriction and the problem becomes NP hard.

3.6 Direct Reuse in Network Inventories

Although the management of containers and reusable packaging are classical examples of reverse logistics, they have always been studied separately. Yet a container can almost always directly be reused and the inventory control of empty containers, or rather the positioning of empty containers over a network of depots, is a very important logistics problem for container transportation companies. Here the problem is to determine how many containers are needed at each depot for a given time horizon, how much to lease in or out, and how many to disposition over the network. An example of a decision support system for this problem is given in Shen and Khoong (1995).

3.7 Disposal

When a product reaches the end of its life cycle, extremely high return rates may occur. At this time return rates may even exceed demand rates, which makes it reasonable to include disposal options in inventory policies. In fact, we observed this also in the spare parts inventory of a refinery (see de Brito and Dekker, 2001) where over four years, an item had two demands and two returns, leaving an inventory of two for two years, while the maximum prescribed inventory level was one. These cases are caused by projects that have separate procurement channels and return the leftover parts to the warehouse at the end of the project. In internal warehouses it is then common practice to accept these returns, but they may lead to overstocks.

Although there are very simple and natural ways to incorporate disposals in inventory models, it may also complicate the mathematical analysis (see Heyman, 1977; Inderfurth, 1997; Van der Laan et al., 1996; Van der Laan and Salomon, 1997) as more decision variables need to be considered.

4. Inventory Control for Value-Added Recovery

In contrast with direct reuse, *value-added recovery* involves more elaborate (re)processing so that throughput times of returned items can be substantial. Moreover, variation in quality makes throughput times variable, while uncertainty with respect to quality makes it more difficult to predict reprocessing needs. Typical products that are associated with value-added recovery are products that have been extensively used and are returned /collected in order to be restored to perfect working conditions.

A class of inventory control problems that has received a lot of attention in the scientific literature since the late sixties is *inventory control for repairable inventory*. In repairable inventory management, items that have failed during operation at a certain base are restored to perfect working order either by the base itself or a central depot, and put back into operation. Usually, only a certain fraction of failed products can be repaired, so that some items have to be discarded and new items have to be procured from outside to level the total number of items in the system (see Figure 2).

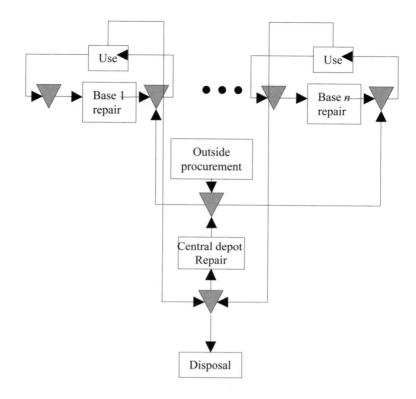

Figure 2: A repairable inventory system with n bases and a central depot

Typical examples of repairable inventory are military equipment (airplanes, tanks, etc.), heavy equipment (industrial machinery), office equipment (computers, printers, etc.), and transportation equipment (trains, buses, etc.). The main issue here is to solve the *imbalance* between demand and supply that occurs, because not all items can be repaired and there is a (stochastic) lead time associated to repair operations. Basically, the inventory problem then is to determine

- the safety stock level at each base,
- the repair *capacity* and repair *quantity* at each base and/or the central depot, and
- the outside procurement quantity,

such that costs are minimized either with or without service level constraints. The scientific literature on repairable inventory control is quite developed. Excellent reviews can be found in Nahmias (1981) and, more recently, Guide and Srivastava (1997).

The fact that after repair the items stay with or return to the original owner/ user, makes that repairable inventory systems are truly closed-loop systems. There are, however, other types of value-added recovery systems that are not *physical* closed-loop systems but rather *functional* closed-loop systems. By this we mean that a recovered item does not necessarily return to the original owner/user, although it is restored to fulfill the same function. This applies mainly to commercial products that have been discarded by the customer either because they reached their technical lifetime or because they are no longer needed. These products can be collected, remanufactured, and subsequently resold (see Figure 3).

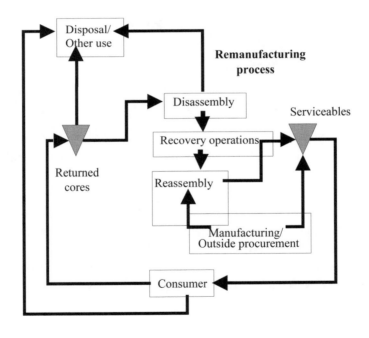

Figure 3: A remanufacturable inventory system

Although there are a lot of similarities between inventory management in a remanufacturing environment and repairable inventory management (i.e., recovery of products, uncertainty in timing and quality of product returns, integration of recovery and manufacturing, and imbalance between supply and demand), there is one important difference. In a repairable inventory system, a demand is *always* triggered by a failure. This means that a demand and a product return always coincide. In a remanufacturing system, this one-to-one correspondence between product returns and product demands does not exist simply because not all demand is triggered by a product failure, and not all product failures generate a new demand. The consequence of this is that the imbalance between supply of remanufacturables and product demand is even more prominent. Supply can even exceed demand, which in principle is never the case if product returns are triggered by product demands only. The consequence is that disposal of remanufacturables becomes part of the inventory policy. So, the inventory problem is to determine

- the procurement policy of remanufactured products (timing and quantity),
- the procurement policy of newly manufactured products (timing and quantity),
- the disposal policy (timing and quantity), and
- the remanufacturing capacity,

such that costs are minimized either with or without service level constraints. In contrast with repairable inventory management, inventory control in a remanufacturing environment has only recently received the attention that it deserves, but is now developing rapidly. Therefore, and also because recovery of commercial goods is more in line with the spirit of this book, we will focus on product remanufacturing rather than repairable inventory management in the remainder of this section.

4.1 Product Remanufacturing

Product remanufacturing is the process that restores used products or parts to an 'as-good-as-new' condition, after which they can be resold on the market. This market may be the original one, but also other markets can be targeted, for instance by offering a 'green' line to environmentally conscious customers, by offering a cheaper alternative, or by selling in a different geographical region.

The operations involved with remanufacturing, like disassembly, testing, cleaning, repair, overhaul, and refurbishing, are usually of a very stochastic nature due to the variability and uncertainty, with respect to quality of returned products. The variability and uncertainty in the timing and quantity of product returns make it hard to balance supply with demand. Imbalances may be solved by integrating manufacturing and remanufacturing operations and by implementing a disposal strategy for excess inventories. The additional interactions that arise due to all these joint operations make production planning and inventory control a difficult task. Examples in practice of this type of systems are the following.

- Toktay et al. (1999) report on the remanufacturing of Kodak single-use cameras. After use, customers turn in their single-use cameras at a photo finishing laboratory where the films are separated from the cameras. The cameras are returned to Kodak that reuses the circuit board, plastic casing, and lens in the manufacture of new cameras. However, imbalance between demand and supply occurs because i) the demand process is independent of the return process, ii) only reusable parts that are of sufficient quality are reused in the production of new cameras, and iii) Kodak does not get all cameras back, despite the fact that laboratories receive a rebate for each returned camera. Consequently, new parts have to be ordered and integrated in the production process.

- In a case described by Van der Laan (1997), car parts, varying from injection pumps to complete engines that have failed during operation are collected by the original manufacturer. After remanufacturing, these are resold as spare parts for almost half of the price of newly manufactured parts. Due to normal fluctuations in both demand and supply and due to a lack of control of the average return stream, there may be periods in which the number of collected car parts does not match the number of demands. Then, in case of supply *shortage*, additional manufacturing of new car parts takes place, or, in case of supply *overage*, products are disposed of.

- A recovery system for copiers at Océ is described in Krikke et al. (1999). Océ is an international copier manufacturer with operating companies in over 80 countries. End-of-use returns occur because of ending lease contracts and active buy-back by the operating companies. If a used copier is not too old, the operating company can choose to refurbish the machine. Otherwise, the copier is sent to a recovery location of Océ for which the operating company receives a fee. Returned products are divided into four quality classes. Depending on the quality of the machine, three recovery strategies are considered. After disassembly, cleaning, repair, replacement and reassembly operations, the machine is put back into 'as good as new' condition and sold in a *secondary* market. Or, additionally, extra functionality is added and the copier is sold as a newly manufactured machine. A third option is to disassemble the machine into parts, use some as spare parts, and recycle or scrap the remainder. To cope with uncertainties in demand and supply, large stocks of returned copiers are built up. The machines of highest quality are used up first. Excess inventories are scrapped.

In the following section we will go into more detail regarding possible inventory policies to control this type of system.

4.2 Inventory Control Policies

In section 3, where we discussed direct reuse environments, it was mentioned that a netting approach is often not appropriate to handle product returns. This applies even more to a remanufacturable products environment. Apart from dual sourcing and an unreliable source of product returns, one also has to take the remanufacturing lead times into consideration.

The reader should note that a remanufacturable inventory system is somewhat different from the inventory systems that have been studied through traditional two-supplier models. A typical two-supplier model consists of a main supplier, who is inexpensive but slow, and an emergency supplier, who is fast but expensive. The latter is used for emergency deliveries in case that an order placed at the main supplier does not arrive in time and stocks fall below the emergency order level. The idea is thus to protect against excess demand during the lead time. In a remanufacturing system, though, the manufacturing source (the 'emergency' supplier) is there to protect against an unreliable remanufacturing source (the main supplier). Note also that a two-supplier system only makes sense if the emergency source is more expensive *and* faster. As a contrast, remanufacturing makes sense as long as the manufacturing source is more expensive.

Reducing safety stocks by order splitting is another motivation to use multiple suppliers (see e.g., Kelle and Silver, 1990), but then both suppliers need to be available. Some papers within the multiple supplier literature consider random availability of suppliers. However, all of these use simplifying assumptions such as deterministic demand, zero lead times, and equal characteristics for all suppliers.

The scientific literature on inventory control for a remanufacturing environment is relatively young, but is growing fast. In the remainder of this section, we report on the most important findings regarding (optimal) inventory policies that have been studied up to the present. To put things in the right perspective, we first list the most common assumptions made in quantitative inventory modeling for remanufacturing environments.

- *Inventory systems are single item, single component systems.* This is a huge simplification, since durable products typically consist of more than one component. Moreover, some remanufacturable products have a modular design such that components are interchangeable among different product types.

- *Product returns are independent of product demands.* Although a product demand is not necessarily triggered by a product return, a return is naturally always preceded by that product being demanded by a customer. This temporal dependence, however, is very difficult to model analytically. Usually one has to rely on simulation studies instead.

- *The demand and return processes are (compound) Poisson processes.* This is a very common assumption that facilitates analysis, but is lacking an empirical foundation (see discussion in Section 3.5).

- *Yields are certain.* In some cases the yield of a remanufacturable product can only be assessed completely at the time of disassembly. This makes planning harder since the processing times are not known beforehand.

- *Processes are stationary.* This assumption is also quite common in traditional inventory control. Stationary processes are easier to analyze than nonstationary processes, but the latter prevail in real life. Trends in demand and supply are continuously changing as a product moves from one stage in its life cycle to another. Seasonal effects complicate things further.

- *Lead times are constant and independent of the order size.* This is another assumption that commonly appears in traditional inventory control. In environments with high utilization of resources, it is likely to be invalid, even more so in case of unreliable supply.

Although all these assumptions together form a huge simplification of real life systems, without them little can be said about their behavior. Nevertheless, some authors have relaxed some of these assumptions to study their impact.

Optimal Policies. Consider the system depicted in Figure 3 for a discrete time setting, in which every period a decision has to be made regarding the manufacture, remanufacture, and disposal of a remanufacturable product. If the remanufacturing lead time equals the manufacturing lead time and there are no fixed setup costs, the optimal policy, a so-called (L,M,U) policy, is given in Figure 4 (Inderfurth, 1997). Its parameters have to be chosen in an optimal way each period. It is interesting to note that the manufacturing decision is based solely on information regarding the *sum*, x, of serviceable inventory, x_s, and remanufacturable inventory, x_r, whereas the remanufacturing and disposal decision is based on x and x_s.

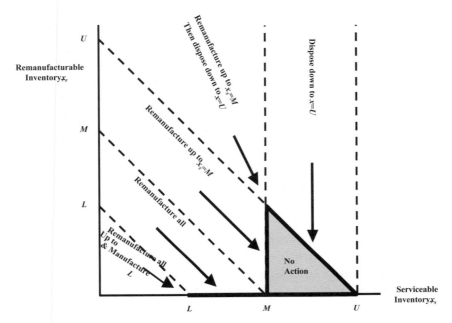

Figure 4 : State space and action set of the (L, M, U) policy
(The arrows indicate the direction of the actions.)

The fairly simple structure of this policy breaks down as soon as the manufacturing and remanufacturing lead times differ one period or more. In general, the optimal policy has no simple form and is very hard to determine, not to mention to implement. Accordingly, we also do not expect optimality of simple policies in the continuous-time case, especially if fixed costs are considered. It seems reasonable then to restrict oneself to simple, heuristic classes of policies that make use of reorder levels and order quantities.

The results of Inderfurth concerning the structure of optimal control policies also hold for nonstationary demand and return processes. A complication under these circumstances is the determination of optimal policy parameters, even in case of simple policy structures. Recent contributions by Minner and Kleber (1999) and Kleber et al. (2000) use optimal control techniques to determine, in a deterministic setting with dynamic demand and return patterns, which combinations of manufacturing, remanufacturing, and disposal operations take place and how they alternate. Although these studies provide some insights in to the structure of optimal policies, and simple numerical procedures can be employed to optimize the policy parameters, the deterministic setting and the absence of lead times and fixed costs limit their practical relevance and utility.

An extension of Inderfurth's model is given in Inderfurth et al. (2001). Here the authors study a system with n different remanufacturing options, each sold on a separate market. A product return is either allocated to one of these n options or disposed of. Since they do not consider a manufacturing source and demands are backordered, it is implicitly assumed that the demand rate is smaller than the return rate. It is shown that the optimal policy is very complicated, but under the assumptions that the allocation of product returns follows a linear rule and the inventory positions are properly balanced, a simple policy is (approximately) optimal. This so-called (nM,U) policy consists of remanufacture up to levels M_i, $1=i=n$, and a disposal down to level $U=\sum_i M_i$.

Heuristic Policies. In the previous section we discussed the difficulty of finding optimal policies in settings with nonzero lead times and fixed (re)manufacturing costs. As a first try, it seems natural to extend traditional (s,Q) and (s,S) policies to allow for product returns. A paper by Muckstadt and Isaac (1981) is one of the first to consider a stochastic remanufacturing environment with nonzero lead times for manufacturing and remanufacturing. Manufacturing is controlled by a continuous review (s,Q) policy, whereas product returns are remanufactured upon arrival by a remanufacturing facility with stochastic service times and limited capacity. Since the product returns are pushed through the system as soon as possible, this is also referred to as a 'push' system. If the unit remanufacturing cost is relatively high and remanufacturing lead times are not too large or too variable, it may be more profitable to defer remanufacturing through a so-called 'pull' policy, until the parts are really needed (Van der Laan et al., 1999a, 1999b).

In Van der Laan et al. (1997) a specific class of continuous review push and pull policies is introduced to cope with fixed (re)manufacturing costs, nonzero lead times and unit disposal (Figure 5). The push policy remanufactures Q_r products as soon as they are available, and manufactures Q_m products as soon as the inventory position (serviceable inventory plus outstanding orders minus backlog) hits order level s_m. Product returns are disposed of upon arrival if the inventory position is at or above U. The pull policy only starts remanufacturing if the inventory position is low enough (s_r) and the necessary

Q_r products are available. Disposal of product returns takes place if the remanufacturable inventory is at or above U. The figure indicates that the push policy concentrates stocks in serviceable inventory rather than remanufacturable inventory, and the pull policy results in the opposite.

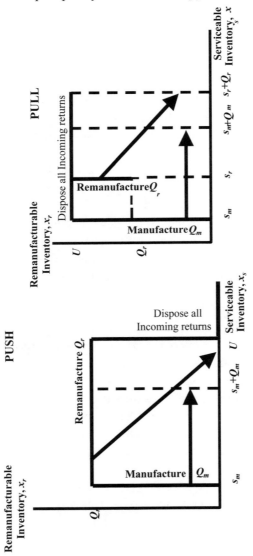

Figure 5: State space and action set of the push (left) and pull (right) policy
(The thick lines indicate the trigger levels, the arrows the direction of the actions.)

Inderfurth and Van der Laan (1998) show that these simple push and pull policies are easily improved upon by redefining the inventory position in an appropriate way. One way of doing this is to treat the remanufacturing lead time as a decision variable, rather than an exogenous constant that has to be set in an optimal way. Another option is to use different information sets for the manufacturing, remanufacturing, and disposal decision, instead of basing them on the same inventory position. As said before, however, the structure of the optimal policy is very complex and only known for very specific cases. At this time a lot of research is underway to investigate and improve the performance of the above heuristic approaches and results are to be expected soon.

One of the common elements of the models discussed up to now is the assumption that product returns are independent of product demands. Knowledge about the dependency relation between demands and returns enables forecasts with respect to timing and quantity of product returns. If good forecasts are available, these should, in principle, be incorporated in the inventory policy, since they considerably improve system performance (Kiesmüller and Van der Laan, 2001). Although *tracking and tracing* of individual products leads to superior return forecasts, the advantage, with respect to the use of just aggregated data, is rather small (Kelle and Silver, 1986; Toktay et al., 2000). The issue of forecasting is dealt with in depth elsewhere in this book.

5. The Use of Accounting Information

A Net Present Value (NPV) approach is widely seen as the most appropriate tool for financial decision making since it explicitly takes into account the time value of money. This should also hold for inventory control problems, since these are basically financial decision making problems too. However, in most literature on inventory control, authors employ an Average Cost (AC) framework in which the time value of money is implicitly taken into account through the holding cost parameters. Several authors have shown that for 'traditional' inventory control models, the AC approach is a reasonable approximation for most practical applications if certain conditions are satisfied (see Corbey et al., 1999 for an overview). However, this is not necessarily the case for inventory control with dual sourcing.

Using the AC approach, holding cost rates are typically calculated as the sum of so-called out-of-pocket holding costs per product and some factor to account for the opportunity costs of capital tied up in inventory. The latter factor is commonly obtained by multiplying the value of the product by some interest rate. In dual sourcing the value of a product return is not defined in a straightforward way. Is its value the acquisition cost, its potential profit, or maybe the difference between the manufacturing and remanufacturing cost? What is *the* value of a serviceable product if some have been manufactured and some have been remanufactured? Depending on the accounting regime, one might opt for different alternatives, each having different operational consequences.

The NPV framework does not face these dilemmas since it takes the time value of money explicitly into account by directly looking at timing and value of cash flows, rather than average costs. Sticking to the AC framework in a meaningful way means that one should assign constants to the holding cost parameters such that the resulting operational decisions are similar to those that would follow from the NPV framework. Recent results show that this is difficult at best (Teunter et al., 2000; Van der Laan, 2000), but sometimes even infeasible (Van der Laan and Teunter, 2000). Moreover, using an intuitive choice for the holding cost rates may lead to very bad system performance.

6. Summary and Outlook

In this chapter we focused on inventory control for product recovery. In this context we distinguished between *direct reuse*, which is closely related to warranty returns or commercial returns, and *value-added recovery*, which is more related to end-of-use and end-of-life returns. Inventory control for product recovery is very much different from traditional inventory control due to the highly variable and uncertain nature of product returns. It is therefore not appropriate to use a netting approach in order to employ traditional inventory control techniques, which are simpler than specialized techniques. Specialized techniques should simultaneously determine trigger levels and quantities for manufacturing, recovery, and disposal operations, given the characteristics of the specific environment, such as procurement lead time, the form of the product life cycle, and seasonal influences. In case of value-added recovery, also the *interaction* of recovery and manufacturing lead times plays an important role.

Observing the recent literature on inventory control for product, recovery we may conclude that the interest of the scientific community in this field is growing. Due to the complexity of these systems, however, attention has been limited to (over) simplified models that are far from the systems that are observed in practice. At the same time, there seems to be a lack of communication between academics and practice, considering the very limited amount of empirical studies that have been conducted up to now. In order to have a better knowledge and understanding about the needs of practice, more case studies should be carried out as well.

References

Corbey, M., K. Inderfurth, E. van der Laan, S. Minner. 1999. The Use of Accounting Information in Production and Inventory Control, Preprint 24/99 (FWW), University of Magdeburg, Germany.

De Brito, M., R. Dekker. 2001. An empirical study on return lags. Report Econometric Institute EI/2001-27, Erasmus University Rotterdam, The Netherlands.

Gentry, C. R. 1999. Reducing the cost of returns. *Chain Store Age* **75**(10) 124–126.

Golany B, J. Yang, G. Yu. 2001. Economic lot-sizing with remanufacturing options. *IIE Transactions* **33**(11) 995–1003.

Guide, V. D. R, R. Srivastava. 1997. Repairable inventory theory: Models and applications. *European J. Oper. Res.* **102**(1) 1–20.

Federgruen, A., Y. S. Zheng.1992. An efficient algorithm for computing optimal (r,Q) policy in continuous review stochastic inventory systems. *Oper. Res.* **40** 808–813.

Fleischmann, M. 2001. *Quantitative models for Reverse Logistics*. Lecture notes in economics and mathematical systems **501**, Springer-Verlag, Berlin.

_____, R. Kuik, R. Dekker. 1997. Controlling inventories with stochastic item returns: a basic model. Management Report Series 43(13), Erasmus University Rotterdam, The Netherlands (to appear in *European J. Oper. Res.*).

Heyman, D. P. 1977. Optimal disposal policies for single-item inventory system with returns. *Naval Res. Logist. Quarterly* **24** 385–405.

Inderfurth, K. 1996. Modeling period review control for a stochastic product recovery problem with remanufacturing and procurement leadtimes. Preprint 2/96 (FWW), University of Magdeburg, Germany.

_____, 1997. Simple optimal replenishment and disposal policies for a product recovery system with leadtimes. *OR Spektrum* **19**(2) 111–122.

_____, A. G. de Kok, S. D. P. Flapper. 2001. Product recovery in stochastic remanufacturing systems with multiple reuse options. *European J. Oper. Res.* **133** 130–152.

_____, E. van der Laan. 2001. Leadtimes effects and policy improvement for stochastic inventory control with remanufacturing. *Intern. J. Prod. Econom.* **71** 381–390.

Kelle, P., E. A. Silver. 1989. Forecasting the returns of reusable containers. *J. Oper. Management* **8**(1) 17–35.

_____, _____. 1990. Safety stock reduction by order splitting. *Naval Res. Logist.* **37** 725–743.

Kiesmüller, G., E. A. van der Laan. 2001. An inventory model with dependent product demands and returns. *Internat. J. Prod. Econ.* **72**(1) 73–87.

Kleber, R., S. Minner, G. P. Kiesmüller. 2000. Multiple options in dynamic product recovery systems. Pre-Prints of the 11-th Internat. Working Seminar on Prod. Econom. 147–166, Igls/Innsbruck, Austria.

Kokkinaki, A.I., R. Dekker, J. van Nunen, C. Pappis. 1999. An exploratory study on electronic commerce for reverse logistics. *Logistique et Management* **7** 27–36.

Krikke, H., A. van Harten, P. Schuur. 1999. Business case Océ: Reverse logistics network re-design for copiers. *OR Spektrum*, **21** 381–409.

Minner, S., R. Kleber. 1999. Optimal control of production and remanufacturing. Preprint 32/99 (FWW), University of Magdeburg, Germany.

Muckstadt, J. A., M. H. Isaac 1981. An analysis of single item inventory system with returns. *Naval Res. Logist. Quarterly* **28** 237-254.

Nahmias, S. 1981. Managing repairable item inventory systems: a review. *TIMS Stud .Management Sci.* **16** 253–277. North-Holland Publishing Company, The Netherlands.

REVLOG website: http://www.fbk.eur.nl/OZ/REVLOG/

Richter, K., M. Sombrutzki. 2000. Remanufacturing planning for the reverse Wagner/Whitin models. *European J. Oper. Res.* **121** 304-315.

Shen, W. S., C. M. Khoong. 1995. A DSS for empty container distribution planning. *Decision Support Systems* 15, 75–82.

Teunter, R. H., E. A. van der Laan, K. Inderfurth. 2000. How to set the holding cost rates in average cost inventory models with reverse logistics? *Omega – Internat. J. Management Sci.* **28**(4) 409–415.

Toktay, L. B., L. M. Wein, S. A. Zenios. 2000. Inventory management of remanufacturable products. *Management Sc.*, **46**(11) 1412–1426.

Van der Laan, E. A. 1997. *The effects of remanufacturing on inventory control.* PhD. thesis, Erasmus University Rotterdam, The Netherlands.

_____. 2000. An NPV and AC analysis of a stochastic inventory system with joint manufacturing and remanufacturing. ERIM Report series, ERS-2000-38-LIS, Erasmus University Rotterdam, The Netherlands.

_____, R. Dekker, A. Ridder, and M. Salomon. 1996. An (s,Q) inventory model with remanufacturing and disposal. *Internat. J. Prod. Econ.* **46–47** 339–350.

_____, M. Salomon. 1997. Production planning and inventory control with remanufacturing and disposal. *European J. Oper. Res.* **102**(2) 264–278.

_____, _____, R. Dekker. 1999a. Lead-time effects in PUSH and PULL controlled manufacturing/ remanufacturing systems. *European J. Oper. Res.* **115**(1) 195–214.

_____, _____, _____, L. N. Van Wassenhove. 1999b. Inventory control in hybrid systems with remanufacturing. *Management Sci.* **45**(5) 733–747.

_____, R. Teunter. 2000. Average costs versus net present value: a comparison for multi-source inventory models. ERIM Report series, ERS-2000-47-LIS, Erasmus University Rotterdam, The Netherlands.

Vlachos, D., R. Dekker. 2000. Return handling options and order quantities for single period products. Report Econometric Institute EI2000-29/A, Erasmus University Rotterdam.

Yuan, X.-M., K. L. Cheung. 1998. Modeling returns of merchandise in an inventory system. *OR Spektrum* **20**(3) 147–154.

Contacts:

Rommert Dekker
Econometric Institute
Erasmus University Rotterdam
Room H11-33, H-building
Burg. Oudlaan 50
3062 PA Rotterdam
The Netherlands

Email: rdekker@few.eur.nl

Erwin van der Laan
Research Fellow of Reverse Logistics
Department of Decision and Information Sciences
Faculty of Business Administration
Erasmus University Rotterdam
P.O. Box 1738
3000 DR Rotterdam
The Netherlands

Email: elaan@fac.fbk.eur.nl

Part III – Listening to the Customer

Forecasting Product Returns

Beril Toktay, INSEAD, France

1. Introduction

Reverse logistics activities consist of collecting products from customers and reprocessing them for reuse. Returned products can take the form of end-of-life returns, where the product has been used by the customer, or commercial returns, where the product is returned before use.

Some products are leased to customers (e.g., Xerox copiers to corporate customers) and are collected by the manufacturer at the expiration of the lease. In this case, the timing and quantity of products to be returned are known in advance. The major uncertainty is about the condition of the product. Other products are sold to the customer and are returned when their useful life is over or when the customer wants to trade in the product for an upgrade. In the former category are products such as single-use cameras, toner cartridges and tires. In the latter category are durable products such as personal computers, cars and copiers. Predicting the proportion of such returns is important at a tactical level for procurement decisions, capacity planning and disposal management. At an operational level, detailed predictions of the quantities to be returned in each period, as well as the variability of these quantities, is useful, especially for inventory management and production planning.

Unlike end-of-life returns that have already been sold for profit and now have the potential of generating additional benefits through value recovery, commercial returns represent a lost margin. In catalog sales, an average return rate of 12 percent is standard, with return rates varying by product category: 5 - 9 percent in hard goods, 12 - 18 percent for casual apparel, 15 - 20 percent for high-tech products, and up to 35 percent for high fashion apparel [9]. Commercial returns impose high costs on retailers and manufacturers alike. The Gartner Group estimates that the cost of processing returns for Web merchandise in 2000 was twice the value of the merchandise itself [22]. Currently, only 44 percent of returns are sold as new, 2 percent are trashed, 13 percent are liquidated, and 41 percent are sent back to the manufacturer [19].

Retailers and manufacturers strive to design reverse logistics systems that increase the visibility and speed of the return process to maximize asset recovery for commercial returns, especially for seasonal or short life-cycle products. Firms vary in how they address this problem. For example, Ingram Micro Logistics, the distribution arm of Ingram Micro, opened the first automated returns facility in the United States in early 2001 [19]. Others increasingly rely on third-party reverse logistics providers such as GENCO Distribution System, UPS, USF Processors, and Returns Online [13]. Various software products that are specifically targeted towards returns processing are now available on the market, provided by such companies as Kirus Inc., Retek.com, ReturnCentral, and The Return Exchange [13]. Like end-of-life returns, an important lever in managing commercial returns is to predict accurately the return quantities for both tactical and operational level decisions.

Forecasting product returns, narrowly defined, is predicting the timing and quantity of returns within a given system based on past sales and return data. Methods that have been proposed in the literature for either end-of-life or commercial returns are described and compared in section 2. The goal of such forecasting schemes is to provide input at an operational level; this section also reviews the literature on integrating forecasts of returns into inventory management decisions.

In this chapter, we take a broader view of forecasting product returns. The proportion of products returned depends to a large extent on a number of factors, including the design of the product, the collection system, and the customer interface, among others. Significant potential for profit maximization therefore lies in understanding what drives the proportion of returns and designing the system accordingly. In section 3, we survey the academic literature, articles from the business press, and some case studies to identify factors influencing return rates. In section 4, we conclude with directions for future research in exploiting this information for better returns forecasting and management.

2. Forecasting Returns

One method for forecasting return volumes would be to use the time series consisting of past return volumes and apply time-series forecasting methods to it directly, but such a method would ignore the information contained in past sales data. Indeed, the key to forecasting returns is to observe that returns in any one period are generated by sales in the preceding periods. Alternatively, a sale in the current period will generate a return k periods from now with probability $v_k, k = 1, 2, \ldots$ or not at all. All the methods used in the literature exploit this structure to postulate a return delay distribution and estimate its parameters.

A particular characteristic of the return delay data is that it is right-censored: At a given time, if an item has not been returned, it is not known whether it will be returned or not. For accurate estimation, it is important that the estimation method distinguish between items that are not yet returned and items that will never be returned.

We classify the forecasting methods used in the literature according to the data that they exploit. We say that period-level information is available if only the total sales and return volume in each period are known. For beverage containers, single-use cameras and toner cartridges, this is typically the only data available. We say that item-level information is available if the sale and return dates of each product are known. Electrical motors with electronic data logging technology [17], copiers and personal computers are typically tracked individually, so this data can easily be obtained for these products. POS (point-of-sale) data technology in retailing also can allow for item-level tracking.

2.1 Period-Level Information

A simple estimate of the return probability is to use the proportion of cumulative returns to cumulative sales. This method is known to be used in industry [11, 26]. It is useful only in estimating the return probability; no information about the return delay can be inferred. We refer to this method as "naive estimation."

Let n_t and m_t denote the sales and returns of products in month t, respectively. Goh and Varaprasad [11] propose a transfer function model of the form

$$m_t = \frac{w_0 - w_1 B - w_2 B^2 - \ldots - w^s B^s}{1 - \delta_1 B - \delta_2 B^2 - \ldots - \delta^r B^r} n_{t-b} + \varepsilon_t$$

where B is the backshift operator, b is the time lag, and ε_t is the noise term.

The determination of the appropriate transfer function model follows the steps of model identification, parameter estimation, and diagnostic checking as described in Box and Jenkins [2].

Note that the transfer function model can be rewritten as

$$m_t = \left(v_0 + v_1 B + v_2 B^2 + ...\right) n_t + \varepsilon_t \ .$$

Once the parameters of the transfer function model have been estimated, the coefficients $\{v_k, k \geq 1\}$ are easily calculated. The statistically significant values of these coefficients are used as estimates of the probability of return after k persionds, for $k \geq 1$. The probability that a product is eventually returned is given by $\sum_{k=1}^{\infty} v_k$.

Goh and Varaprasad use this method to estimate the return quantities of Coca-Cola bottles. Data on sales and returns are available over sixty months from two bottling plants. They find that close to two thirds of the bottles are returned within one month of sales, and almost all containers that will ever be returned will be returned by the third month. The probability that a Coca-Cola bottle will never be returned is found to be less than 5 percent.

In practice, the data is augmented in each period as new sales and return information becomes available. The incremental nature of the information received makes Bayesian estimation a natural choice. Toktay et al. [26] assume that the return process can be modeled by

$$m_t = pr_D(1)n_{t-1} + pr_D(2)n_{t-2} + ... + pr_D(t-1)n_1 + \varepsilon_t \quad t = 2,3,..., \tag{1}$$

where p is the probability that a product will ever be returned, $r_D(k)$ is the probability that the product will be returned after k periods, conditional on ever being returned, and $\varepsilon_t \sim N(0, \sigma^2)$. In this model, if a camera was sold in period t, the probability that it comes back in period $t+k$ is $pr_D(k)$. This quantity corresponds to v_k in [11].

The type of relation in Equation (1) is referred to as a "distributed lag model" in Bayesian inference [27]. Usually a specific form of distribution involving one or two parameters is assumed for the lag, which reduces the number of parameters to be estimated. The estimation procedure for a geometrically distributed lag with parameter q (the probability that a sold camera is returned in the next period, given that it will be returned) is illustrated in Toktay et al. It is also shown how to extend this method to a Pascal distribution, which allows more flexibility in the shape of the delay distribution.

Toktay et al. apply this method to data obtained from Kodak that consists of 22 months of sales and returns of single-use flash cameras. Using a geometric return distribution, they obtain estimates $\hat{p}$ and $\hat{q}$ equal to 0.5 and 0.58, respectively.

Since only two parameters need to be estimated, this method requires less data than the transfer function analysis proposed by Goh and Varaprasad. On the other hand, it lacks the generality of the latter method, since a given distribution is imposed on the data. A partial remedy is to do hypothesis testing with Pascal delay distributions, which allow for a more general delay distribution while remaining relatively parsimonious in the number of parameters to be estimated.

Toktay et al. test the hypotheses of geometric, Pascal lag one, and Pascal lag two distributions on the Kodak data. The result supports using a geometric lag model. A geometric return delay makes practical sense for single-use cameras: Since most purchases are impulse decisions [12], prompted by a special occasion, it is likely that the camera will be used and returned quickly after the sale, which is consistent with a geometric distribution.

2.2 Item-Level Information

When items are tracked on an individual basis, it is possible to determine the exact return delay of returned items. For items that have not been returned yet, it is known that the delay is longer than the elapsed time, or possibly infinite (corresponding to a product never being returned). Dempster et al. [7] introduced the Expectation Maximization (EM) algorithm to compute maximum likelihood estimates given incomplete samples. This algorithm can be effectively used to estimate the return delay distribution using censored delay data. The EM algorithm is illustrated in Toktay et al. for a geometric delay distribution.

Hess and Mayhew [14] consider commercial returns and propose a split-adjusted hazard rate model and a regression model with logit split to estimate the return probability and the return delay distribution. In contrast with the papers cited earlier, they augment their models with dependent variables such as the price and fit of the product. The logit model is a discrete choice model, which simultaneously estimates a baseline return rate and the impact of external factors on that rate. By combining the logit model with basic hazard rate or regression models estimating the return delay, the authors avoid the inaccuracy (due to the right-censoring of the data) that would be engendered if only the latter models were used.

2.3 Comparison of Forecasting Methods

The naive estimate only requires the aggregate sales and return information to date. The data requirements of this method are the lowest. On the other hand, this method ignores the effect of the return delay, and consequently generates a biased estimate of the return probability when the time horizon is short (although it is asymptotically unbiased when the return delay is finite). The bias is larger if the return delay is larger. All other models avoid this bias by explicitly modeling the return probability and the return delay.

The naive estimate, the distributed lags Bayesian inference model, and the EM algorithm are particularly suited to updating return flow parameters over time. We illustrate the performance of these methods in Figures 1-3, which are generated as follows: The number of sales in each period is a Poisson random variable with parameter 200, 2,000 and 20,000, respectively, labeled as low, medium and high sales volumes, respectively. The return probability is $p = 0.5$. The return delay is geometric with a mean return delay of eight periods ($q = 0.125$). Parameter estimation starts three periods after returns are first observed; estimates are updated in each period using the most recent sales and return volumes. The evolution of $\hat{p}$ and $\hat{q}$ over the forty periods of data estimation is plotted in Figures 1 and 2 by method and by volume. Figure 3 makes a direct comparison of convergence rates across methods for a fixed sales volume. The estimates are averages over thirty simulation runs.

As expected, the EM algorithm clearly outperforms Bayesian inference, which depends on the sales volume per period. In this example, two periods, five periods, and twenty periods, respectively, are needed for the confidence interval of the return probability estimate to include the true value of the parameter in the cases of high volume, medium volume, and low volume, respectively. While it is to be expected that the accuracy of the estimate in the EM algorithm directly depends on the volume of data, it is particularly striking that the algorithm achieves such accuracy after only two periods in the high-volume scenario.

With period-level data, the convergence of the estimate depends primarily on the number of periods of data available. In Figure 2, the estimate for the return probability reaches the vicinity of 0.5 after eighteen periods of returns for all sales volumes. The demand volume does not impact the point at which the estimate converges, but it is significant in determining the accuracy of the method in the periods up to that point.

Figures 1 and 2 further show that the estimate of the return delay is more robust than the estimate of the return probability; it fluctuates less from period to period under both algorithms.

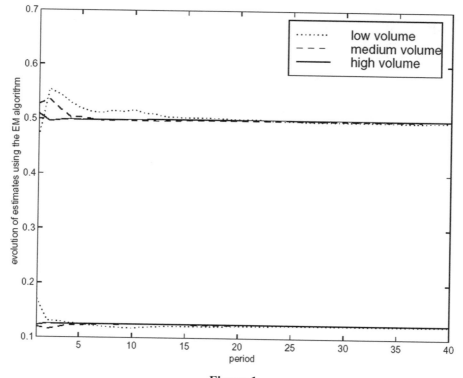

Figure 1

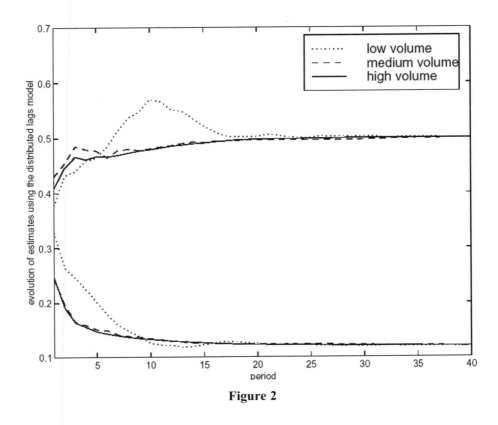

Figure 2

Figure 3 shows that the methods taking into account the return delay clearly dominate naive estimation, which systematically underestimates the return probability. The bias of this estimate decreases in time, but in this example, it is still 20 percent less than the true value after forty periods.

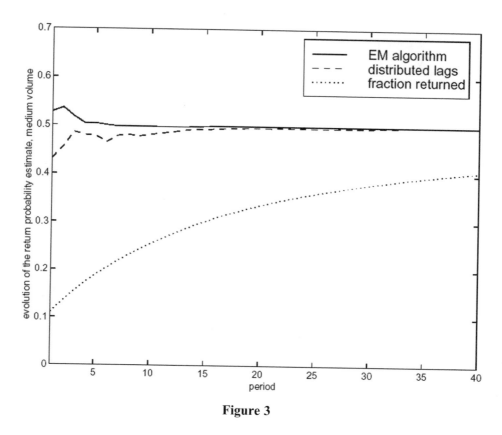

Figure 3

Hess and Mayhew [14] apply their methods to simulated data containing 2,000 sales whose return delay is exponential with a mean of 3.3 weeks, and show that the hazard model outperforms the regression model. The reason for the superiority of the hazard rate model is that a general hazard rate distribution was assumed, whereas the regression model restricts the analysis to normally distributed errors.

2.3.1 Inventory Management using Returns Forecasts

Given past sales volumes and estimates of the return probability and the return delay distribution, it is possible to approximate the distribution of returns in future periods. Given n_t, the vector $(m_{t,t+1}, m_{t,t+2}, ...)$ that denotes returns from sales in period t has a multinomial distribution with probability vector v (or pr_D). Based on this fact, Kelle and Silver [15] develop normal approximations for demand over a time horizon of L periods under both period-level and item-level information. For a base-stock level defined by $E[D_L] + k\sigma_{D_L}$ they compare the deviation between the base stock levels obtained under the two information structures. For the range of parameter values that they investigate, the difference ranges between 0.5 percent and 30 percent.

These experiments are for a single order only, and assume that the return flow parameters are already known. Kelle and Silver [16] formulate a deterministic dynamic lot sizing problem, taking into account future returns in net demand forecasts. The impact of future returns is that net demand may be negative. The authors develop a transformation into the nonnegative demand case. The Wagner-Whitin deterministic lot-sizing procedure can then be applied to determine procurement quantities in each period. In practice, since new sales and returns are recorded in each period, and return flow parameters could be updated periodically, rolling horizon decision making would be more appropriate. In this case, a heuristic that is more robust than the Wagner-Whitin algorithm [1] could be used. It would be interesting to compare the value of the additional information provided by item-level information in this setting.

Toktay et al. [26] develop adaptive procurement policies using dynamically updated return flow parameter estimates in the context of the single-use camera supply chain. They use discrete-event simulation to compare the system (inventory, lost sales and procurement) cost under period-level versus item-level information, and investigate the impact of sales volume and product life-cycle length on the relative benefits of the two informational structures. They conclude that the accurate estimation of the return probability and of the quantity of products that will be returned are the most important levers in achieving low operating cost. In addition, they demonstrate that the relative benefit of using item-level instead of period-level information is highest when the total demand volume for a product over its life cycle is low. This is consistent with the results discussed in the previous subsection concerning the convergence rate of the two algorithms exploiting different levels of data aggregation. The EM algorithm does significantly better than Bayesian inference using the distributed lags model over a given initialization period when the demand volume is low.

3. Factors Influencing Returns

The literature review in section 2 shows that papers forecasting end-of-life returns use only sales and return data. Explanatory factors that could increase the accuracy of prediction are not incorporated in the analysis. Hess and Mayhew [14] bring in this dimension in their paper on forecasting commercial returns. They hypothesize that a higher price will increase the probability of return and that items where fit is important are more likely to be returned. On data from a direct marketer of apparel, they find that the return probability is positively correlated with price, but that differences in fit have little impact on the return rate. Hess and Mayhew [14] suggest that for commercial returns, estimation can be carried out at a customer level to identify individual return patterns. If this data is not available, they propose that it be carried out on aggregate data to identify patterns at the product or product-family level. The goal is to identify higher-profitability customers and products by taking into account not only the sales information but also the return information.

Hess and Mayhew [14] only consider price and fit as dependent variables. In practice, many factors could affect the probability and the delay in returns, for both end-of-life and commercial returns. Incorporating explanatory variables into predicting return flow characteristics could therefore increase the accuracy of the prediction. Equally, if not more important, are the benefits of quantifying the impact of such factors on the volume and timing of returns. Such information would be very valuable in maximizing the profitability of a given product line by optimizing over these factors.

As one possible example of the use of quantifying the effect of explanatory variables on return flows, consider the Kodak single-use camera. Customers take the used cameras to a photofinishing laboratory, where the film is taken out and processed. The laboratories receive a small rebate for each used camera that they subsequently return to Kodak. Due to economies of scale in transportation, small photoprocessors either wait for a long time before sending a batch back to Kodak or do not send in cameras at all, significantly adding to the return delay and influencing the return percentage. The reusable parts (the circuit board, plastic body and lens aperture) of the returned cameras are put back into production after inspection. The circuit board, which can be used several times, is the most costly component in a single-use camera. Therefore, used boards are valuable to Kodak as long as the product design allows them to be reused, although they have minimal salvage value.

The initial design of the product was constrained by the size of the circuit board. Subsequently, Kodak introduced a pocket-size camera that required a smaller circuit board. As a result, a number of larger-size boards would become obsolete by the time they were returned to Kodak. In this setting, an integrated design of the collection policy and the new product introduction decisions would have been valuable to Kodak. To carry out this analysis, the impact of changing incentives provided to consumers and to photoprocessors would need to be assessed. The hypothesis is that the higher the rebates, the more and quicker the returns; the elasticity of return rate and delay to the rebate quantity is a concise measure that captures this interaction.

Once a model of the dependence of returns on such factors as rebate level and ease of return has been developed and its parameters estimated, a cost-benefit analysis can be carried out to investigate the value of investing in collecting used products more rapidly versus delaying the introduction of the new product line. When take back is mandatory, such that the return percentage is close to 100 percent, the return delay can have a huge impact on the bottom line, especially in the electronics industry where value depreciation is high. In general, the trade-off between investing in collection versus the value that would be generated by this effort needs to be quantified.

One problem that Kodak faced in collecting its products was that opportunistic third parties would load the used camera with new film and sell the camera at a lower price, sometimes claiming it to be a Kodak camera. In addition to reducing potentially the quality perception of consumers regarding the product, this phenomenon also reduced the return rate. In the tire industry, the technology to remanufacture a tire is relatively cheap, resulting in a proliferation of small third-party remanufacturers. Investing in and promoting a higher-quality proprietary remanufacturing technology allows Michelin to remain one of the main remanufacturers of its own products. As these two examples highlight, the choice of production technology and product design can influence the return rate.

In the tire industry, 5 percent of car tires, 30 percent of light truck tires and almost all commercial truck tires are retreaded [3]. Tires are bulky items that are costly to transport. Therefore, there are important economies of scale in their collection. They are typically collected by garages and dealers, parties that are difficult to reach at low cost by tire manufacturers or retreaders. For this reason, companies exist whose sole business is to purchase tires from garages, and sell them to tire remanufacturers. Clearly, the geographical dispersion in the market, the size of the outlets, and the transportation costs per unit play a role in determining returns. The structure of the collection channel, which is to some extent in the control of manufacturers, also impacts returns. Savaşkan et al. [24] show that if the retailer is in charge of collecting used products (as opposed to the manufacturer or a third-party), then the fraction returned will be higher. Thus, the impact of the collection channel on returns should be incorporated into decisions regarding supply chain design.

The environmental consciousness of consumers would be expected to impact positively the return probability. According to OECD data [20], countries differ in recyling rates. In 1997, glass recycling rates were 26 percent in the United States, 52 percent in France and 79 percent in Germany, and paper recycling rates were 40 percent in the United States, 41 percent in France and 70 percent in Germany. On the other hand, 65 percent of Americans and 59 percent of Germans expressed their willingness to pay a premium on an eco-safe product [10], suggesting that the receptiveness to recycling in Germany is lower than in the United States. The significant difference observed in practice could be a function of a variety of other factors such as infrastructure and promotional expenditures. Clarifying the reasons for this difference is relevant to a company who will expand to a new market.

According to CEMA (Consumer Electronics Manufacturing Association) research, a store's return policy is "very important" for 70 percent of consumers in their decision to shop there [21]. This is also true for e-tailers: In a survey by Jupiter Media Metrix, 42 percent of online shoppers said they would buy more from the Internet if the returns process was easier [23].

E-tailers vary widely in terms of the returns policies they offer. A search on www.buyersindex.com reveals return policies ranging from conditional returns within several days to unconditional lifetime returns in various product categories. Lenient return policies may increase demand for a retailer's products, but they may also increase the return rate. There are conflicting opinions about this tradeoff. While some managers say that it is a myth that "if a company makes it easy for consumers to return products, they will send back more items" [19], theory claims that this is not a myth, but reality [6].

The reason for this dichotomy may be that the outcome depends on the product, the customer, and the market. A lenient return policy acts as a signal of quality, much like a warranty. Moorthy and Srinivasan [18] show that money-back guarantees are effective signaling devices as customers assume that it is costly for a low-quality retailer to offer this service. This effect would be higher for products for which achieving high quality is costly. Return policies allow the customer to test the good before making the final purchase decision. Che [4] shows that full-refund return policies maximize retailer profits only if customers are sufficiently risk averse or if retail costs are high. The sales medium (on-line versus in-store) would be expected to impact the profitability of a given returns policy because it changes the point at which customers are able to test the good. Tailoring the return policy to the target market, the distribution medium, and the product remains a significant challenge.

It is claimed that to reduce commercial return rates, retailers can resort to a number of strategies such as clear packaging, follow-up calls, toll-free help lines, and information sharing about reasons for returns [21]. Determining which of these factors are those that significantly impact commercial returns would be instrumental in allocating resources spent on attempting to reduce return rates.

4. Conclusions

In this chapter, we reviewed the existing literature on forecasting product returns, both for end-of-life and commercial returns. Despite the clear financial impact of product returns on profitability, the literature on this topic is relatively limited. Research has focused on pure forecasting [11, 14, 15] and inventory management incorporating updated forecast information [16, 26].

Integrated returns forecasting and inventory management has been analyzed primarily in the context of end-of-life returns. However, the timing and quantity of commercial returns is a significant determinant of the profitability of a product offering, especially for short life-cycle items. Developing methods to incorporate forecast information about commercial returns in stocking decisions is a potential avenue of research.

Inventory management, an operational-level problem, is not the only facet of supply chain management that is affected by return flow characteristics. We have discussed several system design issues - rebate policy, collection channel design, product design, timing of new product introduction - that would benefit from an integrated approach incorporating the impact of design on return flows.

To address these design problems, two complementary methodologies need to be pursued: empirical and model-based. Return forecasts typically do not take into account explanatory variables that would improve forecast accuracy. Relevant factors are price, rebate level, ease and cost of return, environmental consciousness of consumers, structure of the collection channel, return policy, sales medium, and level of after-sales follow up. Empirical research is necessary to test hypotheses concerning the impact of these explanatory variables on returns behavior. The resulting information can then be used as an input to models of integrated supply chain design or product design and returns management.

References

[1] Blackburn, J. D., R. A. Millen. 1980. Heuristic Lot-Sizing Performance in a Rolling-Schedule Environment. *Decision Sciences*. 11 (4) 691 - 701.

[2] Box, G. E. P., G. M. Jenkins. 1976. *Time Series Analysis, Forecasting and Control*, revised edition, Holden-Day, San Francisco.

[3] Bozarth, M. 2000. Retreadonomics 2000: Retread Production Costs and Industry Forecast. *The Tire Retreading/Repair Journal* 44 (4) 3-15.

[4] Che, Y.-K. 1996. Customer Returns Policies for Experience Goods. *Journal of Industrial Economics*. 44 (1) 17 - 24.

[5] Cox, D. R., D. Oakes. 1984. *Analysis of Survival Data*. Chapman and Hall, London.

[6] Davis, S. E., M. Hagerty, E. Gerstner. 1998. Return Policies and Optimal Levels of Hassle. *Journal of Economics and Business*. 50 (5) 445 - 460.

[7] Dempster, A. P., N. M. Laird, D. B. Rubin. 1977. Maximum Likelihood from Incomplete Data via the EM Algorithm (with Discussion). *J. Royal Stat. Soc. Series B*. 339 1-22.

[8] Dhrymes, P. J. 1985. *Distributed Lags*. North-Holland, Amsterdam.

[9] Dowling, M. 1999. Getting Less in Return. *Catalog Age*. 16 (4), pp. 1,18.

[10]   Gallup International Institute. 1992. *The Health of the Planet Survey*. Gallup International Institute, Princeton, NJ.

[11]   Goh, T. N., N. Varaprasad. 1986. A Statistical Methodology for the Analysis of the Life-Cycle of Reusable Containers. *IIE Transactions*. 18 (1) 42 - 47.

[12]   Goldstein, L. 1994. The Strategic Management of Environmental Issues: A Case Study of Kodak's Single-use Cameras. M.S. Thesis, Sloan School of Management, MIT, Cambridge, MA.

[13]   Gooley, T. G. 2001. Diminishing Returns. *Logistics Management and Distribution Report* 40 (6), p. 43.

[14]   Hess, J. D., G. E. Mayhew. 1997. Modeling Merchandise Returns in Direct Marketing. *Journal of Direct Marketing*. 11 (2) 20 - 35.

[15]   Kelle, P., E. A. Silver. 1989. Forecasting the Returns of Reusable Containers. *Journal of Operations Management*. 8 17-35.

[16]   Kelle, P., E. A. Silver. 1989. Purchasing Policy of New Containers Considering the Random Returns of Previously Issued Containers. *IIE Transactions*. 21 349 - 354.

[17]   Klausner, M., W. M. Grimm, C. Hendrickson. 1998. Reuse of Electric Motors in Consumer Products. Journal of Industrial Ecology. 2 (2) 89-102.

[18]   Moorty, S., K. Srinivasan. 1995. Signaling Quality with Money-Back Guarantee: The Role of Transaction Costs. *Marketing Science* 14 (4) 230 - 247.

[19]   Morrell, A. L. 2001. The Forgotten Child of the Supply Chain. *Modern Materials Handling*. 56 (6), 33 - 36.

[20]   OECD Environmental Data: Compendium 1999.

[21]   Pinkerton, J. 1997. Getting Religion about Returns. *Dealerscope Consumer Electronics Marketplace*. 39 (11) p. 19.

[22]   Richardson, H. 2001. Logistics in Reverse. *Industryweek*. 250 (6), 37 - 40.

[23]   Rosen, C. 2001. Ready for the Returns? *Informationweek*. January 8, 22 - 23.

[24]   Savaşkan, R. C., S. Bhattacharya and L. N. Van Wassenhove. 1999. Channel Choice and Coordination in a Remanufacturing Environment. INSEAD Working Paper 99(14/TM).

[25]   Thierry, M., M. Salomon, J. van Nunen, L. N. Van Wassenhove. 1995. Strategic Issues in Product Recovery Management. *California Management Review*, 37 (2) 114 -135.

[26]   Toktay, L. B., L. M. Wein, S. A. Zenios. 2000. Inventory Management of Remanufacturable Products. *Management Science* 46 (11) 1412 - 1426.

[27]   Zellner, A. 1987. *An Introduction to Bayesian Inference in Econometrics*. Robert E. Krieger Publishing Company, Malabar, Florida.

Contact:

Beril Toktay
Technology Management Area
INSEAD
Boulevard de Constance
77305 Fontainebleau Cedex
France

Email: beril.toktay@insead.edu

Reuse and Technology Diffusion

Jonathan D. Linton, Rensselaer Polytechnic Institute, USA*
Shantanu Bhattacharya, INSEAD, France

1. Introduction

Technological change and obsolescence has a tremendous impact on both the generation of post-consumer product – with retained functional life – and the rate of decline in the economic value of product. The effect of technological change on the generation of raw materials and the viability of remanufacturing is poorly understood. While technology change can impact the reuse content of some of a product's components, the fact that other components remain the same across generations of the product make remanufacturing a viable option even under rapid technological change. Hence, the potential of reusing parts from older products in new generations depends on a host of design parameters of the products, in addition to the degree of technological change.

Most of the relevant literature is peripheral to this subject, but offers both useful insights and a good base for future study. There exist streams of research in the areas of technological obsolescence on markets, the role of secondary markets, the phasing out of products based on older technologies to make way for newer technologies, and other related topics. However, the subject of reuse of older products due to technology change has not been addressed directly in the literature. In this chapter, we consider the development and diffusion of new and newer technology and its impact on remanufacturing and reuse of older generation products. To accomplish this we consider:

- The reselling of products with old technologies in different markets which are less advanced: There are a number of examples in the industry of products that are based on older technologies, are recovered from advanced markets, and are then refurbished and sold in less advanced markets where the older technology is still in use. We outline the fac-

* In 2001 Dr. Linton was at Polytechnic University-Brooklyn. In 2002 Dr. Linton moved to Rensselaer Polytechnic Institute.

tors that impact the decision to order from suppliers who recover products based on the older technology, and the decision on the markets to be served.

- The effect of upgrades on technological obsolescence: The impact of upgrades on technological obsolescence is twofold. The upgraded versions of a product make it easier for manufacturers to replace only the components of the product whose technology has evolved. Adopting the upgrade also makes it easier for the customer, as the upgrade provides a hedge against technological obsolescence. Buying the upgrade is also cheaper for the customer, as the entire set of components that make-up the product does not require replacement.

- Reuse of components from products of the same generation of technology: For some categories of products e.g., consumable products like one-time use cameras, the products can be sent back to the manufacturer or retailer immediately after the use of the product. The manufacturer can then replace the consumable components of the product with new components, but keep the durable parts in the product. This provides the manufacturer with direct cost-saving incentives for recovering used products.

- Impact of the technology diffusion of the old generation of products on remanufacturing in the new generation: Sometimes products with technologies from older generations can be recovered and components can be used for products of the next generation e.g., in personal computers. This kind of remanufacturing provides manufacturers with an incentive to recover older products from the market for use in the next generation of products.

2. An Overview of Related Literature

The rate of technological advance, diffusion, time, and economic value are interrelated. Some of these interrelations have been explored for a variety of reasons other than product take back and remanufacture. Before exploring current issues and questions relating to reuse and technology diffusion, this literature is briefly considered.

The diffusion of ideas, services and products has been the subject of thousands of studies (Rogers, 1995). The general model of diffusion suggests that the adoption of products can be described by a diffusion curve that can be approximated by the standard normal distribution (Bass, 1969). The modeling of product adoption is extensive. This modeling includes verification, invalidation, extension, and the offering of alternative models to Bass' original model. (For further consideration of this subject refer to Parker [1994]). While this research stream describes the buying pattern of customers over time and therefore, an inter-temporal effect of product adoption by customers, this research stream in itself offers little insight into either the effect of technological advancement or the abandonment (and disposal or redeployment) of older technology. This stream of literature typically also does not consider the potential of reuse from products that have either been bought in the past or the issues of durable components being reused in products. However, the effect on diffusion of an older generation of technology on a newer generation of technology has been considered in semiconductor industry, mainframe computers, and cellular telephony (Norton and Bass, 1987, 1992; Mahajan and Muller, 1996; Islam and Meade, 1997).

Norton and Bass (1987) consider the effect of newer generations of products through the integration of adoption and substitution models. This study raises the question of how much of the market do the older and newer generation products compete for. They assume that the coefficients are the same for each successive generation. While this paper focuses on the degree of cannibalization exerted when a new product generation is introduced into the market, the paper does not consider supply side dependencies between the two products. Hence, while the paper considers issues related to substitution for the introduction of new product generations, the reuse issue is not addressed.

Mahajan and Muller (1996) consider the replacement of successive generations of IBM mainframe computers. It is important to consider the unusually high market share that IBM possessed in this market. The lack of such market share may limit the applicability of this example. They, like Norton and Bass, assume that the coefficients are constant across generations and do not look at the prospect of reuse from the products of the older generation in the new one.

Islam and Meade (1997) consider both IBM mainframes and cellular phones. They suggest that a better model is offered by allowing the coefficients to vary for each successive generation. In the case of mainframes, this led to an eventual decrease in the market for mainframes, as the potential market size in the Bass diffusion model is decreased owing to reasons of previous purchases hampering the sales of future products. Whereas, in cellular telephony it has resulted in increases in market size, as the potential market size increases owing to the diffusion of the previous generation. However, in this study as well, supply side economies leading to sharing of components across the different generations of products have not been considered.

It is clear from the research to date that there are many cases where the specific mix of characteristics of the different generations may be preferable to different groups of people. Some additional insights that could be useful to understand the impact of diffusion and substitution better would incorporate the effects of newer technologies on the utilities of the customers. Customers with increased utility from the new generation of technology are more likely to switch to the new product, as the increased utility gives them a higher surplus than the price of the new product. Additional experience must be gained in understanding how much of the initial market is specific to the older generation product, how large a market could be served by either product, and how large a market is created through the introduction of the new product. It is clear that the introduction of a newer product is affected by the existence of an older one. The sales of the new product are more attractive to the firm than the sales of the older product, since the new product at the start of the life cycle typically has much higher margins compared to the older product because of better technology and performance content. It is not clear, however, if the existence of an earlier product results in either a larger market for the newer generation or a smaller market. The argument in favor of the smaller market is that the existence of the older product satisfies the needs of the existing market. The older product cannibalizes the sales of the new product; this is true for the case of consumer durables, where if a customer does not have foresight, and adopts a product based on an older technology that satisfies his needs, he will not purchase a product based on the new technology unless the surplus utility exceeds the price. The argument in favor of a larger market suggests that the knowledge and learning that has occurred due to the existence of the older product creates an environment in which the potential market is larger and the readiness for new adopters to try the product is greater. In addition, when certain technologies are introduced into the market, they may not have use for some potential customers who are risk-averse, and would like to see the technology usage grow before their adoption. Such customers become part of the potential market once the newer technology is in use by more risk-neutral customers.

The change from one technological trajectory to another has not yet been addressed in the diffusion literature. This is an important distinction since change in product can be a result of performance improvements along a specific technological trajectory or as a result of a change from one technological trajectory to another (Clark and Abernathy, 1985; Foster, 1986). Performance improvements in a product that take place due to minor process or design efficiency successes are incremental in nature, but a large number of such changes across product generations can result in radical change. However, when the core technology behind the product is changed, one can have a radical change in product performance within one product generation. One example would be the move of the laptop industry from using Nickel-Cadmium-based battery cells to Lithium-ion-based battery cells. The performance of Ni-Cd batteries was steadily improving; however, it was difficult to improve significantly the battery life over three hours. However, when the battery based on the lithium-ion technology was introduced in laptops, it was found that the battery life increased significantly to seven or eight hours. The difference between a change in technology trajectory and movement along a trajectory is depicted in Figure 1. Movement along a technology trajectory occurs due to learning about a technology through research and/or use. Changes in technical trajectory occur, because at some point in time, a new technology becomes attractive due either to overtaking the existing technology in some set of performance characteristics, or the potential to overtake the existing technology at some point in the future due to a superior physical limit (as shown in Figure 1). A more historical example (Foster, 1986) is the change from sailing vessels to steam vessels. This difference is significant since the skill-set, infrastructure and requirements for stakeholders may vary extensively with a change in technological trajectory. Whereas, generational improvements in a product result from movement along a technological trajectory—not from one trajectory to a different trajectory. Having considered the diffusion literature, a separate but related literature on the disposal/replacement decision is reviewed.

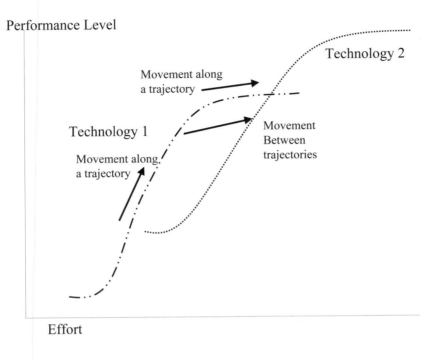

Performance Level

Movement along
a trajectory

Technology 2

Technology 1

Movement along
a trajectory

Movement
Between
trajectories

Effort

**Figure 1: The two pathways for technological advancement leading
to generational changes in products**

The maintenance versus replacement literature offers further insights into the disposal of older products in favor of a newer generation of technology. This literature focuses on the replacement of older, more expensive to maintain, capital equipment with new maintenance-free and more efficient machines. While these models do consider the evolution of process technology, they do not consider again the supply side economical issues of reuse or remanufacturing of older technologies into the newer one for cost reduction. Initially, these models took into consideration the cost of new equipment, capital and increasing maintenance costs for older equipment (Kalymon, 1972; Derman et al., 1978; Kwon et al., 1981; Ye, 1990). More recently, the effect of the rate of technological change is considered. This technology change can either be reflected in a lower cost of manufacturing per unit (implicitly assuming that while the design of the product does not change substantially, new technologies can process units faster or more efficiently resulting in lower unit manufacturing costs), or can also result in an increased capacity for manufacturing. This literature suggests that as systemic risk—technology advances faster or other drivers—increases, the advisability of postponing equipment repurchase increases (MacDonald and Siegal, 1986; Nair and Hopp; 1992; Kulatilaka and Perotti, 1993; Mauer and Ott, 1995). It is important to note that the literature often assumes that the salvage value of disposed equipment/products is zero (Derman et al., 1978; Jesse, 1986; Eschenbach; 1995; Park, 1997). This is important since it is indicative to a belief that products have no residual value at disposal. Such a belief often prevents the direct capture of this residual. The consideration of reuse or remanufacturing can significantly change this assumption, as the salvage value is obtained not only in the secondary markets, but also in a lower unit cost for the machines with the new technology, as certain components in the older machines can be reused. Both Verheyen (1978) and Mauer and Ott (1985) recognize that products can decline in salvage value over time, as they both model the salvage value as an exponential function. In addition, consideration has been given to perishable goods (Rosenfeld, 1989; Gupta and Dai, 1991; Fujiwara et al., 1997). These models apply well to products with clearly defined lifetimes (agricultural products). Rosenfeld (1989) considers what to dispose of, given a known salvage value. In contrast, Gupta and Dai (1991) and Fujiwara et al. (1997) are concerned with establishing a pricing and inventory policy. These models may be relevant to certain classes of reusable products; therefore, it is worth noting the literature for future consideration.

The related literature either considers very specific problems (like perishability of meat) or models based on a set of assumptions with weak or unstated attachment to actual applications. Prior to the development of models for understanding the effect of technological change on products and their reuse, it is necessary to better define the field. Consequently, the rest of this chapter considers the affect of technology and obsolescence on products. We accomplish this by first considering selling of older technology into different markets.

3. The Reselling of Products with Old Technologies in Different Markets Which are Less Advanced

There are a variety of opportunities to sell products that appear to be obsolete in one market, because they may not be obsolete in some other market(s). Sale of old stock or post-user product can be within a country, between countries, or for a different application.

Redmond (1994) found that the rate of diffusion of a product varies within a country. This is a result of difference between regions or as a result of differences in socioeconomic conditions. For many products, the difference between regions or socioeconomic groups is insufficient to make selling of used product attractive. For other products, such as automobiles, these differences are great and have led to a large used car industry and a growing car leasing industry in the United States. A large second-hand market has always existed due to classified advertising, garage sales, flea markets, and charity sales. The Internet has also contributed to further growth of the used product market by increasing the ease of sellers and buyers locating each other. Diffusion rates can vary within a country, but also between countries. Kalish, Mahajan and Muller (1995) consider the different strategies that a firm can adopt in introducing products into global markets. They find that under certain conditions, the firm is better off introducing a product based on a new technology simultaneously in all the markets, whereas under other conditions, the firm is better off adopting a piecemeal approach, where the different markets are entered sequentially. When the fixed cost of introducing a product (like advertising costs) in a less advanced market is small, and the initial number of adopters (coefficient of innovation in the Bass diffusion model) is high, the firm introduces the products into all the global markets simultaneously. Alternatively, if the fixed cost of introduction is high for a foreign market, and the coefficient of innovation is low, the firm should introduce products into different markets sequentially, as this enables the firm to get some word of mouth effects across different countries.

Cross-border sales of products based on the older technology may be a result of either differences in the rate of technology diffusion, technological change, or differences in relative wealth (income effects may make a sizeable difference in the ability of a country to adopt a new technology immediately when it becomes available). Research on mobile phones suggests that diffusion rates for technology are considerably different in different countries (Gruber and Verhoven, 1998; Dekimpe et al., 1998; Johnson and Bhattia, 1997). This offers a tremendous opportunity to transfer discarded telephones from one market to another. Another factor influencing this decision is the compatibility of the new technology with the existing standards being used in the country. In software, for example, some features possible with a new technology may be unsupported by products based on older technologies. When certain items like documents are shared between different people, having the latest software version may limit the ability of the purchaser to share documents with others. This reinforces the point that unless a sizeable fraction of the market is ready to adopt the new technology, consumers may have an incentive to purchase products with older technologies that are compatible with the existing standards in the country. In this particular example, the rate of diffusion and technological change is not completely dependent on relative wealth. To determine when and where it is worth collecting obsolete equipment and when and where it is worth reselling this equipment, requires an understanding of the global markets for different products.

In other cases, including resale of telecommunications equipment and the sale of used clothing, export from richer countries to poorer countries is common. One can partially recapture the value of products with older technologies quickly by transferring older products from the market where it is obsolescent to geographically different markets where it is not. This gives rise to a pseudo-salvage value for an older technology, where the product may be obsolete but it may be possible to refurbish the product and sell it in other markets. In this case, the less developed market acts as a secondary market for the product with the older technology. The reasons for the existence of this geographically disparate secondary market include lower costs of cannibalization and a satisfactory surplus being obtained by the consumer. Resellers only sell the low-end product in the less advanced market, hence they do not cannibalize the sales of the product with the new technology. The other reasons for this strategy to work from the customer's perspective are as follows.

(i) An overfunctionality of the product with the new technology in the less developed market. Often, the customers prefer the products with the older technologies because they do not need, and do not want to pay for the additional features in the new product, or do not have other infrastructure in their country to support all the features of the new product.

(ii) Retail selling price advantages can often be obtained by buying products with older technologies, as these products are typically cheaper compared to the products with newer technologies. The lower price is often accompanied by a lower price to performance ratio as well. Technology products fall faster in price after introduction in the advanced market and can be recovered at a lower unit cost, and sold at a lower price in the less advanced market.

To be able to import products to a poorer country, it must be established that the products are saleable and are not being dumped on less advanced markets.

This is an important criterion since there are international conventions to prevent the shipment of waste from richer to poorer countries (Shearer, 1993; Porter and Welsh Brown, 1996).

One additional possibility is the sale of the product in either original or modified form for another application. This repositioning of a product may take place with or without a change of geographic market. In this form of secondary market, the product satisfies the utility for a different purpose and the content of cannibalization of the new product sales is very low. For example, older personal computers can be used for less demanding applications. Newer personal computers are required for applications that have either extensive use of sophisticated graphics or intensive calculating powers. Older personal computers are adequate for a wide range of applications including industrial and building control systems, low-graphics educational purposes, word processing, and many other applications that are not dependent on fast processor speed. Another example is equipping rental cars with older cell phones. The cell phones may be too old or large to be saleable within the country. However, they are adequate for the temporary use of visiting business people and tourists, since this market segment is not sensitive to age and style of the telephone. Often, components of older products can be used for the same purpose, for example, when one wants to dispose of an old computing system, the monitor may be small or obsolete for the new line of products, but may be able to satisfy display needs for other systems.

The remaining functional value of obsolete new product or used product may be captured by selling the product to less technologically advanced price-sensitive markets in the same country, to less advanced price-sensitive customers in different countries, or selling the product to customers in the same or different countries for use in different applications that only require the level of performance offered by this technology that is now obsolete in its original market. Having considered the resale of new or used product, the effect of upgrades on technological obsolescence is considered.

4. The Effect of Upgrades on Technological Obsolescence

The effects of upgrades on technological obsolescence are manifold. Since customers do not lose value from the older generation of products, they can always be upgraded to a new level of performance and customers are more willing to purchase the product at every level of technology. This can also be analyzed using the options theory framework. This gives them surplus utility for longer periods of time since a small upgrade price offers an added level of performance, and also minimizes the impact of price. In addition, the firm is often better off by providing an upgrade, as it provides a remanufacturing option to the firm. The firm provides the upgrade to the customer who performs the task of upgrading the product by adding some components in hardware products or features in software products themselves. This enables the firm to provide the higher-end version of the product to the consumer at a much lower unit cost, and also eliminating some additional overhead expenses in the process. Since both the firm and the customer can benefit from the upgrade option, the use of upgrades has excellent possibilities in certain circumstances. Consequently, we offer some insights into the management of the process of providing upgrades to customers, and delineate successful applications of upgrading with examples.

4.1 Type of products that suit upgrades

Product upgrades have historically been of two types: to correct deficiencies and to improve performance. The correction of product deficiency through an upgrade is often referred to as a recall. Recalls are unintended, but necessary since they involve deficiencies in the product that have the potential to create safety hazards, break existing laws, or seriously affect the functionality and/or longevity of the product. In certain industrial products, the firm may provide upgrades to rectify problems that are not critical at a later stage. For example, in the software industry, firms often provide a basic version of the software application to consumers at an earlier stage, to gain the first-mover advantage, or to introduce a placeholder in the market. This basic or beta-version may often have bugs that do not cause serious problems to the consumer, but may result in the software operating at a lower efficiency with some breakdowns. The firm continues the development of the software in the interim, and provides an upgraded version to the consumer at a later stage; this enables the consumer to derive some initial utility from the product, and also to get full performance when the upgrade is introduced. In the absence of such a strategy, the firm may face a competitive threat, as some other firm may introduce a product earlier than they can develop their full version, and consumers also gain as they obtain the beta-version earlier, and typically at a lower price. There are examples of this strategy being used for hardware products also (Applied Materials, 1986).

Other times, upgrades are conducted to improve the functionality of the product. In such examples, the firm provides the basic version of the product first, at a certain price, and then provides components that can be added or replaced to obtain a greater level of functionality. Depending on the market norms and the nature of existing agreements with customers, firms may charge for upgrades or provide them at no cost. Usually, upgrades that are provided for error rectification, as in the case of recalls, or fixing bugs, are provided at no cost to the product owner, while upgrades that result in performance enhancements are sold to the product owner. The nature of product design, technological change, industry norms, and the manufacturer/consumer relationship all affect the viability and potential profitability of product upgrades. Since all of these factors interact, each will be dealt with briefly.

Products may be designed to facilitate or inhibit product upgrades. If product upgrades are desired, the design is made to keep the cost of modifications low and the modification process as easy and foolproof as possible. This is often necessary for consumer products, as the firm may lack the ability to upgrade the product at the place of use for each individual consumer. The consumer should be able to undertake the upgrade himself. For industrial products, this may not be essential, as field service engineers can do the upgrading for the nominal number of individual consumers. This process of design-for-upgrading involves the use of modularity in design. By using a series of easy to assemble/disassemble modules, removal of one module and replacement with a new generation model becomes easier. The use of software, instead of hardware, encourages upgradeability since changes to the function of the product can be obtained through the change of code and may not require either any physical modification or contact with the product. With proper design this requires at worst the swapping out of an integrated circuit. However, it is easy to design a product so that no physical changes to the product are necessary for modifying the software. A reliance on software instead of hardware is common in control systems across many industries, making these products easier to upgrade. Using techniques, like design for modularity, has the added advantage that the product is easier to assemble and manufacture the first time, and suppliers can be closely integrated in the product development process by making each supplier responsible for the design of their module. This strategy has been used effectively for cars, as suppliers bear the responsibility of the design of most of the core systems and components. A modular design has other advantages, as a number of different products can be based on the same components by using a mix-and-match strategy. Repair and testing activities are also easier to do, as the modular-designed product can be tested for each component separately, and defective items can be repaired or replaced. The same logic works during the replacement of the consumable components during the remanufacturing process. Some products are even easier to upgrade because the system has been designed to allow the manufacturer remote access. Remote access by the manufacturer can be obtained through fixed telephone link (allowing either the product or the manufacturer to contact each other), connection to the Internet, or provision of a wireless link. Such an interface not only allows for remote upgrades, but remote monitoring. The remote monitoring provides additional information valuable for managing the product over its entire life. However, designing products to be modular has costs as well. Sometimes some performance content is lost, as the interaction of different components cannot be guaranteed as well as in an integral architecture. Modular designs also may sometimes result in a higher cost of offering the same level of functionality, since interactions between components can be taken advantage of to a lesser extent.

Differences in established practices between industries also greatly affect what is currently done and how easy it is to modify practice in the future. Established practices depend partially on history and partially on the structure of the industry—product standards, nature of supplier/customer relationships, number of customers, and number of suppliers. The existence of product standards may allow for OEMs as well as a non-OEM to provide upgrades; this supports upgradeability in an industry. If product design can be made modular, third parties can develop applications that can result in the upgrade of the core product. One example that would be familiar to most readers are add-in packages in software applications like Microsoft Excel. A number of users can write add-ins in programming languages like Visual Basic to enhance the functionality provided by the software application. Similarly, the Wintel standards and plug-and-play features in PCs facilitate upgrading. Similar examples can be found in hardware. The automotive industry, in part due to the large number of standards, has a huge after-market allowing, for upgrades of existing parts (like Engine Control Modules) and increasing functionality of the vehicle, like mobile telephony. A small number of suppliers and customers, product complexity, and/or strong relationships between customer and supplier support the provision of post-sales interaction. All increase the likelihood of upgrades being economically attractive for both the OEM and customer to pursue (Baumgartner and Wise, 2000). These structural factors encourage the use of product upgrades. An example is the modification of cockpit electronics in airplanes, where strong relationships between a small number of manufacturers and customers exist, to enhance their performance and extend their technical life so that it is in-line with the functional life of the rest of the airplane.

The nature of technological change is of great importance to the degree that the product can be upgraded. Components must be placed in modules, so that any components that may interact are placed together. This will ensure that if one module is replaced, the product does not lose functionality due to incompatibility between old and new components. However, it may not always be possible to separate parts of the product into modules for upgrading, depending on how technology changes all attempts at modular design can be thwarted. For upgrades to be successful, upgrades to the in-field product must be affordable. Better product design, modularity, and programmability, increases the likelihood that this is the case. It is possible, however, that technology changes in an unforeseen way, and as a consequence, it is not possible to upgrade the product. We now return to the concept of the technological trajectory (see Figure 1) and the possibility of obtaining improvements by either moving along a technological trajectory or changing to a new technological trajectory. In the case of movement along a technological trajectory, performance improves over time. This is easy to upgrade for, since it usually involves swapping one part or system for another in order to obtain better performance along some series of dimensions. One example would be replacing an existing computer monitor with a monitor that offers a larger screen size and lower power consumption. However, switching technological trajectories is more problematic for upgrades. Identifying technological trajectories that will be superior at some point in the future are, at best, difficult to predict. Consequently, it is difficult to design for compatibility with new technological trajectories. Different technological trajectories are often based on very different bodies of knowledge and fundamental assumptions, therefore increasing the likelihood of incompatibility. These differences in technology often result in different and incompatible sets of standards that further hinder the upgrade process, since additional parts of the product need to be upgraded. It is possible that products utilizing different technological trajectories are compatible with upgradeability. An example is the replacement of traditional sensor technology with smaller and cheaper microtechnology-based sensors. These sensors are often designed to interface with other parts of a product in a manner similar to traditional sensors. Consequently, the aerospace industry has been upgrading to microtechnology-based sensors for decades. In summary, technologies that are either disruptive or are from competing technological trajectories may make upgrades difficult or impossible. It is more likely that when product increments are introduced later in the diffusion cycle (the growth, maturity and decline phases of the Bass diffusion model), that one can have the upgrade option. When a product creates a completely new market, it may be difficult to have a high degree of similarity with the old technology product and it may be more difficult for the product to be upgraded.

Having considered the factors that effect upgradeability, we can summarize by stating that the following features generally encourage upgradeability:

- Upgrade opportunities resulting from changes in technological trajectories
- Modular design
- Use of software, instead of hardware
- Product is remotely accessible and upgradeable
- Compliance with established product standards
- History of upgrades occurring in industry
- Sale of benefit or service, not product
- Small number of customers
- Small number of manufacturers
- Large market share
- Close relationship between manufacturer and customer
- Product is expensive and has potentially a long functional life

The following features generally discourage upgradability:

- Changes in standards

Special consideration should be given to situations that involve:

- Upgrade opportunities resulting from changes in technological trajectories

We now present a simple model of the beneficial effects of upgrading in product development to the consumer and to the firm; the model is based on Bhattacharya, Krishnan and Mahajan (1999). A simple multiperiod model of product introduction is used. The lower performance level product and the product at the higher performance level are referred to as the low-end product and high-end product, respectively. In the first period, the firm introduces the low-end product, and in the next period, it introduces the high-end product when the technology improves.

We model the unit variable cost of the product to be an increasing and convex function of the product's performance quality q_i. In other words, the marginal cost of delivering higher performance increases with the level of performance. Specifically, we assume the unit cost of product i to be independent of demand volume and to be given by cq_i^2, where c is a constant. This form of the unit cost offers the added benefit of tractability, and is also used in the literature (Moorthy and Png, 1992). We also assume that the fixed costs of developing products are negligibly small compared to the gross profit, since the products are introduced in the mass market.

To model demand, we assume consumers to be rational in that they purchase the product with a performance level that maximizes their net utility surplus. Each consumer has a certain valuation of performance, denoted by v, which is the amount the consumer is willing to pay for a unit of performance. For product i which has a performance quality of q_i, a customer with a valuation of v is willing to pay a maximum of vq_i. If a consumer has a higher valuation for performance, s/he would gain more utility, and would be willing to pay more for a unit of product performance. The linear form of consumer utility is commonly used in the literature, because it enables a simpler analysis of consumer choice. The surplus that a consumer with valuation v derives from a product of performance quality q_i is given by $vq_i - p_i$, where p_i is the price of the product.

The surplus derived by the consumer from a product is also a function of the time of consumption, as a product offered earlier provides greater utility than a product with the same performance offered later. In other words, consumers discount the surplus accrued from a product at the rate of δ. The firm too prefers early accrual of profits, and it discounts profits from products at the same rate, here, we assume a perfect capital market. As is the case in the high technology industry, we model that the firm communicates the roadmap of its products (timing of introduction and the performance levels of the products) to its consumers. We also assume that this announcement is credible, i.e., consumers will wait to purchase the product that is introduced later if their discounted surplus from that product is higher.

The performance and price of the low-end produced are denoted by q_1 and p_1, respectively, and that of the high-end product are denoted by q_2 and p_2. Since consumers with higher valuations of performance are willing to pay more for a product, the firm targets the higher-end product at these consumers. Consumers with lower valuations of performance either adopt the low-end product, or do not purchase any product. The two market segments are characterized by the variables v_1 and v_2 (see Figure 2), whose significance is as follows.

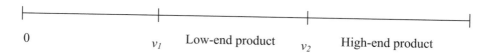

Figure 2: Market segmentation for two products

Consumers with a valuation lower than v_1 do not buy any of the products, as the utility $v_i q_i$ they derive from a product is less than p_i, the price of the product. Consumers with valuations between v_1 and v_2 buy the low-end product, as they get a higher surplus from the low-end product than the high-end product. Consumers with valuations higher than v_2 derive the maximum surplus from the high-end product, and consequently buy the higher-end product. The reason for such a market structure is as follows. Consumers with very low valuations of quality (low v) will not be willing to pay for either product, as their reservation price, given by vq, is low. If a consumer with a valuation of v_1 buys the low-end product, then a consumer with a higher valuation (who derives greater utility) will also buy the low-end product. Consumers with very high valuations of quality will buy the high-end product even if it is more expensive, because the excess utility from quality $v(q_2-q_1)$ is higher than the difference in the prices of the products p_2-p_1.

To simplify the analysis, we assume that the consumer valuations are uniformly distributed between 0 and 1. In that case, the demand volume for the low-end product is simply $v_2 - v_1$, as every customer whose valuation lies between v_1 and v_2 purchases the low-end product. Similarly, the demand volume for the high-end product is given by $1 - v_2$. The profit maximization problem for the firm can be formulated mathematically as follows.

$$\text{Max } \Pi = (v_2 - v_1)(p_1 - c\,q_1^2) + \delta_s\{1 - v_2\}(p_2 - c\,q_2^2)$$

such that:

$$vq_1 - p_1 \geq \delta(vq_2 - p_2) \qquad v1 \leq v \leq v2$$
$$vq_1 - p_1 \leq \delta(vq_2 - p_2) \qquad v2 \leq v \leq 1$$
$$vq_1 - p_1 \geq 0 \qquad v1 \leq v \leq v2$$
$$vq_2 - p_2 \geq 0 \qquad v2 \leq v \leq 1$$

The objective function P (firm's profit) is the sum of two terms representing the contributions from the low-end product and the high-end product. The profit of each product is equal to the demand volume multiplied by the margin (which is equal to $p - cq^2$), and is discounted appropriately. The first two constraints are the self-selection constraints, which ensure that consumers select (get more surplus from) the products targeted at them. The last two constraints are the participation constraints, and they ensure that the utility that the consumers obtain from the product is positive.

In the model, consumers with valuations of v_1 and v_2 in Figure 2 are the marginal consumers in the market, as they are indifferent between the two options that they have. The consumer with a valuation of v_1 for performance is indifferent between buying and not buying the low-end product, and the consumer with a valuation of v_2 is indifferent between buying the low-end product and the high-end product. Equating the utilities of the marginal consumer from their two options gives us the optimal prices. From the equations, we obtain

$$p_1 = v_1 q_1; \; p_2 = v_2 q_2 - \frac{1}{\delta}(v_2 - v_1)q_1$$

The marginal consumer valuations are:

$$v_1 = \frac{p_1}{q_1}; v_2 = \frac{\delta p_2 - p_1}{\delta q_2 - q_1}$$

Substituting these values into the profit function, we obtain

$$q_1 = \frac{6\delta - 4\sqrt{9\delta^2 - 8\delta}}{(64 - 54\delta)c}$$

$$q_2 = \frac{16 - 9\delta - 3\sqrt{9\delta^2 - 8\delta}}{(64 - 54\delta)c} \cdot v_1 = \frac{32 - 24\delta - 2\sqrt{9\delta^2 - 8\delta}}{64 - 54\delta} \quad \text{and}$$

$$v_2 = \frac{32 - 18\delta - 6\sqrt{9\delta^2 - 8\delta}}{64 - 54\delta}$$

In the analysis so far, we assumed that consumers did not have the upgrade option, so they had to self-select one of the two products at the beginning. However, if the upgrade option is provided, then consumers do not have to choose one of the two products in the beginning; all consumers with positive surpluses will purchase the low-end product in the first period. Then, only consumers with positive surpluses from the upgrade will upgrade to the high-end product in the second period. The profit maximization problem for the firm can be formulated mathematically as follows.

$$\text{Max } \Pi = (1 - v_1)(p_1 - c q_1^2) + \delta_s \{1 - v_2\}[p_U - c(q_2^2 - q_1^2)]$$

such that:

$$v(q_2 - q_1) \le p_U \qquad v_1 \le v \le v_2$$
$$v(q_2 - q_1) \ge p_U \qquad v_2 \le v \le 1$$
$$v q_1 - p_1 \ge 0 \qquad v_1 \le v \le v_2$$

The objective function Π shows that the price of the upgrade (p_U) minus the cost of the upgrade is the margin of the upgrade. The profit of each product is equal to the demand volume multiplied by the margin, and is discounted appropriately. The first two constraints say that only consumers with greater valuations than v_2 obtain a positive surplus from the upgrade (the surplus from the upgrade is the net gained utility minus the price of the upgrade).

Equating the utilities of the marginal from their two options gives us the optimal prices. From the equations, we obtain

$$p_1 = v_1 q_1; p_U = v_2(q_2 - q_1)$$

The marginal consumer valuations are:

$$v_1 = \frac{p_1}{q_1}; v_2 = \frac{p_U}{q_2 - q_1}$$

Substituting these values into the profit function, we obtain

$$q_1 = \frac{18 - 16\delta - 3\sqrt{9 - 8\delta}}{(27 - 32\delta)c}$$

$$q_2 = \frac{81 - 80\delta - 9\sqrt{9\delta^2 - 8\delta}}{3(27 - 32\delta)c}. \quad p_1 = \frac{q_1}{2} + \frac{c q_1^2}{2} \text{ and } p_U = \frac{q_2 - q_1}{2} + \frac{c(q_2^2 - q_1^2)}{2}.$$

A numerical comparison across different values of the discount factor δ shows that the profits from the upgrade are always higher than if the consumer has to choose a new product, which is completely different. From this model, we can see that the upgrade option always does better than the situation where the product based on the new technology replaces the product with the existing technology. Therefore, firms can profit be redesigning their products to be upgradeable.

4.2 Traditional upgrade processes

There are substantial differences between upgrade processes depending on whether they take place at the customer or manufacturer's site. For industrial products, most upgrades occur at the manufacturer's site. Consequently, this will be considered first. Even in the case of product recalls, the customer returns the product to a site designated by the manufacturer. It enters an incoming inventory, the product is upgraded and then the product is returned. In many instances care is taken to ensure that the product returned to the customer is the product that was sent in for upgrading (consider for example automobiles). In other cases, this is not considered necessary since all products are considered totally interchangeable and are covered under a warranty or service guarantee. For example, Linton and Johnston (2000) describe in detail a typical upgrade process for telecommunications products.

Alternatively, the product may be upgraded at the customer's site. This is frequently the case for consumer-based products, where the established base of the market is too diverse for the manufacturer to be able to offer an upgrade to all consumers; therefore, the manufacturer designs the upgrade to be such that the consumers can effect the upgrade themselves. For example, in the car industry, a number of audio systems have been developed which are compatible with the existing electrical outlets in the car. These audio systems are designed to increase the functionality of the existing audio system in the car as made by the manufacturer. In cases such as these where the manufacturer has to give detailed instructions for upgrading to the consumer, an agreement must be made regarding upgrade date and time, product downtime, and customer-provided resources required for the upgrade. For commercial products such as photocopiers and telecommunications products, upgrades are typically conducted on-site by representatives of the OEM.

There have been no observations of the nature of the technological change affecting the type of upgrade process used. However, the resources provided for and the structure of the upgrade process will have a tremendous impact on the rate of diffusion of the new technology through the existing field population of product.

5. Reuse of Components From Products of the Same Generation of Technology

Reuse of components depends in part on: the durability of a product, the rate of technological change, and the nature of that change. In the case of a consumable or nondurable product, every time a technological change is made to a product, manufacturing will involve a ramp-up phase, a steady-state phase, and a phase-out as a new introduction occurs. During the ramp-up, phase increasing quantities of new technology product will enter the market and later enter the waste stream. If these technological changes prevent the reuse of components, an increase in manufacturing capacity is required to make the new components and a new pathway—remanufacture, recycle or disposal will have to be created for the old parts that can no longer be reused. The need to treat previously reusable components differently and manufacture large volumes of alternative components depends on the lifespan of the product—both new and older generation(s).

Alternatively, the rates of usage of durable goods with even a low rate of technological change and significant standardization tend to differ greatly over time. There are two issues relating to the reuse of components or materials. First, the reuse of components from products where the technological change has been gradual, and is primarily based on movement along a technological trajectory, can be managed better. Second, when an alternative technological trajectory is introduced, this creates major disruptions to the reusability of parts.

Savaskan (2000) has a comprehensive review of the different kinds of products that can make use of remanufacturing from products of the same generation. For products like one-time use cameras, Kodak has an established system of collecting cameras from retailers that develop film for customers. From these used cameras, the company recovers a large proportion of the nonconsumable parts of the camera in the production of new cameras—this includes the cartridge and packaging. The retailer is given a fixed fee in exchange for every camera returned to Kodak. Print and copy cartridges, where the consumable component of the cartridge is not high, are directly collected back from the customers using prepaid mailboxes provided by the manufacturer. These cartridges are then disassembled and remanufactured into new products. Often, third parties undertake this effort, by either repairing products that are defective, or by refurbishing them with components of acceptable quality. In the case of copier machines, Xerox has set the standard by using the components from copiers that are at the end of their lease in the manufacturing of new copiers. Similarly, Hewlett-Packard encourages customers to return their used computers or peripherals to any HP office from where the products are later sent to one of HP's hardware recycling centers in the UK, France, or Germany for refurbishing, remanufacturing or recycling (Savaskan, Bhattacharya and Van Wassenhove, 2000).

In such cases, there are two main issues connected with reuse: (1) market penetration of the product determines the presence/absence of an established base for recovering and reusing these products and (2) determination of the parties that should be made responsible for the take-back effort on behalf of the manufacturer. Since all of these consumable products are sold in the recent past, the remanufacturing content that is available in the older products can be high, as even components, which have lower degrees of durability can be reused within the next few months for new products. If there is a sufficient number of older products already purchased by consumers, then integrating such products into the steady state production for new products is not difficult, as there can be some base level of supply that can be ensured in a reasonable lead time. Depending on the reach of the different parties within the market, the responsibility for the take-back effort can rest with different parties. Since retailers already have an established network of outlets to interact with customers, they can be one possible source of take back. Kodak entrusts the task of take back to their retailers. Often, manufacturers may be able to reach out to their customers by providing easy methods of returning used products, such as providing financial incentives or costless methods. Xerox uses this method by providing prepaid mailboxes to customers for returning their copier cartridges. When there are economies of scale in undertaking the take-back effort, third parties may be the most efficient method to undertake the take back of the product. Savaskan, Bhattacharya and Van Wassenhove (2000) find that for supply chains that are not integrated, if the costs of collection are the same for all three agents, then retailers are the most efficient agents for undertaking the take back as they have the incentive of accelerating the diffusion process so that products may be sold earlier in the market, and then used for recovery later.

In summary, whether the product is a durable or consumable is important to the economic viability of the reuse of components from products. Consumable products can often be used within the same generation for reuse, and this content of reuse depends on the extent to which the product diffuses into the marketplace. Another important question is which agent in the supply chain should undertake the take-back process on behalf of the manufacturer. Depending on the nature of the product and the supply chain, the firm should choose their strategy for recovering used products from the market, and using them for manufacturing new products.

6. Impact of the Technology Diffusion of the Old Generation of Products on Remanufacturing in the New Generation

Technology change may make older products obsolete prior to the end of their functional life. Firms frequently discontinue the sale of older technology products once new technology is introduced. Existing stock is often scrapped or sold at a greatly discounted price. Often, retail items such as fashion goods may demonstrate the same feature, as customers expect that products that have been introduced in previous seasons are not in vogue anymore, and will not purchase items from the previous season at full-ticketed prices. However, the degree to which the older-generation products can be reused for products of the new generation depends on the degree of change and the durability of the older generation of products. In fact, companies may provide customers with a product using the new technology even if the customer wants the product with the old technology (downward substitution). This is justified by cost benefits in inventory carrying costs obtained from carrying one product instead of two. This does not imply, however, that firms must take tremendous write-downs on the older generation product.

If there are similarities between the new and the old product, components from the older generation can be used in manufacturing new products. Usually, some of the components in the older generation of products can be used in the new generation. Hence, take-back older products from customers and reusing the components for the new generation of products is an effective tool for extraction of value from older generations of products. Xerox is an example of one firm currently pursuing this manufacturing strategy. Firms profit through the reuse of components, as there are cost savings associated with reusing these previously used components. These unit cost savings can be passed on to some extent to the consumer or retained, offering an increase in margin. Below, we provide a model for determining the optimal price and quantity to be recovered from the market.

We consider a system where the manufacturer can either make a product from new components entirely, or use some durable old components in addition to new ones to make a new product. For simplicity, we assume that the channel is coordinated, that is, the manufacturer undertakes the take-back process. Savaskan, Bhattacharya and Van Wassenhove (2000) provide a detailed discussion on product take back and reuse in uncoordinated channels. Denote c_m as the unit cost of manufacturing a new product, and c_r as the unit cost of remanufacturing a returned product into a new one ($c_m > c_r$, as the prospect of reuse results in lower unit costs). Let τ denote the fraction of the current demand supplied from returned products. The average unit cost of manufacturing can be written as $c = c_m(1-\tau) + c_r\tau$. If we denote the unit cost savings from take-back by Δ, where $\Delta = c_m - c_r$, then the average unit cost can also be represented by $c_m - \tau\Delta$.

With p the retail price charged by the manufacturer and F the demand curve with respect to price, we make the standard assumption that $F(p)$ is decreasing in p. Typically, the cost associated with the take back of used products from consumers is expensive (using pre-paid boxes to encourage consumers to return used products, for example), and the greater the fraction of products to be reused, the greater is the cost of take back. The cost of take back is also higher if the volume of units sold is higher. To model these effects, we model the cost of take back as $G[\tau, F(p)]$, where G is increasing in τ and increasing in $F(p)$. The profits of the firm can then be represented as:

$$\Pi = F(p)[p - c_m + \tau\Delta] - G[\tau, F(p)]$$

The first term represents the product of the demand volume and the margin, as the unit cost is now $c_m - t\Delta$. The second term is the cost of undertaking the take-back process. The first-order conditions for the optimal price and the fraction to be recovered are given as follows:

$$p = c_m - \Delta\tau + \frac{\partial G[\tau, F(p)]}{\partial F(p)} - \frac{F(p)}{\dfrac{\partial F(p)}{\partial p}}$$

$$\frac{\partial G[\tau, F(p)]}{\partial \tau} = \Delta F(p)$$

In the absence of remanufacturing, the retail price would be given by

$$p = c_m - \frac{F(p)}{\dfrac{\partial F(p)}{\partial p}}$$

Hence, we see that the retail price is lower if $\Delta\tau > \dfrac{\partial G[\tau, F(p)]}{\partial F(p)}$ implying that both the consumers and the manufacturer can benefit from reusing old components in new products. If G is convex in τ, then the first-order condition provided above for τ shows the optimal level of the fraction to be recovered. If G is concave in τ, then the firm either does not use remanufacturing ($\tau=0$), or remanufactures all its products ($\tau=1$).

There are additional considerations in the capture and reuse of components for remanufacturing on the new technology generation of product. The two major issues are the reuse of components to alleviate the need for manufacturing and inventorying replacement parts, and the use of components that have been rendered obsolete through the introduction of new technology.

First, we consider reuse of components in the automotive industry as an alternative supply of after-market components. Reuse of components from durable goods is most clearly developed in the automotive industry (de Hond and Groenwegen, 1993). The automotive industry involves substantial, but conservative, changes in technology from model-year to model-year. Reuse in the automotive industry is directed towards servicing the remaining product that exists in the field. In the automotive industry, suppliers maintain capital equipment and tooling and responsibility to support the after-market for parts and components. The take back and reuse of components from automobiles that have entered the waste stream could reduce either the need or duration of the need to retain inventory and production readiness, thereby reducing the inventory cost of the product for the supplier. This take back and reuse exists currently, but is independent of and competes with the supplier of the original parts and components. Through the coordination of the take back of parts with the firm that has the responsibility to maintain a supply of after-market parts, the overall cost of inventory and the profitability of after-sales service could be improved. Having considered the reuse of components as an alternative to absorbing the high set-up and inventory costs associated with manufacturing small batches of parts and components to service after-markets, the consideration of reuse activities in the case of technological advances rendering a part obsolescent is now considered.

The introduction of components or products that include technological advances may render some components of earlier product obsolete and unusable for its current application. In this case, the alternative is to find an alternative application for the component. A current example of this is the eventual displacement of analog Cathode-Ray Tube (CRT)-based television with digital Flat-Panel (FP) display televisions. This technological change prevents the reuse of the lead-bearing glass of the old CRTs. This is a problem, since lead is hazardous and the CRT glass has special requirements for its transportation and disposal in some jurisdictions. This example and its implications are addressed in detail in Linton et al. (2001). The implications are summarized here. The rate of diffusion of the new product is clearly important; the rate of abandonment of the existing technology is also important. This is problematic, since little is known about abandonment behavior and since diffusion researchers have shown a pro-innovation bias—they only consider accepting the new and not rejecting the old (Rogers and Shoemaker, 1971). Abandonment not only relies on the rate of adoption of new technology, but other factors as well. Frequently, when people adopt new technology, the old technology does not enter the waste stream. Instead the product is either used by the owners (but in a different way), sold, given to someone, else or placed into storage (Linton, 1999). The effect is to create tremendous uncertainty regarding the rate and duration of the supply of this component as a raw material for alternative products. Linton et al. (2001) modeled the disposal of CRT-based televisions using resampling to capture the uncertainty caused by different factors and their likely distributions. Unlike earlier predictions (DEP 1998), Linton et al. found that:

- Quantity of disposable/recoverable CRTs needed to be predicted as a range of values for a given year, not as a single value.
- Disposal of CRTs changes over time.
- Even assuming the most aggressive adoption behavior, there will be substantial disposal of CRTs each year over the next fifty years; disposal of all CRTs within ten years is not likely.

An extended period of time is required for durables that rely on older technology to become completely displaced from the field. Consequently, alternative uses of technically obsolete durables are worth investigation. Great care should be taken with forecasts, policy, and business decisions relating to components from durable products.

In addition, the study of the effect of new technologies on use by customers has focused on the effect of new technologies on replacement decisions for old equipment. However, if there is a high likelihood of technological evolution and obsolescence, the customer may not always want to purchase the new equipment, but may hold on to the old equipment, and skip a generation of the new technology. This is often the case since it may be better to wait to purchase the next generation of a more advanced technology. This situation also creates a secondary market for the technology that has recently been disposed of. Whether this market is sought by the OEM or left to third parties varies from industry to industry. Telecommunications firms like Lucent and Nortel Networks have long been involved in the sale and resale of older equipment (in addition to current equipment). However, many other firms have left opportunities in this market to third parties fearing that participation in this market would cannibalize their sales.

Other than consideration of mainframes, semiconductors and cellular telephony, an understanding of diffusion of generational technology is lacking. Closed-loop considerations have not been studied in the context of diffusion, yet. This void must be filled to understand better diffusion and market life cycles in a closed-loop market or economy.

7. Conclusions

The focus of this chapter has been on the role of remanufacturing and reuse in profitable operations, and the impact of technological change on this role. Products or components that can be reused by the OEM can be reused if the components are durable. However, this reuse of components from previous products depends on the extent of change introduced in the product by the new technology, and the speed at which the market adopts the products, enabling older products to be recovered. There is a need for a better understanding of the effect of changes in technology and succession in product generations on diffusion. Initial studies indicate the use of Bass's diffusion model is of value in this regard. A better understanding of the abandonment of older products is required, which may assist in forecasting the supply-side potential for reuse and remanufacturing. In turn, the effect of remanufacturing and/or reuse on diffusion of new products has not been considered—but should be.

Within the context of remanufacturing under technology change, we looked at four basic situations and identified issues and results in the literature to understand their relation: (i) reselling products based on older technologies in new markets, (ii) offering product upgrades to obtain superior performance, (iii) remanufacturing new products using old products from the same technology generation, and (iv) remanufacturing new products using old products from previous technology generations. In all of these cases, we identified situations where remanufacturing and reuse are easier to achieve. One of the primary sources of difficulty in reusing components from older products is the nature of the technology trajectory(ies). The difference between technological advancement that is along the same technical trajectory versus a change to a different technological trajectory has been established. Changes in technological trajectories are less likely to support product upgrades. When the technology improves performance along the same trajectory, existing standards can be maintained, and components can be reused in different types of products.

The nature of the product and industry must be considered. These factors include:

- Existence of standards
- Ownership of product versus lease or purchase of benefit
- The agents of remanufacturing and take back of used products
- Ease of designing products for disassembly
- Similarities in design between firm's products
- Extent of relationship between customer and manufacturer
- Tradition of upgrades

There are questions associated with the effects of time and application on the value of a product. We must gain a better understanding of the rate of reduction in value of a product or products under different circumstances:

- In the current geographic market for the same application
- In the current geographic market for a different application
- In a different geographic market for the same application
- In a different geographic market for a different application
- Based on the use of its parts in the new generation product
- Based on the use of its parts in other products

Furthermore, an understanding is required of how the perceived rate of change affects investment decisions in reuse and remanufacturing. By understanding better the rate at which the technology diminishes in value, better decisions can be made about using the value of the technologically obsolete product. By considering mechanisms to identify alternative uses of technology, or to maximize value harvesting, we may actually increase the rate of diffusion of new technology. The rate of diffusion may increase because if the salvage value of old technology increases, earlier adoption of the newer technology will increase. This is a statement worth reflecting on since pessimism in many firms towards a closed-loop environment is based on the concern that life extension of older products will cannibalize the market for and profits from newer generation products.

References

Abernathy, W.J. and K.B. Clark (1985) Innovation: Mapping the winds of creative destruction. *Research Policy* **14** 3-22.

Applied Materials 1986. Harvard Business School Case, 86-019, Harvard Business School Press.

Bass, F.M. (1969) A new product growth model for consumer durables. *Management Science* **15** 215-227.

Baumgartner, P. and R. Wise (1999) Go downstream: The new profit imperative in manufacturing. *Harvard Business Review* **50(5)** 133-141.

Bhattacharya, S., V. Krishnan and V. Mahajan (1999) Operationalizing technology improvements in product development decision-making. INSEAD Working Paper Series.

Dekimpe, M.G., P.M. Parker and M. Sarvary (1998) Staged estimation of international diffusion models: An application to global cellular telephone adoption. *Technological Forecasting and Social Change* **57** 105-132.

den Hond, F. and P. Groenwegen (1993) Solving the automobile shredder waste problem: Cooperation among firms in the automotive industry, in K. Fischer and J. Schot (eds.), *Environmental Strategies of Industry: International perspectives on research needs and policy implications*, Washington, DC: Island Press, 343-376.

Department of Environmental Protection (DEP) (1998) Hazardous and solid waste regulations for Massachusetts: 310 CMR 30.000 and 310 CMR 19.00, Public hearing draft regulations for the management of discarded cathode ray tubes. Boston: Department of Environmental Protection.

Derman, C., G.J. Lieberman and S.M. Rossi (1978) A renewal decision problem. *Management Science* **24** 554-561.

Eschenbach, T.G. (1995) *Engineering Economy: Applying Theory to Practice*, Boston: Irwin.

Foster, R.N. (1986) *Innovation: The Attacker's Advantage*, New York: McKinsey and Company.

Fujiwara, O., H. Soewandi and D. Sedarage (1997) An optimal ordering and issuing policy for a two-stage inventory system for perishable products. *European Journal of Operational Research* **99** 414-424.

Grubber, H., and F. Verboven (1998) The diffusion of mobile telecommunications services in the European Union. Tilburg University, Center for Economic Research, Discussion Papers.

Gupta, D. and Z. Dai (1991) A heuristic procedure for determining ordering and price-discount policies for commodities with two-period perishability. *Engineering Costs and Production Economics* **21** 177-190.

Islam, T. and N. Meade (1997) The Diffusion of Successive Generations of a Technology: A More General Model. *Technological Forecasting and Social Change* **56**, 49-60.

Jesse, R.R. (1986) On the retention of finished goods inventory when reorder-occurrence is uncertain. *Journal of Operations Management* **6** 149-157.

Johnson, W.C. and K. Bhatia (1997) Technological Substitution in Mobile Communications. *Journal of Business and Industrial Marketing* **12** 383-399.

Kalish, S., V. Mahajan and E. Muller (1995) Waterfall and sprinkler new-product strategies in competitive global markets. *International Journal of Research in Marketing* **12** 105-119.

Kalymon, B.A. (1972) Machine replacement with stochastic costs. *Management Science* **18** 288-298.

Kulatilaka, N. and E.C. Perotti (1993) What is lost by waiting to invest? Working Paper #9343, Boston University, Boston, MA.

Kwon, I., J. Fang and J. Hubard (1981) A Bayesian approach to replacement theory using robust method – A case of small sample. *Industrial Management* 9-13.

Linton, J.D. (1999) Electronic products at their end-of-life: Options and obstacles. *Journal of Electronics Manufacturing* **9(1)** 29-40.

Linton J.D. and D.A. Johnston (2000) A decision support system for the planning of remanufacturing at Nortel. *Interfaces* **30(6)** 17-31.

Linton, J.D., J.S. Yeomans and R. Yoogalingam (2001) Forecasting the Waste Flow of Televisions: An Enabler for Industrial Ecology and Sustainability. Working Paper, Polytechnic University, Brooklyn, NY.

Mahajan, V. and E. Muller (1996) Timing diffusion and substitution of successive generations of technological innovations: The IBM mainframe case. *Technological Forecasting and Social Change* **51** 109-132.

Mauer, D.C. and S.H. Ott (1995) Investment under uncertainty: The case of replacement investment decisions. *Journal of Financial and Quantitative Analysis* **30** 581-605.

McDonald, R. and D. Siegel (1986) The value of waiting to invest. *Quarterly Journal of Economics* **101** 707-728.

Moorthy and Png (1992) Market Segmentation, cannibalization, and the timing of new product introductions. *Management Science* **38** 345-359.

Nair, S.K. and W.J. Hopp (1992) A model for equipment replacement due to technological obsolescence. *European Journal of Operational Research* **63** 207-221.

Norton, J.A. and F.M. Bass (1987) A diffusion theory model of adoption and substitution for successive generations of high technology products. *Management Science* **33** 1069-1086.

Norton, J.A. and F.M. Bass (1992) Evolution of technological generations: The law of capture. *Sloan Management Review* **33(2)** 66-77.

Park, C.S. (1997) *Contemporary Engineering Economics*. Addison-Wesley: Reading, MA.

Parker, P.M. (1994) Aggregate diffusion forecasting models in marketing: A critical review. *International Journal of Forecasting* **10** 353-380.

Porter, G. and J.W. Brown (1996) Global Environmental Politics, 2nd Edition, Boulder Co: Westview.

Redmond, W.H. (1994) Diffusion at sub-national levels: A regional analysis of new product growth. *Journal of Product Innovation Management* **11** 201-212.

Rogers, E.M. (1995) *Diffusion of Innovation*. Free Press: New York.

Rogers, E.M. and F.F. Shoemaker (1971) *Communications of Innovations: A Cross-Cultural Approach*, Free Press: New York.

Rosenfeld, D.B. (1989) Disposal of excess inventory. *Operations Research* **37** 404-409.

Savaskan. R.C. (2000) Management of closed-loop supply chains for recoverable products. Unpublished Ph.D. dissertation, INSEAD.

Savaskan, R.C., S. Bhattacharya and L.N. Van Wassenhove (2000) Channel choice and coordination in a remanufacturing environment. INSEAD Working Paper Series.

Shearer. C.R.H. (1993) Comparative analysis of the Basel and Bamako conventions on hazardous waste. *Environmental Law*, 23(1) 141.

Verheyen, P.A. (1978) Economic interpretation of models for the replacement of machines. *European Journal of Operational Research* **3** 150-156.

Ye, M. (1990) Optimal replacement policy with stochastic maintenance and operation costs. *European Journal of Operational Research* **44** 84-94.

Contacts:

Jonathan D. Linton
Lally School of Management and Technology
Rensselaer Polytechnic Institute
110 8th Street
Troy, NY 12180

Email: linton@rpi.edu

Shantanu Bhattacharya
Technology Management Area
INSEAD
1 Ayer Rajah Avenue
138676 Singapore

Email: shantanu.bhattacharya@insead.edu

Information Technology in Closed-Loop Supply Chains

Harold Krikke, Tilburg University, The Netherlands,
Angelika Kokkinaki, and Jo van Nunen, Erasmus University Rotterdam,
The Netherlands

1. Introduction

Similar to all chapters in this book, the key question is: what is new in closed-loop supply chains and what are the implications of exploiting information technology? However, before investigating the use of Information Technology (IT) in closed loop supply chains, it seems appropriate to explore the use of IT in Supply Chain Management (SCM) at large. Supply Chain Management is defined as "the integration of key business processes from end user through original suppliers that provides products, services and information that add value for customers and other stakeholders" (Stock and Lambert, 2000). Its actual realisation occurs by implementing concepts such as Efficient Consumer Response (ECR), Continuous replenishment, Supply and Demand planning, Installed Base, Business Intelligence, which in turn enable strategies such as alternate sourcing, responsiveness and mass customisation. Supply Chain Management basically avoids local inefficiencies by integrating business processes.

Nowadays, many companies are implementing enterprise resource planning (ERP) solutions to attain more efficient intra-enterprise transactions and a single data model. However, ERP systems alone do not deliver what many companies need to survive and prosper in today's marketplace. To compete effectively, companies are moving to collaborative planning and execution between divisions as well as between trading partners. Electronic Data Exchange (EDI), the Internet, and mobile networks enable easier transaction of information. Moreover, by using electronic networks for doing business, certain players in the chain become redundant (disintermediation). High potential areas of IT applications in supply chains include CAD/CAM systems, MRP/ERP-systems, Warehouse Management Systems, and E-commerce.

Closed-loop supply chains (CLSCs) deal with the set of interrelated sub-processes enabling the recovery of commercial, end-of-use and end-of-life items

(Guide and Van Wassenhove, 2000). Let us first point out some special characteristics of CLSCs and the role of Information Technology (IT).

To start, new players (such as waste management companies, energy firms, specialised recycling firms) enter the supply chain, thus establishing new and maybe more complex alliances. The roles of existing players also change, e.g., the customer is now also 'supplier' of discarded goods. New EU legislation puts responsibility for product take back and recovery on the OEMs. In turn, OEMs will try to share this responsibility with other players in the supply chain. Now a logical question is, which of the (new) supply chain players becomes responsible for which portion of the product life cycle. Supply chain objectives become more complicated, since supply chain optimisation is subjected to legal compliance. Advanced planning software may help to evaluate and improve economical and ecological performance of both the product and the (closed-loop) supply chain. In the latter category, IT can support choosing optimal recovery options or determine the logistics network structure. Life cycle tools support a reconsideration of several business functions, in particular product design. Information on returns can give important feedback to designers, not only about recovery but also with respect to, e.g., quality issues.

Regarding markets, alternative 'secondary' or reuse markets are developed in parallel with primary markets. Often, there is a mismatch between returns and demand for secondary products, often referred to as push-pull effects. In many cases, collection rates and costs appear to be serious issues. Electronic markets can facilitate returns acquisition and help balance demand and supply of used parts or products. Lack of information and control mechanisms on upcoming returns increase uncertainty in the system regarding quantity, quality, composition and timing and place of origin, leading to much inefficiency and missed opportunities (for reuse). IT can help lower uncertainties, e.g., by implementing remote monitoring systems, providing accurate data on the products condition, composition and location. Furthermore, reduction of operational costs can be accomplished by applying extended decision support, such as optimisation of route planning for the combined collection and distribution of returned goods or increase revenue through E-access to expanded, de-fragmentised markets.

To put it short, success factors in CLSCs include, among others, product design for recovery, disassembly, repairability, etc. (also known as DfX), product acquisition, development of secondary markets, management of increased system complexity and uncertainty, choice of optimal recovery options, and reduction of collection and handling cost.

Managing CLSCs requires specific information, both on a strategic and on an operational level. Common supply chain information systems have so far neglected the issue of closed-loop supply chains. Instead, specialised tools have been developed. Table 1 indicates how the four high potential areas can support the management of CLSCs.

SC IT area	CLSC IT area	Supports	Type of return
CAD/CAM	Product eco-tools	Product design and optimise EOL scenarios	End Of Life (EOL)
Warehouse Systems (WMS) (RLS)	Reverse logistics system (RLS)	Control handling cost	End Of Use (EOU)/ commercial
E-commerce	Electronic marketplaces for reusable products	Product acquisition and to development of secondary markets	EOU/commercial
Material Requirements Planning (MRP)	Reverse MRP	Deal with system complexity and uncertainty	EOU

Table 1: Information Technology Areas in Closed-Loop Supply Chains

In Section 2 we discuss each of the four major IT areas in view of closed-loop supply chains. We do so by taking a fictitious copier firm, nicknamed CopyMagic, as an illustrative example. We will show the benefits CopyMagic realises by using efficient and effective IT support to manage return flows.

It appears however, that not all benefits are fully exploited because of the lack of consistent product data that can be used throughout the products' life cycle. This also prevents the integration of the specialised CLSC IT tools with common SCM IT. Therefore, we discuss Product Data Management Systems and the integration with common 'forward' IT-systems in Section 3. In Section 4, we discuss our findings, draw conclusions and point out the research agenda.

2. CopyMagic and IT in closed-loop supply chains

The CopyMagic case was first described by Thierry (1995). It is a fictitious, Netherlands-based, large manufacturer of high quality copiers, selling world-wide, but in particular in Europe and Northern America. Most of the products are leased, however some (in particular refurbished products) are being sold in the Eastern European markets. Although fictitious, the case strongly resembles business practice, since it is based on experiences of the authors with a number of copier firms (see e.g., Krikke et al., 1999).

Since the early 1990s recovery activities have developed steadily through a number of development stages. It started with local repair by Operating Companies (OPCOs). Next, the management of CopyMagic instructed the R&D department to adapt product design to enable easier repair, disassembly and recycling. After that, it started up a centralised asset recovery plant for large-scale refurbishing and remanufacturing. By now, recovered machines account for 50 percent of sales and 60 percent of net profit. The current closed-loop supply chain of CopyMagic is reflected in Figure 1.

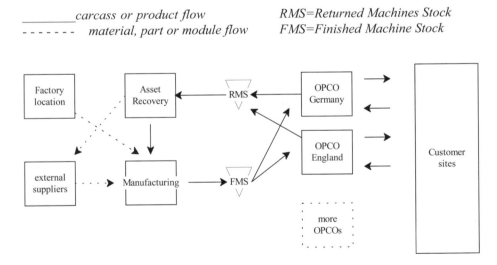

Figure 1: Closed-Loop Supply Chain of CopyMagic

CopyMagic machines are returned from the market due to the ending of lease contracts or active buyback because of market demand for recovered machines. The operating companies (OPCOs) are allowed to repair the machines in local workshops and put them back into the market. In case operating companies are not interested in repair, they return the machine to a recovery location of CopyMagic, for which they receive a fee. The cores are put in stock. Depending on their quality, the cores are fit for one or more of the following options:

- **Refurbishing (X->X+).** A returned machine X is disassembled to a fixed level and cleaned. New or repaired parts, that are the (sometimes improved) equivalent of the released parts, are built in. The new machine X^+ is thus an upgraded version of the returned machine.

- **Remanufacturing (X->Y).** A returned machine X is converted into a new model Y that contains all features and functions of a new product. In fact, model Y can also be manufactured from brand new components only. The return process is basically the same as for refurbish, except that not only released parts are replaced, but also entirely new parts and units are added to provide additional functionality.

- **Scrap (X->parts/materials).** The returned machine X is dismantled completely. Good components for which there is a demand are cannibalised for reuse; other components are recycled to the material level. Nonrecyclables are disposed of.

In addition to adapting product design and installing the physical returns operations, CopyMagic also had to change its information systems. In the next subsections we will describe reverse MRP, reverse logistics systems, E-market places and virtual networks for returns and product eco-tools.

2.1 MRP-I systems for product recovery

Since the regular MRP system, part of the ERP software package, is not geared for recovery operations, CopyMagic has developed its own MRP system. It is partly implemented using ERP software and partly implemented separately.

Let us first describe the process in more detail. If there is a demand for refurbished or remanufactured, or some cannibalised components, cores are actually taken from stock and disassembled. In remanufacturing and refurbishing, cores are first disassembled to a certain fixed level and a predetermined set of components, either good or bad, is removed. Released parts are tested and inspected. Approved parts are restocked directly or after repair. Disapproved parts are scrapped.

Always, the stripped carcass is cleaned and reassembled. In case of refurbishing, this is done in a specialised asset-recovery reassembly line. In case of remanufacturing the carcass enters the regular assembly line as a subassembly. The assembled machines are tested and packaged by the manufacturing department and put in to final machine stock before being delivered to the Operating Companies.

With respect to MRP, we need two additional types of Bills Of Material (BOMs): a disassembly BOM represents the yield of reusable/repairable components from the disassembly process as well as the repair time of repairable components; the recovery BOMs concern the output, i.e., the remanufactured or refurbished machines.

Disassembly BOMs need to be differentiated for the alternative recovery options, due to varying degree of disassembly, quality requirements, disassembly times and yield. Since ERP software does not provide this functionality, these BOMs are kept and maintained in a separate information system.

Also, disassembly scheduling needs to be done outside the ERP software system. Periodically, a disassembly planning is made in which disassembly operations are scheduled. The expected yield is entered in ERP software as negative requirements on a component level. In this way, unnecessary external orders for new components are prevented and hence reuse is maximised. Yield factors are monitored and in case of structural deviance, adapted. If, after disassembly, the actual yield is more than expected (oversupply), the quantity of negative requirements is adjusted downwards accordingly in the next planning cycle. In case of undersupply, negative requirements are shifted backwards in time, assuming that the average yield will be achieved over time hence by oversupply later on in the next period. If not, a manual correction of the negative requirements is necessary, automatically leading to external orders.

Disassembly of cores leaves a stripped machine and a set of single components, which can either be repaired or scrapped. For reassembly of the stripped machines, CopyMagic uses recovery BOMs. A recovery BOM specifies the components to be reassembled (replaced) and the reassembly times, and hence does not apply to the scrap option. Recovery BOMs can be represented within the structure of ERP software. Because CopyMagic is replacing a predetermined fixed set of components, this BOM is simply a sub-BOM of a full BOM (in case of quality-dependent replacement, the replacement factors would have been somewhere between 0 and 1, representing average replacements). Also here, different recovery options have different recovery BOMs. This introduces the problem that one product type is represented by multiple BOMs. Therefore, an additional meta-identifier is needed on top of standard ERP software product structures.

As we mentioned, model Y machines might be 'remanufactured' machines or built from entirely new components. Again, a labelling feature is added on a component level, by which a planner can identify which components might be obtained from (which) cores. This situation, where a planner can choose between (multiple) cores or new component/subassembly supply, is referred to as multisourcing. The eventual choice is determined by availability, lead times, internal capacity and disassembly/procurement cost. Regarding final stock, CopyMagic distinguishes between remanufactured and new instances of the same product type enabled by the same meta-identifier mentioned above.

In conclusion, on the recovery side, BOMs can be represented within ERP software. Alternative BOMs represent to some extent alternative routings, namely, as far as dependent on the recovery option chosen. However, additional routing variance may result from input variance and hence stochastic repair lead time or even different repair processes at different locations. Current ERP software cannot handle this. On the return side, various routings can also be represented by alternative disassembly BOMs, however, as explained outside the current ERP system. Also these systems cannot deal with variance in disassembly lead times. This appears to be a fundamental MRP characteristic. Therefore, CopyMagic is looking for product design solutions to reduce disassembly time and variance.

With regards to inventory control, returned cores are mostly registered in a separate information system, because ERP software is not capable of distinguishing between different types (statuses) and owners of returns inventory. Note that cores and disassembled components can be found in different states, e.g., 'to be dismantled', 'scrap, 'repairable' or 'reusable'. This was solved by adding a status identifier to the article code and by distinguishing different lead times for different states.

The improvements in the MRP system have enabled CopyMagic to efficiently implement refurbishing and remanufacturing operations. They were able to deal with the system complexity and uncertainty in recovery and realised enormous cost savings by reusing capital-intensive components. After a slow start, the recovered machines are now a major cash generator for the company. CopyMagic is working together with the ERP software supplier to integrate fully its current reverse MRP methodology in the ERP software package. Once that is established, there are still a number of areas for improvement:

- **Master Production Plan.** Next to demand, returns also must be forecast. This can be solved, for example, by adding a line with a returns forecast to the Master Production Plan. This works best in the dual bill method, which is being used by CopyMagic (Thierry, 1995). At the level of components, one would like a replanning functionality after core disassembly since actual quality of the components is known then. To the best of our knowledge, no solution has been found for this.

- **Commonality**. Inventory control of returns has, among other characteristics, the additional complexity of multisourcing. (Remember, this refers to the possibility to retrieve certain components from various types of cores or even completely new.) Labelling of these components as described can solve identification of identical components retrievable from various cores. However, some components might not be identical but fulfill the same function. For this, CopyMagic is seeking a solution, again by labelling.

- **Visibility of lower-level assemblies**. Often, cannibalising cores or modules can obtain specific components; however, the availability of these components is not visible in the inventory control system, since only the modules are registered as a whole.

- **Facilities for final assembly in manufacturing and remanufacturing are often shared**. However, the subassemblies from which final products are assembled can either be new or remanufactured. Due to dual sourcing, the integration of both input streams adds planning complexity to inventory control (as described above) and also capacity planning, because in hybrid (re)manufacturing systems, facilities are shared. To the best of our knowledge, no solutions have been found for this problem.

Based on (Thierry, 1995) and (Krikke et al., 1999) we summarise the requirements as well as possible adaptations to the MRP system in Table 2.

CLSC characteristic	Adaptation MRP-System
System complexity	
1. Select return products with best quality	Cores inventory with status classifiers
2. Support disassembly process	Disassembly BOM
3. Support inventory control of returns	Inventories status can be 'core', 'repairable', 'repaired', or 'new' Visibility of various disassembly levels
4. Support different recovery options	Labeling to identify commonality Alternative BOMs
5. Support multi-sourcing (i.e., new procurement and returns)	Labels at component level to identify commonality and availability
6. Support parallel routings (different dependent recovery options)	Alternative BOMs per recovery option quality
7. Support shared resources in manufacturing and remanufacturing	?
System uncertainty	
8. Deal with uncertainty in return quality	Fixed replacement rates labels for quality classes
9. Support re-planning after testing (new information on quality of components)	?
10. Deal with varying return quantity, timing and composition	Fixed replacement rates Labels for quality classes
11. Support re-planning after arrival of cores or new forecast information	Returns forecast in MPP

Table 2: CLSCs and Adaptations in MRP-I

Notes:

In the early days, disassembly and hence reassembly were partly quality-dependent. In other words, the degree of disassembly yield and replacement rate were variable, which leads to more nervousness in the system compared to fixed replacements. Therefore, CopyMagic has chosen the fixed replacement method, where removed reusable components are repaired for reuse and put on stock separately. A disadvantage of this method is additional disassembly and inventory control operations.

CopyMagic enters the negative requirements for components in ERP software before actual disassembly (based on expected yield), which introduces additional uncertainty both in yield and repair lead times. This can be solved by postponing the inclusion of returns in the planning until after disassembly (but before repair) because quality, availability and repair cost are then known more accurately. However, it may also lead to unnecessary external orders since the cores inventory and disassembly pipeline are neglected.

2.2 Reverse logistics/warehouse management systems

Recently, CopyMagic has reorganised its logistics. In the forward channel direct shipping has been implemented, eliminating inventories and Distribution Centers (DCs) and reducing lead times drastically. Although out-of-pocket costs have increased, reduced risk of obsolescence and improved customer service through JIT delivery justify this. Also, CopyMagic has forbidden the OPCOs to repair machines in local workshops; all machines must be returned to ensure quality of recovered machines.

Until recently, reverse logistics and forward DCs were combined, but the streamlining of the forward channel made it necessary to set up a specialised return centre. Transportation will remain combined pickup and delivery. After careful consideration, CopyMagic has decided to hire Genco to manage the return centre.

In 1898, Genco was founded by Hyman Shear, and delivered commodities to Pittsburgh and its surrounding area. During the 1940s and 1950s warehousing and distribution were added. In 1970, Herb Shear, the third generation of the family, expanded the company's base of operations. In 1988 Distribution Resources was formed, including product assembly, refurbishment, manipulation and general distribution services. In 1990 returned goods management and software development were added to the services. Today, reverse logistics is Genco's core business. It processes in excess of $6 billion (U.S.) worth of returns annually in over 15,000 retail locations, and operates in 14 million square feet of distribution and reverse logistics space. Recently, Genco has set up European headquarters in London. CopyMagic might become one of its first customers in Europe. CopyMagic is particularly interested in the information system that Genco is using: R-log. This software program controls the process of returns of no longer wanted products, by managing a specialised warehouse called 'return centre', often also operated by Genco. It tracks each product delivered to a return centre by labelling it with a barcode. Within the return centre, each product is tracked by its unique number, and for its container and/or storage area. Also, R-log selects an optimal recovery or disposal option, based on secondary market channel opportunities (vendors, salvage, charity), cost, and constraints such as condition of the returned product, hazardous contents, or specific customer demands (some customers do not want their secondhand products to be sold again). In order to optimise the returns process, the R-log software is able to use original product specifications provided by the OEM and link to the original delivery, as well as secondary market information. After determining optimal recovery/disposal channels, it bundles similar products to reduce handling and shipping costs, and provides management control to check whether intended recovery/disposal operations are actually carried out. Because radio frequency computers and barcode scanners are used, the amount of paperwork regarding the returns is strongly reduced as well as the number of human errors. For management information, a couple of dozen standard queries and reports are available, e.g., to analyse compliance on recalls, reason of return, returns per vendor, etc. Finally, it interfaces into many other information systems, such as financial systems to facilitate the crediting of customers and debiting of vendors, ERP for MRP scheduling, and so on.

GENCO's approach to project is twofold 1) minimise costs 2) maximise benefits. In keeping with this two fold approach, we recommend the installation of R-Log. In this environment R-Log will control the operational flow of the Return Centre, Data Flow (financial, etc.) and the Disposition Management. The first step in the process would be individual item-level scanning or tracking. This will determine what units are being returned from what customers and what financial credits should be transacted, if any. This initial scan or tracking also begins the Disposition Management process. Due to the nature of CopyMagics products, an appropriate Disposition Management program is key to the success of the Return Centre. R-Log's Database would be populated with specific Disposition requirements for each of CopyMagics products. Example; upon scanning or item entry, R-Log would direct the unit to its Disposition path, refurbishment, reconditioning, break down into reusable parts inventory, destroy resale into a secondary channel, etc. Once directed down the appropriate Disposition path, the units will then be inspected for Quality Data and then carried through the physical Disposition process. In all, R-Log is the key mechanism in capturing the information and & carrying out the Disposition Management.[1]

---

[1] Written by Jason Shivett, Genco, London, November 6, 2001

R-log is an example of a dedicated reverse logistics warehouse management system for dedicated returns centres. Most companies, however, handle their returns via the normal warehouse and hence their regular WMS. According to (de Koster et al., 2000), a warehouse usually has to deal with three kinds of returns: retailer returns, supplier refusals and packing returns. Returns cause additional labour-intensive processes in the warehouses, which constitute around 6 percent of total logistics costs. The Warehouse Management System (WMS) fulfils administrative tracking and handling support. Ideally, it determines the next steps to be broken further down the channel (recovery options) and communicates this information to the players involved. It also collects product information to optimise processing.

Table 3 summarises the basic features a reverse logistics system (RLS) should have in order to handle returns, either as part of a WMS or as a separate system, which can bring large benefits. Caldwell (1999) describes the Estèe Lauder case. This cosmetics company invested $1.3 million in scanners, business intelligence tools a,nd an Oracle-based data warehouse, and was able to realise a yearly cost saving of $475 thousand through increased reuse and less handling. It also reduced the amount of products scrapped from 37 percent to 27 percent, improving its green image with the consumer.

1. Disapproved supplier lots blocked for delivery
2. Sales to alternative secondary markets must be registered with separate article number or lot number
3. Scrapped lots must be written off
4. In case of refused supplier lots, supplier should be debited
5. In case of customer returns, customer should be credited according to conditions as defined by return policy
6. Customer returns must be traced back to original delivery and reason of return codes are necessary
7. Original product specifications must be made available for recovery operations
8. Returns waiting for further processing must be registered separately at a distinct location
9. Inventory levels must be adjusted according to process option (recovery, sell, etc.)
10. Testing and inspection instructions must be given to support recovery option choice, and recovery options assigned must be registered
11. Returns being recovered must be registered as (temporary) shipments and receivables, and recall functions must support control
12. Repair/recovery instructions must be given
13. Report functions, for example, to analyse returns per channel or retailer

Table 3: Requirements to RLS/WMS, based on de Koster et al., 2000

2.3 E-marketplaces and virtual networks for returns

One of the key characteristics of closed-loop supply chains is the mismatch between supply of cores and demand for remanufactured and refurbished products and parts cannibalised from cores. In case of too much core supply, this can be handled by storage and returns inventory control. In case of shortage, CopyMagic needs to buy actively back from the market, either being the OPCO's or the open market.

Management is exploring possibilities to set up an internal trading place for OPCOs in order to give better insights in field inventory, as well as incentives to actually return. This concerns leased products, which are under the control of the OPCOs. Moreover, management considers using eBay.com for acquiring machines for parts cannibalisation to support service operations in Eastern Europe. Because these machines are being sold instead of leased, it is relatively difficult to buy them back from the market.

Founded by Pierre Omidyar in 1995, eBay, which has recently celebrated its half-billionth listing, is often described as the most popular online marketplace on the Internet. From a closed-loop supply chain perspective, eBay is an example of an electronic marketplace for end-of-use and commercial returns. eBay enables sellers to list items for sale and buyers to bid on items of interest using eBay's fully automated transaction processing system and dynamic pricing mechanism. eBay's secret lies with the defragmentation of a market operating in less efficient forums, such as classified ads, collectibles shows, garage sales, flea markets and auctions with an estimated value of $200 billion (USD). eBay's business model is transaction based: sellers pay a nominal fee for placing a post and when a transaction is completed, the seller is charged a transaction fee based on the final sale price. Financial details and logistics aspects are agreed upon between the trading parties (Bradley and Porter, 1999; Hill and Farkas, 2001).

eBay's main competitors include Yahoo, Onsale and Amazon, which incorporated electronic auctions in March 1999. To guard and increase its critical mass, eBay has formed a marketing alliance with AOL Time-Warner and has enhanced its international presence by launching new trading Web sites for users in Europe and Southeast Asia/Oceania.

CopyMagic relies on eBay's exemplary reputation for the reliability of the sourcing cores and its many buying alternatives to acquire them at a fairly low price, and within a short time interval. But, due to eBay's demographics, CopyMagic has difficulty buying cores in bulk. Even when it is feasible to gather a large number of cores, its trading parties are distributed over a widespread area, driving logistics costs for transporting individual units quite high. Another complication is quality control. Although providing some security checks, the actual quality of the part returned remains uncertain until arrival. Therefore, CopyMagic might consider setting up its own website, dealing with a closed community, like the business models of ReCellular or AUCNET. The advantage of this is an increased reliability and trust between the trading partners; however, the market coverage is smaller.

In an attempt to identify other more suitable business models of electronic marketplaces, CopyMagic opens up to the opportunities offered by Web technology applications for closed-loop supply chains. More generally speaking, Web technology can be used to streamline existing business processes or to support new e-business models (Kokkinaki, et al., 2001). With respect to contributing towards more efficient returns handling, Web technology has been used to control the volume of returns, to lower the uncertainty factors when returns actually occur, to enable data sharing and interoperability of IT systems between companies and third party logistics operators that handle their returns, and to establish new channels for returns redirection towards new destinations.

Regarding new e-business models we have identified three: returns aggregators, speciality locators and integrated solution providers. These are distinguished on the following characteristics: (i) degree of inclusion of reverse logistics activities (support only direct reuse through trading mechanism or provide a whole range of value-added activities such as fulfilment), (ii) the level of control exercised upon their trading partners (i.e., how open is the marketplace to participants), and (iii) the value proposition offered to their participants.

Table 4: An Overview Outline of E-business

Table 4 An overview outline of E-business models in Reverse Logistics

E-business Model	Inclusion of Reverse Logistics Activities	Level of Control	Added Value
Returns Aggregators	Reuse	Open to all	Searching mechanisms. High transaction throughput.
Returns Aggregators	Reuse, Remanufacture	Buyers: Free Suppliers: Participation fees	Focused searching for complex, expensive, hard to find Returns. Developing a community of like-minded customers.
Speciality Locators	Collection, Selection,	Free Registration Charges for services	Handling returns with high impact on core business processes
Integrated Solution Providers	Reuse, Remanufacture		

Models in Reverse Logistics

Table 4 An overview outline of E-business models in Reverse Logistics

Ways to generate income	Industry Sectors	Competitive Advantage	Examples	Remarks
Transaction Fees Advertizing	Commoditized returns, focus at: production waste commercial returns all returns cars	Scope and liquidity	[Metalsite] [QXL] [eBay] [OnSale] [180Commerce] [ViaVia]] [AUCNET] [Autodag]	Strong geographic orientation, USA, Europe, Asia closed community
Participation fees Data mining Advertizing	Restoration, Maintenance	Specialized Knowledge Qualified suppliers Timely results	[FindaPart] [BigMachines]	
Direct profits Locking-in customers	Pharmaceuticals Re-engineered tools, machinery	Technical Expertise One-stop shop	[Return-Logistics] [Pharmacy-Return] [Milpro]	database with 80.000 items
	Cellular phones		[ReCellullar]	

Returns aggregators bring together suppliers and customers, automate the procurement of returns, and create value through high throughput and minimal transaction costs. The returns aggregators handle returns from many different OEMs, without owning the product and are specialised in different kinds of returns flows. Returns aggregators typically do not control the returns, with which they are stored at their initial location until a transaction is completed. Logistics aspects of electronic marketplaces cover a great variety of services. Many returns aggregators follow subcontracting third parties to do some or all of the described logistic functions.

Web design, searching mechanisms and efficient price-setting mechanisms are essential tools for returns aggregators. Through user-friendly and clever Web design, returns aggregators aim to increase their visibility and extend their population of participating traders. Moreover, a dynamic price-determining mechanism (often an e-auction) enables high throughput of transactions, volume increase by the defragmentation of a highly fragmented market and uncertainty reduction, overcoming difficulties associated with conventional means for managing returns. A price-setting mechanism can be available online as in the case of consumer electronics, or be subject to interpersonal communication through conventional means.

U.S.-based returns aggregators concentrate within the North American market due to their demographics or to logistics requirements. In the EU, returns aggregators are country-oriented, as they tend to cultural, logistic, linguistic, and financial diversities between different member states. There are some trading communities open only to partners who have established relations through conventional interaction or to new members that are introduced by some existing members.

Beyond the described functionality, some returns aggregators have promoted new e-business models by which new processes have been devised to accomplish certified inspection, description, and multimedia representation of the products to be sold, e.g., car dealers bid from their computer and transport is arranged between traders.

Speciality locators are vertical portals, which focus on niche markets for highly specialised used parts or products, such as authentic antiques, exact replicas parts or equipment in historic restoration projects, or the maintenance process for vehicles and industrial equipment. Speciality locators are region-bounded and vertically structured, focusing on a limited range of used parts or equipment over a geographical region. These electronic marketplaces provide specialised (and thus highly prized) services and do not aim for large volumes or many hits. Their services include training, frameworks for catalogue search, selection and configuration, and financing and technical support. Speciality locators are mostly used for information dissemination and address the marketing aspect of electronic commerce.

Besides participation fees, value is generated from reference fees, advertising fees, and from mining buyer's profiles. This business model has high entry barriers; for someone to enter this business it requires the design and imposition of new standards in a specialised topic, structuring of information, and market liquidity.

Identification of the part or product in request is key to the success of this business model and it implies the use of a common, unique and unambiguous description. Contrary to suppliers coding systems, they enable them to interchange spare parts from different suppliers. Standards and structure vary from one implementation, whereas conventional catalogues of spare parts offer a unique coding system. Identification of a part can be enhanced through oral communication or through the use of Web-accessible search engines that are based on some prominent features of the part (brand, description, code, etc.).

Addressing urgency is a determining factor for speciality locators' competitive advantage. In the future we expect that speciality locators will address this point and their competitive advantage will likely shift to provide dynamically customised on-line expertise.

Integrated solutions providers go a step beyond facilitating and matching demand and supply of returns. They capitalise on their distinctive expertise and use www-technologies to offer unique services for handling returns. Furthermore, they actually become the owners of the returns instead of implementing a brokering mechanism as in the previous two models. This model aims to forge strong relationships with long-lasting customers in industries where the cost of a return itself may not be high, but its speedy handling is essential to its core business process. By definition, each integrated solution provider focuses on the reverse logistics network in an industry/sector.

Integrated solution providers enable returns processors to track seamlessly and document authorisation for returns. Furthermore, they assist users with the appropriate packaging and shipping documentation. They provide the full range of logistics services, including destruction of controlled substances, depackaging and repackaging of products. They also provide software wizards that guide customers through questions about problematic processes (such as chatter marks), and then recommend particular remanufactured spare parts or equipment.

The model for Integrated Solution Providers does not view e-commerce as a migration of existing practices and services over a new infrastructure, but as a new tool to restructure a business activity and offer new services. This e-business model creates value through escrow and processing fees and locking in the customer for add-on services or products.

2.4 Product eco-tools

In June 2000 the European Union has revised its proposal for a "Directive on Waste Electrical and Electronic Equipment (WEEE)." The guidelines for the member states in this proposal are (EU, 2000):

- producers should take the responsibility for EOL phases of their products;
- appropriate systems for separate collection of WEEE should be put in place;
- producers have to set up appropriate systems in order to ensure accurate processing and re-use/recycling of WEEE; and
- users of electrical and electronic equipment must be informed about their role in this system, in order to achieve high collection rates and to facilitate recovery of waste of electrical and electronic equipment.

The management of CopyMagic is convinced that the greening of industry is becoming a major trend. It feels increasingly uncomfortable with the idea of just complying with legislation, hence the management wants to create ecological alternatives for its current economically driven recovery system. It feels that the (re) design of copiers is a good starting point, using DfX tools instead of mere common sense. TNO-industry from Delft, The Netherlands has developed such a tool and is asked to assist in the DfX process (source: internal documents TNO).

The tool the TNO team uses is called "DFE-tool" (Design for Environment), and assists in estimating environmental effects of production and end of life of a product. Also, the costs and benefits of disposal, recycling and reuse can be estimated. With graphical feedback, the software helps to explore scenarios and to find an optimal design strategy in order to reduce environmental effects and costs. Environmental effects are expressed in so-called MET points (Material cycles, Energy use and Toxic emissions), which resemble a simplified LCA.

When starting a new analysis, information about the product is entered. By selecting various parts and subassemblies, one can build up a disassembly sequence. For parts and subassemblies details about disassembly, production and end of life are given.

Based on the input, the software uses its disassembly and environmental databases to calculate outputs on two levels: strategic, determining optimal EOL recovery options, and product design, including disassembly optimisation. For both, one can make quick scenarios by changing labour rates, disposal rates, cost benefits of reuse and recycling, item weights, disassembly sequences, etc.

TNO helped the product development team of Electrolux Commercial, Culemborg, The Netherlands, to analyse the strategic and design consequences of revision, reuse and recycling. From a list of eight options, three were chosen as relevant and likely for the Electrolux situation:

- **Reuse of components.** The most valuable parts that still function are reused as service parts or as parts in new display cabinets. In most cases, display cabinets are disposed of because of aesthetic or stylistic outdating, but only few components are out of order.

- **Revision of used display cabinets.** Malfunctioning components are repaired or replaced; scratched or bent parts are replaced. In this way, an additional life span of several years can be achieved with a reasonable effort.

- **Full recycling of materials.** Materials in the display cabinet are recycled as much as it is economically feasible.

In real life, a mixture of options will occur. However, it was decided first to analyse strict scenarios to obtain a good understanding of the key parameters for retaining economic and environmental value.

Economically speaking, the revision option is the most attractive one. Also, environmental results are good. Revision could be a new service for customers. The reuse option also renders decent economic and environmental results. The option assumes that customers will buy a product with secondhand parts in it. At this point, no marketing strategy has been defined for this situation. The recycling option is hardly attractive in an economical comparison with the revision and reuse option. However, still a profit is made and the recycling rate is increased strongly, which is relevant in view of EU legislation. Also, products that have been revised and parts that have been reused will at some point be recycled. Therefore, this option is relevant in any case. This ended the strategic part of the study. It was decided that product design would be directed at improved revision and recycling.

In spring '97, a new development was started for a cooling display cabinet. This model, the Chameleon, featured an increased modularity so that the number of configurations and the amount of customisation could be increased while reducing the number of different components: a good opportunity for improving ease of disassembly and suitability for revision and recycling. For example, disassembly time was reduced by over 40 percent for the revision option, recovery of materials by recycling was improved from 89 to 96 percent, meeting even the strictest EU targets proposed.

A quick scan suggests that the energy use of the copier causes the most severe environmental impact, whereas the remanufacturing option is commercially most feasible. Therefore, it is decided to aim for product design improvements to support the remanufacturing of energy-friendly copiers.

In general, product eco-tools are categorised into LCA tools, DfX tools and waste management tools (Caluwe, 1997). Their main purpose is enhancing sustainability of products over the full life cycle. Although product oriented, these tools in fact analyse the environmental impact of the product supply chain processes and express this in a score at the product level.

LCA tools analyse products as feedback for improvement of the environmental behaviour over the product life cycle. They have a methodology that involves four steps: i.) defining goals and boundaries, ii.) inventory analysis, iii.) impact analysis, and iv.) improvement analysis. In setting goals and scope, it can be decided to focus on a single product or a related group of products. Inventory analysis concerns quantifying inputs (processes) and outputs (e.g., emissions or toxicity) of a product's processes and activities over the life cycle. Next, an impact analysis qualitatively or quantitatively computes the environmental impact of these outputs, both in direct effects (e.g., ozone depletion) and long-term damage (e.g., increased risk of skin cancer). The improvement step (not present in all LCA tools) systematically evaluates opportunities to reduce the environmental impact over the entire life cycle, encompassing all product-related processes.

The biggest differences in tools can be found in the way they transform direct effects into long-term damage. This is a rather subjective process, which gives rise to many discussions. Some tools give the possibility to evaluate long-term effects by different methodologies (representing different interpretations). Another major difference lies in the scope of the system (supply chain) as defined by the tool. For example, sometimes energy consumption in mining and quarrying raw materials is excluded.

Most LCA tools have an interactive database; the problem of obtaining accurate data remains the largest obstacle for applying LCA in practice. Therefore, several authors have advocated the use of simplified approximation methods, based on energy, waste and toxicity, such as the MET method of TNO.

Methodologically, DfX tools are to a large extent similar to LCA tools, but focus on improvements of the product design for only a part of the life cycle and provide additional functionality to optimise this. In particular, they advise on construction methods, fastening methods and materials used. DfX tools can be subcategorised in Design for Assembly, Design for Operations (service and maintenance) and Design for Disassembly/Recovery. The Design for Disassembly/Recovery tools explicitly focus on the EOL/EOU stage, by enhancing reusability/recyclability of components, or at least reducing the environmental burden of incineration and landfill. In addition to standard LCA data, data are necessary on the specific design issues.

As opposed to design tools, waste management tools compare materials and processes to generate alternatives at different levels of environmental impact, given product design and use characteristics. Also, they optimise product EOL options, taking into account time and context-dependent characteristics such as return quality, geographic location, legislation, and secondary market prices. Most of the tools are related to regulatory compliance and tracking of materials and emissions and matching their values with defined checklists of materials and maximal emission values.

2.5 Concluding: the need for life cycle data and systems integration

We conclude that many special-purpose tools with extensive functionalities are available in the market. Although there is room for functional improvement, it appears that most is to be gained from the integration of data models. All applications have heavy database requirements, which are labour intensive and sensitive to errors. Moreover, there appears to be a strong overlap in the kind of data used by various applications of different players in the chain. Therefore, there is a need for shared product life cycle data. This is referred to as product data management (PDM).

Once PDM is established, a next step would be systems integration, e.g., integrating DfX in CAD/CAM or reverse MRP in ERP software systems. In turn, this would enable the integrated planning and control of CLSCs. CopyMagic has not yet explored these possibilities. Therefore, we end our state-of-the-art discussion here and in the name of CopyMagic take a look into the future, based on scientific research results.

3. Product Data Management and systems integration

The management of closed-loop supply chains requires the use of IT throughout the product life cycle. Figure 2 illustrates the use of the IT tools described in Section 2 at various stages of the product life cycle.

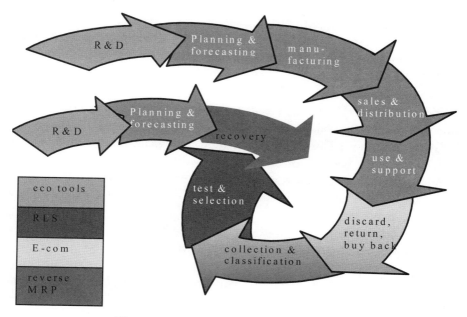

**Figure 2: IT Tools in Closed-Loop Supply
Chains over the Product Life Cycle**

Product Data Management (PDM) systems aim to capture, process and disseminate, product data during the product's entire life cycle, in which it goes through different configuration and condition stages. Usually various supply chain players generate such information. More specifically, PDM systems:

- maintain accurate data on complex products (many parts, variants, alternatives),
- record maintenance changes on a product during its life cycle, and
- disseminate product data at an intraorganisational or interorganisational level.

Product Data Management Systems include data on:

- product or process definition (Bill of Material, Engineering Change Order, MPR, Order Processing),
- control information (location, access, maintenance records), and
- configuration management data (version number, release level, upgrades).

Furthermore, a PDM system may manage or control related technical information, such as CAD/CAM drawings, specifications, engineering analysis and other electronically stored data, collectively termed as Technical Object Data (TOD).

Using PDM, CopyMagic can create a platform for integrating business functions, in particular product design (DfX), maintenance (installed base), and recovery operations. This can result in more ecological, yet low-cost and high quality products, because essential features are built into the product from scratch and vice versa, returns information is fed back to the (re)design. In the following subsections we present three examples of (partial) systems integration thanks to PDM.

3.1 Computer Aided Design (CAD) and DfX

Harper and Rosen (1998) present a methodology for inferring appropriate information from CAD models of a product by incorporating end-of-life data into CAD systems and by extending its modelling and query capabilities. Information requirements involve metric information to enable a recovery assessment. Suppose one wants to assess disassembly times and number of components to be replaced once a product returned must be remanufactured. Standard CAD systems contain insufficient information and must therefore be extended. In particular, one needs data on fastener and construction methods, material types, post-life intent, and functional or disassembly relationships between components. For example, one of the problems in disassembly optimisation is that CAD systems only contain information on assembly level, they lack capability of modelling hierarchical structures. Query methods are needed to retrieve relevant information for evaluation of product design impact on end-of-life scenarios, involving questions like does a part have to be made of a different material, does it facilitate disassembly processes, and so on. For example, disassembly times might be estimated given the number of components in a (sub)assembly, the mating relationships between them, and the fasteners used to attach components. Not all information can be stored in a CAD system; for example, in the current example the number of tests required remains user supplied. Finally, CAD systems might be of use to closed-loop supply chains by enabling redesign. A catalogue of reusable components would help a designer to review quickly opportunities for reuse. This obviously increases (internal) reuse markets and also shortens development time, while at the same time, upgrade possibilities can make the product meet state of the art requirements.

CopyMagic uses CAD for its design activities. However, DfX elements are brought in by designers based on their individual skills and expertise using a separate DfX tool. Integrating with CAD would result in more consistency of product data, less labour intensive manual data entry, fewer errors and more overview in commonality of parts. Also, design flaws that prevent optimal maintenance and recovery can be identified more easily, giving new opportunities for optimisation.

3.2 Reloop: reverse logistics for consumer electronics

Reloop is a pilot project, carried out by a consortium of Hewlett Packard, Cleanaway, TME, the Belgium Metal industry, IAT, Progis and Louvain University. A description is taken from [RELOOP].

The Reloop software is an integrated system, using the GIS (Geografic Information System), which supports all players involved in the reverse chain in planning and control of their reverse logistics activities. It supports the following processes.

The cores are collected from households and companies, sorted and disassembled. The individual components and materials can be reused 'as is' or be submitted to further processing into raw materials for the same or alternative application, or disposed of to a waste processor for incineration and landfill.

Potential users of the software are predefined and include end users, waste collectors, transporters, waste processors, waste management organisations, and government institutions. The software consists of the following modules:

- **Optimisation of processing.** This module evaluates various recovery and disposal scenarios for discarded products, and compares them on costs, environmental impact and compliance with legislation.

- **Route planning and optimisation.** This module optimises the collection and distribution routings. It can be optimised on costs or time, or a combination. Environmental constraints can also be taken into account.

- **Report.** This module assists in generating reports for government institutions, contractors, top management or company shareholders. Reports can be customised both on contents and layout.

- **Internet database.** The final module consists of an Internet database containing information on all possible players of the electronics reverse chain. Users are informed on reuse markets, and also facilitated in promotional actions by means of advertising.

Although designed for consumer electronics, the similarities between copiers and consumer electronics are strong. CopyMagic might consider buying the package as add-on to the Genco R-log system because of its ability to optimise on both economical and environmental criteria and the possibility to find scrap markets quickly.

3.3 Condition monitoring and remote sensing

Whereas PDM systems capture information provided by communicating partners, they may not record information on product condition and configuration that result from the use of the product. New communication protocols can be combined with embedded control systems to monitor product data dynamically and transmit the data logged upon some event. This is referred to as condition monitoring of the installed base, where the installed base is defined as the total number of placed units of a particular product in the entire primary market or a product segment.

Traditional installed base monitoring methods include end-user surveys, competitive interviews, trade associations and maintenance records. Installed base monitoring is used for product improvements, product upgrades, introducing a peripheral device, and repair services. For example, feedback of return info to product design and production stages results in product quality improvements.

Giuntini and Andel (1995) describe a steel mill case where through re-engineering, material costs were reduced by 40 percent, MTBF improved by 27 percent and increased spare parts availability improved service fulfilment from 89 percent to 98.5 percent.

A case example is included to describe the use of condition monitoring for remanufacturing: Electronic Data Log (EDL).

The Bosch Group, a worldwide operation with 190 manufacturing locations and 250 subsidiary companies in 48 countries, is known for automotive supplies, power tools, household goods, thermo technology and packaging technology supplies. In collaboration with Carnegie Mellon University, Bosch was looking for ways to capture data on the use of their range of power tools that would yield better decisions about their recovery options (Klausner et al., 1998).

As a result, the Electronic Data Log (EDL) was developed to measure, compute and record usage-related parameters of motors in power tools, with the aim to use values of the recorded parameters for analysis and classification between reusable and nonreusable used motors. The following components are used in this approach.

- A low-cost circuit (EDL) that measures, compiles and stores parameters that indicate the degradation of the motor, including number of starts and stops, accumulated runtime of the motor, and sensor information such as temperature and power consumption for an accumulated runtime of approximately 2300 hours of operation. EDL also computes and stores peak and average values for all recorded parameters.

- An easily accessible interface to retrieve data from the EDL circuits without disassembling the tool.

- An electronic device (reader) connected to the interface to retrieve the data values.

- Software data analysis and classification into two main categories: reusable used motors and nonreusable used motors.

The main benefits of EDL compared to conventional disassembly and testing can be summarised as follows.

- Easily accessible interface to EDL, which does not require disassembly of the product, offers labour cost saving for nonreusable used products.

- Easy and speedy retrieval of information stored in EDL.

- EDL data reconstruct the entire usage history of a product leading to the assessment of reuse for other components besides the motor.

- EDL data can be used to improve design, support market research and quality management.

The economic efficiency of this method is the subject of Klausner et al. (1998). The trade-off between initially higher manufacturing costs and savings from reuse is analysed, taking into account return and recovery rates as well as misclassification errors. The analysis shows that the use of EDL can result in large cost savings.

Developments such as increased service obligations (product lease, extended warranties, service level agreements), environmental liabilities (producer responsibility/product stewardship, consumer demand for recycling), and product modularisation will enable *and* necessitate the establishment of product life cycle management and hence of closed-loop supply chains. The EDL case presented storing data on the product itself by inserting a chip. However, new sensor and transmission technology enables online and remote sensing. The transaction capacity of (wireless) networks drastically increases, and related transaction costs will decrease accordingly. This enables online monitoring not only of capital-intensive products but also of somewhat cheaper consumer goods such as cars or televisions.

For CopyMagic, PDM systems with remote sensing have great potential for maintenance and service, feedback to designers, and system upgrades. For example, sensoring might enable preventive repair improving customer service and maintenance efficiency. The replenishment might also be pro-active; supplies such as toner and paper can be shipped without a customer order needed. Customer relation management can analyse customer behaviour by monitoring the number of copies made. In this way, early product takeback is possible in case another type of copier would better fit the customer's profile. The same data are also useful for the asset recovery department. The above fits CopyMagic's strategy of providing an optimal 'copying function', i.e., product leasing with agreed service levels to the customer. We note that there are opportunities here for advanced planning and expert systems based on neural networks. Condition monitoring provides a lot of data; however, this data needs to be monitored, filtered and translated in action by some event-triggered system.

4. Discussion, conclusions and outlook

Information technology already has given much support to the establishment of closed-loop supply chains. Critical IT areas in CLSCs are MRP for recovery, electronic marketplaces/virtual networks for returns, reverse logistics (warehouse management) systems, and product eco-tools. Specialised tools with impressive functionalities have been developed and their use is widespread in business practice.

It appears that further exploitation of IT in CLSCs requires a common link between the four areas, which we refer to as Product Data Management systems. These systems enable consistent, less labour-intensive exchange of information between the various players in the closed-loop supply chain throughout the product life cycle. In turn, establishing PDM systems would contribute to new services such as early repairs, proactive take back and system upgrades (both based on remote condition monitoring), sustainable products and longer spare parts availability. PDM also enables integration with current SC IT systems, which are not capable of dealing with closed-loop supply chains. However, it is crucial that current systems be extended with CLSC functionalities to cover the entire product life cycle. This requires a standardisation of modelling, technologies and infrastructure all over the supply chain:

❑ **Modelling.** From a generic modelling perspective, one could look at the inclusion of closed-loop supply chains in SCM modelling languages such as SCML, XSML. At this point, it is necessary to establish what objects are necessary for modelling unique properties of CLSC and what would be their attributes. Using XML-based variants for modelling closed-loop supply chains, offers flexibility and data exchange interoperability between different domains. In today's globalising economy, product data management systems need to communicate and exchange data with possibly incompatible PDM systems that are maintained by other players in a supply chain. Addressing the need of integration of installed legacy systems, international standards (STEP, CALS) enable a user-definable common data representation. Another area of interest is advanced planning models. Since an increased number of parameters can be monitored, lots of data become available, but not necessarily information. Sophisticated mathematics, such as neural networks, can help decision makers to filter relevant information and take appropriate action, help setting critical alarm levels, and enable data mining.

❑ **Connecting to SCM technology.** It appears that acceptation and use of the specially developed CLSC software tools is limited to specialists. One should connect to supply chain management information technology as much as possible. Not only is this better in view of achieving optimal integration of return flows in supply chain management, it may also be cheaper to use technology already available for other purposes. For example, Bluetooth wireless technology is a de facto standard, as well as a specification for small-form factor, low-cost, short-range radio links between mobile PCs, mobile phones and other portable devices. It enables end-users to connect a wide range of computing and telecommunications devices easily and simply, without the need to connect cables. It delivers opportunities for rapid ad hoc connections, and the possibility of automatic connections between devices. Bluetooth can be used for a variety of purposes, which might be applicable to installed base modes [Bluetooth].

❑ **Innovative uses of Web and wireless communication technology enable the substitution of physical operations (i.e., collection and selection) in reverse logistics networks by multi-agent systems.** Multi-agent systems employ computational or monitoring processes (agents) to collect and disseminate information on the installed base of products, their configuration and operational status. It is therefore foreseeable in the future to have virtual or hybrid reverse logistics networks that combine virtual processes and physical operations for the efficient handling of returns.

Acknowledgments

We would like to thank the following:

- Rene de Koster of Erasmus University, RSM/Faculteit Bedrijfskunde, for providing information on WMSs and returns
- Workshop participants, Business aspects of CLSCs, Pittsburgh, May 30–June 2, 2001
- Ron Giuntini of OEM services, for his general advises on IT in CLSCs
- Jason Shivetts of Genco, for providing information on Genco, R-log and for reviewing the manuscript
- Mirjam Korse of TNO-Industry, for providing information on the DfE tool and reviewing the manuscript

References

Bradley, Stephen P. and Kelley A. Porter. Ebay, Inc., Harvard Business School Case 9-700-007, 1999.

Caluwe, Nils de, Ecotools manual – a comprehensive review of DfE tools. Metropolian University of Manchester, 1997.
 http://sun1.mpce.stu.mmu.ac.uk/pages/projects/dfe/pubs/dfe33 {ecotools.htm}

Caldwell, Brice. Reverse Logistics. Information week online, April 1999, www.informationweek.com/729/logistics.htm

(EU, 2000), Document 500PC0347(01), Website European Union, December 2000 (Genco, internal documents): (1) "What is R-log, facts & features", author: Dave Moyer - Senior VP IT and (2) "GENCO Distribution System", anonymous.

Giuntini, Ron and Tom Andel. Reverse Logistics Role Models. *Transportation and Distribution*, April 1995, 97-98.

Guide, Jr. ,V. Daniel R. and Luk N. Van Wassenhove. Closed-Loop Supply Chains. INSEAD, R&D working paper 2000/75/TM, 2000.

Harper, Brian and David Rosen. Computer Aided Design for de- and remanufacture. Harper and Rosen, Proceedings of DETC '98, September 1998, Atlanta.

Hill, Linda and Maria Farkas. Meg Whitman at Ebay, Inc., Harvard Business Scool Case 9-401-024, 2000.

Klausner, Markus, Wolfgang M. Grimm and Chris Henderson. 1998. Reuse of Electric Motors in Consumer Products, Design and Analysis of an Electronic Data Log. *Journal of Industrial Ecology*, 2(2), 89 –102.

Kokkinaki, Angelika I., Rommert Dekker, Rene Koster, Costas Pappis, and Wilem Verbeke. From E-trash to E-treasure: How value can be created by new e-business models in reverse logistics. Proceedings of the Euro conference, Rotterdam, 2001. Also in the Econometric Institute Report Series EI2000-32/A, Erasmus University Rotterdam, ISSN 1566-7294, The Netherlands, 2000.

deKoster, Rene, F.H.W.M. Jacobs, and H.E. van Dort. Informatie binnen Magazijnen. In *Praktijk Boek Magazijnen Distributiecentra,* edited by J.P. Duijker, M.B.M. de Koster, M. J. Ploos van Amstel, 2000 (in Dutch).

Krikke, Harold, A. van Harten and Peter Schuur. Business case Oce: reverse logistic network re-design for copiers. *OR-Spektrum*, 21-3, 381-409, 1999.

Lee, Howard G. AUCNET: Electronic Intermediary for Used-Car Transactions. *Electronic Markets*, 7(4), 24-28, 1997.

Stock, James R. and Douglas M. Lambert. *Strategic Logistics Management*. Fourth edition, McGraw-Hill International Edition, New York, 2001.

Thierry, M. An analysis of the impact of Product Recovery Management on manufacturing companies. Ph.D. Thesis, Eramus University Rotterdam, 1995.

(TNO, internal documents): (1) DFE case study: The Electrolux Chameleon cooling display cabinet. Anonymous. (2) Overview of the software. Anonymous. (3) The MET points method makes Life Cycle Analysis easy manageable for designers. Anonymous.

E-Business Name	E-Business URL
180Commerce	www.180commerce.com
Aucnet	not accessible to the public
Autodag	www.autodag.com
Bigmachines	www.bigmachines.com
Bluetooth	www.bluetooth.com
Dell	www.dell.com
E-rma	www.e-rma.com
eBay	www.ebay.com
Fairmarket	www.fairmarket.com
Find-a-part	www.find-a-part.com
Genco	www.e-genco.com
IBM	www.ibm.com
Metalsite	www.metalsite.com
Milpro	www.milpro.com
Onsale	www.onsale.com
Pharmacy Returns	www.pharmacyreturns.com
QXL	www.qxs.com
RELOOP	http://www.wtcm.be/~reloop/
ReCellular	Not accessible to the public
Return.com	www.return.com
Returnlogistics	www.returnlogistics.com
TheReturnExchange	www.thereturnexchange.com
Yantra	www.yantra.com
Viavia	www.viavia.nl

Contacts:

Harold Krikke
Center Applied Research
Tilburg University
Warandelaan 2
Postbus 90153
NL-5000 Le Tilburg
The Netherlands

Email: krikke@kub.nl

Angelika Kokkinaki
Erasmus University Rotterdam
Burgemeester Oudlaan 50
P.O. Box 1738
3000 DR Rotterdam
The Netherlands

Email: kokkinaki@few.eur.nl

Jo van Nunen
Erasmas University of Rotterdam
Rotterdam School of Management
P.O. Box 1738
3000 DR Rotterdam
The Netherlands

Email: jnumen@fac.fbk.eur.nl

Design Engineering

Chris Hendrickson, H. Scott Matthews, Jonathan Cagan and Francis C. McMichael, Carnegie Mellon University, USA

1. Introduction

Design decisions can profoundly affect the cost and the feasibility of reuse, remanufacturability and recycling of discarded products. For example, choice of adhesive joints rather than snap-fit connections may make disassembly of a product prohibitively expensive. Similarly, use of plastic parts rather than metal components may reduce the value of particular products enough that recycling is not economical. Whenever design decisions increase the cost hurdle of transition to another cycle of reuse, remanufacture and recycling, then the likelihood of discard to landfills or the environment increases.

Of course, narrow cost concerns may not dominate the decisions about the fate of particular products. There are many examples of products for which producers have introduced reuse or recycling even if these operations lose money. The programs may be undertaken for public relations value, due to regulatory requirements (or to avoid possible regulatory requirements), for marketing reasons or others. However, the cost of such programs is always a concern in widespread implementation. Most of the recycling programs losing money handle relatively small fractions of the entire market.

In this chapter, we will discuss some design approaches to aid closed-loop supply chains. We will look at several examples, including aluminum cans, power tools, coffeemakers and computers.

2. Design Objectives and Incentives for Closed-Loop Supply Chains

Most products are designed without consideration for closed-loop supply chains or extended producer responsibility. In many cases, designs are developed with only initial costs and product functionality as objectives, rather than including concerns such as life cycle cost, maintenance or reuse. Providing appropriate incentives and information for designers is likely to be more important than any technical recommendations for good design practices in this area.

Voluntary industry agreements and corporate strategies for extended product use can play an important role in influencing design decisions. For example, aluminum can designers know that they are operating with a closed-loop supply chain for the most part, so they have made changes to the can design to make recycling easier. Voluntary agreements can require recycling of discarded products and minimum recycled content for new products.

A major difficulty in pursuing design changes is devising appropriate objectives to assess alternative designs. How should greater fuel efficiency be balanced against more particulate emissions in assessing diesel versus gasoline-powered vehicles? How much weight should be placed on recycled content versus energy efficiency? Unfortunately, there is little uniformity of opinion on such trade-offs, either in the political or the scientific communities. However, corporate priorities are often devised as part of environmental management systems that can provide guidance for designers on the most important attributes for particular products (Matthews, 2001).

Regarding particular areas of design attention for closed-loop supply chains, experience has shown the following areas to be of greatest concern:

- **Avoid and reduce toxic materials.** Whenever possible, toxic materials should be avoided because of the possibility of release into the environment. For example, Ford Motor Company now bans the use of cadmium additives in plastics.

- **Make disassembly easier.** With easier disassembly, there is a greater chance of reuse, remanufacture and recycle. Permanent joints inhibit disassembly. Computer aids to assess the possibility of mechanical disassembly are available.

- **Use more homogeneous and recycled materials.** There is a tendency for each component designer to use the optimal material for their own part, with the result that complex products may have dozens of different materials. Recycling becomes very difficult, especially if shredding strategies are ineffective.

- **Include information aiding return and reuse**. Information on product content and components can enable reuse of components or material recycling.

3. Environmental Considerations in the Engineering Design Process

Design for the environment is becoming a critical part of the overall engineering and product development process. As consumer expectations and governmental regulations become more demanding, industries need to be more aware of the environmental impact on life cycle costs and consumer attitudes. The engineering design process is part of a larger design process that begins with product opportunity identification; takes into consideration the needs, wants and desires of the user/consumer and other stakeholders; and evolves a concept into a manufacturable, marketable product (Cagan and Vogel, 2001).

The engineering focus is typically an iterative process that takes design specifications of a defined opportunity as input, and determines a physical configuration that meets the behavioral requirements as output. The process requires concept generation and analysis, leading to refinement of the initial concept (see Otto and Wood, 2001, or Antonsson and Cagan, 2001, for a discussion of the engineering design process). Proper engineering design requires both synthesis, the generation of configurations, and analysis and the evaluation of those configurations.

The synthesis problem usually includes idea creation methods such as brainstorming and functional analysis. A useful emerging technique for functional analysis is function mapping based on the work of Pahl and Beitz (1996), and developed further into a useful method by Wood and Otto (2001). In function mapping, each major and minor functional chunk is broken out and mapped in terms of its connectivity to other chunks. An example of functional mapping appears below.

As analytical models become better articulated and represented computationally, optimization of the parameters to best meet design requirements within a configuration becomes feasible (Papalambros and Wilde, 1988). However, in practice there are multiple, conflicting goals or objectives and many physically based, manufacturing-based and performance-based constraints. Further, there

293

are usually many approximations and a limit on how well each objective is articulated (especially nonphysically based objectives). Finally, the importance of each of these objectives and constraints must be balanced. As such, the optimization of parameters is typically, at best, a satisficing solution (Simon, 1969).

The most effective engineering design processes are those that balance concept idea creation with analytical support. Given the above discussion, the more physically based the analysis, the stronger the engineer's confidence in the solution.

The problem with the engineering design approach is that many aspects of product development cannot be clearly and cleanly articulated mathematically. This is true for purely technical solutions, and is even more so for consumer products. In the design of successful consumer products, the three major considerations are features (addressed by engineering design), image and ergonomics (Cagan and Vogel, 2001). The last two categories are difficult, at best, to quantify (at least today); even ergonomics, with Dreyfuss Charts (Dreyfuss, 1967) and other statistical measures useful to quantify the design process, has limited extent in scope of application.

The traditional engineering design process is useful in consumer design once the product opportunity is well articulated. Until that time, a more qualitative approach is required. The early process, called the *Fuzzy Front End*, is seemingly vague and magical for engineers (especially), but it is the most critical part of new product development (Cagan and Vogel, 2001). If the early stages are done right then the rest of the process flows smoothly. But if the early stages are misdirected then there will necessarily be many downstream changes to attempt to correct all of the problems missed upfront. Further, even if the product is finally produced to specification, if it does not meet the needs, wants and desires of the market, then it will fail.

This discussion on the engineering design process, its place within the greater design process, and the necessity of the Fuzzy Front End, is particularly relevant for Green Design. The impact of environmental considerations on the design of products cannot wait until the final, detailed stages of the design process. Instead it must be a part of the design considerations early in the process. As described below, the decision to include microprocessors to monitor the use of power tools to enable refurbishment and resale has important implications in the tools' architecture and features, their manufacture and their design for disassembly and end of use. Designing products with environmental considerations at the forefront is actually an opportunity to add considerable consumer *value* to a product (Cagan and Vogel, 2001).

4. Case Study: Aluminum Cans

4.1 Background and brief history

The aluminum beverage can is a thin-walled pressure vessel used by the beer and soft drink industries. Its cylindrical shape is easily recognized and its volume of 12 oz (355 ml) is a standard size. Annual U.S. production of aluminum cans exceeded 100 billion for the last five years (1995-2000). This industry output is more than one can per person per day for the U.S. population (Aluminum Assoc., 2001).

In the crossover year 1976, the three-piece steel can and the two-piece aluminum can have equal U.S. market shares (44 percent or about 20 billion annual cans). Since that time, the aluminum beverage can has grown and dominated the market. Current and near future competition for the carbonated soft drink and beer container market is between aluminum cans and plastic containers.

Both product design and process design for the aluminum beverage can has received enormous engineering attention over the last 25 years (Hosford and Duncan, 1994; Sanders, 1990; Petroski, 1996). A systems approach to describing the life cycle of a can includes both private and public sector issues. Manufacturing addresses choice of appropriate aluminum alloys for the body, top and tab components. Issues of the use of virgin aluminum from ores and the use of well-described home (pre-consumer) scrap and less homogeneous, post-consumer scrap are important for materials cost analysis and assessing the amount of energy required for the system. Recycling of aluminum alloys provides for reduction in the absolute mass of metal for a can and the possibility of reducing the net energy used over the life cycle of the can.

Product design is centered on lightweighting or reducing the mass of the aluminum for a can (Figure 1). In 1976, approximately 23 cans weighed one pound; this measure of the lightweighting has been increased to more than 33 cans to the pound in 2000. Cans are formed from two kinds of circular blanks cut from sheets. The tab of the can remains attached after opening. This is a feature that played an important role in avoiding the public ban of beverage cans because of the nuisance of separate sharp tabs in can litter.

Lightweighting is an important process and product design issue. It is a complex engineering materials task. While holding the container volume constant, the designer considers: decreasing the thickness of the aluminum sheet for the can wall and the can bottom, decreasing both the top and bottom can diameter, increasing the taper or can necking, and lowering the axial necking loads to control the threshold of can buckling. The metal content of a can makes up nearly 70 percent of the unit cost (Sanders, 1990; Sanders, 1993) and reduction in can weight is an opportunity for major savings. The excess pressure of carbonated beverages, about 90 pounds per square inch, is used in the design to offset buckling loads (Trageser, 1988). Taking advantage of excess pressure is a major reason for the success of the aluminum industry in the soft drink and beer markets, and the lack of success in the market for containers for non-carbonated food products. Incorporating high levels of post-consumer recycling (more than 50 percent) can result in large reductions (order of 50 percent) in the net energy requirements per unit mass of a can.

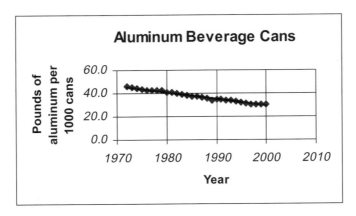

Figure 1: Declining Weight of Aluminum Cans (Aluminum 2001)

Design studies seek priorities between product and process issues. The context of these decisions include interactions between the public [environmental and resource sustainability or social cost issues] and private sectors [efficiency and private cost issues]. Questions include: What is the best level of recycling? What targets are best addressed in the private or public sectors? What behaviors lead to cooperation between sectors and what actions lead to stagnation and unresolveable conflicts? Academic questions include are there technical limits for recycling or are recycling targets social science decisions?

4.2 Process Design

Life cycle analysis is a method for a systematic study of process design issues. An engineering approach identifies an overall system boundary to separate what is inside from what is outside the system. A steady state analysis is a typical approach using a year as the chosen time interval. Boustead and Hancock (Boustead, 1979) apply this method to aluminum can processes. Their simplified analysis selects eleven steps, or unit operations, for the process life cycle. Their mathematical model tracks both mass and energy and uses simple conservation concepts to develop algebraic equations for calculating net mass flows, recycle rates and unit energy requirements. All results are expressed in terms of the production of a kilogram of cans.

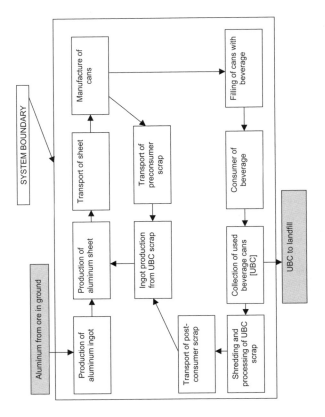

Figure 2: Aluminum Can Process Flow Model

The Boustead and Hancock model shows a simple process flow diagram. The complexity of the systems includes two nested material recycle loops. The preconsumer recycling is controlled by the private industry. The post-consumer recycle loop links private industry and public waste disposal processes.

One result of this model is to illustrate the approximately linear relationship between the net energy per kilogram of can production and the post-consumer recycle rate.

4.3 Product Design

The high technology of aluminum can production is shown by the sophistication of the advanced engineering tools used by designers (Sanders, 1990;

Bhakuni, 1991). Aluminum can production incorporates the skills of materials, process, and manufacturing engineering. Environmental engineers interact with traditional engineering in several ways. They pose questions about waste production and the fate of products and materials. Recycling is a material issue; the aluminum can is not refilled and reused. The beverage can is made of more than a single alloy. Current methods of collection, shredding and baling by the scrap industry results in a blend of alloys for the post-consumer aluminum scrap. The composition of the end and the body alloys differ in the relative amounts of manganese and magnesium in each aluminum alloy. Recycling operations that combine these alloys create potential engineering issues. Desirable magnesium concentrations in lid and tab alloys degrade performance of aluminum body alloys; manganese plays the opposite role for the body alloy versus the top alloys (Sanders, 1990). Unless an additional unit operation is added to the process flow diagram, multiple recycling cycles can result in a scrap alloy that is unacceptable for the body-drawing manufacturing step. Another option is simply the addition of pure aluminum. Presently, the industry estimates that a recycle rate of 65 percent is below the rate for which new operations must be added.

4.4 Recycling Promotion and Target Setting

Environmental concerns about recycling started from issues of litter from bottles and cans. Some states addressed these issues by mandating deposits and returns of soft drink and beer containers. The Container Recycling Institute (2001) reports the significant difference in the estimated recycle rates for eight states with mandated deposits (more than 85 percent collection return rate) versus the rest of the United States (about 55 percent rate). Efforts are ongoing to relate the increase in recycling rate to the size of a mandated deposit.

Transactions in aluminum used beverage cans (UBC) are facilitated by standard specifications developed by the Institute of Scrap Recycling Industries (ISRI, 2001). These specifications are used to prepare can scrap for sale to an aluminum recycling company that will sell to a secondary ingot melter. Because the thinness and strength of finished aluminum can sheet requirements, the specifications address both the handling history and specific contaminates that must be controlled. ISRI defines three kinds of scrap aluminum cans: baled UBC, densified UBC and bricked UBC. For example, of these specifications, baled UBCs are used beverage cans that have been magnetically separated and are free from all other types of materials. Average bale dimensions are 30 to 36 inches by 36 to 48 inches by 60 to 72 inches, and with a density of 14 to 30 pounds per cubic foot. The bales should be kept dry, with maximum moisture content of four percent. The goal is to produce a bale relatively free of contaminating materials with lead, copper, brass and other nonferrous materials as cause for rejection.

The scrap industry operates differently than major process and manufacturing industries. Transactions at the interface between industries must identify and adjust or compensate for these differences. These issues add to the cost and uncertainty of these transactions. The scrap industry has led efforts to classify scrap materials as materials of commerce and not to classify scrap as waste subject to federal and local regulations (ISRI, 2001).

Private cost savings on demand for virgin aluminum from ore and significant reductions in ingot production requirements has driven industry interests in recycling.

4.5 Calculation of Recycling Rates

Calculating recycle rates acquires different context if it is used as a means of environmental regulation rather than a useful, but somewhat arbitrary private sector measure of performance. In 2000, a conflict about the appropriate way to calculate the recycle rate for aluminum cans was reported between aluminum industry, The Aluminum Association and the Container Recycling Institute (CRI). A difference in methodologies resulted in the CRI reporting that the U.S. annual recycling rate for UBCs was 55.2 percent, in contrast to the Aluminum Association estimate of 62.5 percent. The large difference depends on how imported and exported new and scrap cans are addressed. The social context of this disagreement affects measuring annual progress towards a goal of 75 percent UBC recycling established by the aluminum industry in November 1997.

Calculating and reporting of recycle rates is a recurring issue of conflict between government regulators, industry and environmental watchdog organizations. In most cases for scrap and waste materials, the procedures for calculating recycle rates are self-defined and perhaps are self-serving to show the efforts of a particular organization in the best light. Lack of standardization for recycling calculations makes it difficult and typically wrong to compare reported rates between materials and industries. Communications would be improved with more attention to this issue.

5. Case Study: Datalogger for Power Tools

In Germany, manufacturers have banded together to introduce a voluntary recycling program for power tools. Electric saws and drills are examples of these kinds of power tools. Power tools can be returned at no cost to dealers, and the discarded tools are accumulated in bins and shipped to a central recycling facility. At this facility, tools may be repaired or recycled. For recycling, the tools are disassembled into different materials. Materials or combinations of materials without a recycling chain are sent to a landfill. The reverse logistics transportation, disassembly, repair and other costs are larger than the revenues received from material recycling or sale of repaired tools, so the power tool product take-back process operates at a loss. To cover this loss, manufacturers are assessed a fee in proportion to the numbers of their own tools handled.

Klausner (1998-2000) investigated product design changes and take-back system alternatives that might improve the current system. His recommended change would be to introduce a remanufacturing option. In this scenario, returned power tools could be remanufactured or recycled. In remanufacture, the power tools are disassembled into components. Fragile components are replaced (such as rubber parts) and reused components are refurbished, cleaned and tested. The result is a remanufactured power tool that can be resold for a substantial fraction of the price of a completely new power tool. The sale price could cover the costs of remanufacture plus any losses associated with the recycled tools. Interestingly, Klausner found that remanufacturing was less expensive than repair and resulted in a longer-lived product, so the repair option was excluded.

A critical consideration in the recommended operation is the choice for individual power tools between remanufacture and recycle. For power tools, the value still residing in motors is the critical element. As long as the motor is in good shape, remanufacturing is desirable. Unfortunately, external tests on power tool motor quality are not reliable, particularly without initial disassembly. As an alternative, Klausner suggested embedding a datalogger in new power tools.

A datalogger is comprised of a memory chip, sensor(s) and communication capability. Over the lifetime of a power tool, the datalogger could record information about extent of use, temperatures and other information. On the return to the product take-back center, the record could be accessed and an accurate assessment of the potential for remanufacturing accomplished. In effect, the design change of embedding a datalogger enabled much better decision making about end-of-life options. It also provides information on the actual use of a large number of power tools, which can then be used to improve design.

One disadvantage of the datalogger scheme is that the cost of a datalogger is incurred for each new power tool, even though only a fraction of power tools are actually returned in the product take-back stream. Klausner suggested that rebates might be offered for the return of desirable power tools, such as tools purchased within the past five or ten years. These rebates could be used as an incentive to purchase new tools and to insure a reliable stream of remanufactured tools to the marketplace. Again, the profitability of the remanufacturing option would be sufficient to pay for these types of rebates.

The power tool take-back operation has some interesting implications for other products. Remanufacturing is an option to consider in many cases, unless issues of obsolescence emerge. Design changes can affect the possibilities of remanufacture.

6. Case Study: Coffee Makers

Nearly every household has a coffee maker, yet there is significant business available to manufacturers as units are constantly being replaced as they break, get dirty, or their styles become dated. An analysis of coffee makers shows several important implications for Green Design: first, no coffee makers that we are aware of are specifically designed to be repaired or recycled. Second, many coffee makers are designed to prevent disassembly. Third, the result is that coffee makers are sent to the landfill after their short life span.

A life cycle analysis (LCA) of the coffee maker, shown in Figure 3, captures the immense energy and material resources necessary to manufacture the product with the only current output at end of life being disposal in a landfill. There is clearly opportunity to improve the environmental impact of the product. Design for recyclability or take-back programs are reasonable options for this type of consumer product. To consider redesign for recyclability, the first step would be a function relation analysis (Figure 4) indicating the discrete functions necessary to make coffee. An analysis of this breakdown will help the designers reconsider how to design the functionality to enable better disassembly and recyclability later. The other consideration in redesign is the use of materials and the ease of their separation. Coffee makers typically use polypropylene, steel, glass, aluminum, rubber and other materials. As long as a consistent and easily recyclable composition of polypropylene is used, material separation should be straightforward once the product is disassembled.

Life Cycle Analysis

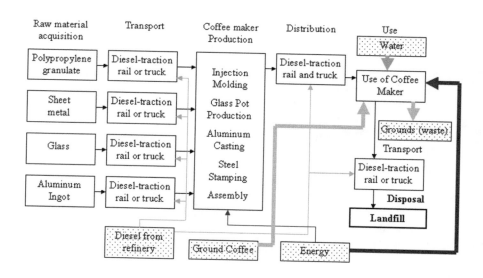

**Figure 3: Illustrative Life Cycle Assessment
Processes for a Coffee Maker**

The final consideration is repairability of the product. It is interesting that some manufacturers go so far as to rivet the base of the product together, preventing repair and ease of disassembly, while others use screws making the process potentially easier. The use of a rivet might be lack of consideration for disassembly or intentional prevention of disassembly. The scope of consideration goes beyond the product itself into implications on overall infrastructure and legal protection. Because coffee makers use water and electricity, manufacturers may be concerned about customers taking the product apart and having electrical components exposed to water. Concern for the consumer's well-being and prevention of potential litigation if someone were to be injured all work against creating a readily disassemblable product. Protection of and from individual components would ease this threat to a recyclable product. However, the issues surrounding the tradeoffs of design under environmental considerations is complex and unique to each product.

Function Relation Analysis

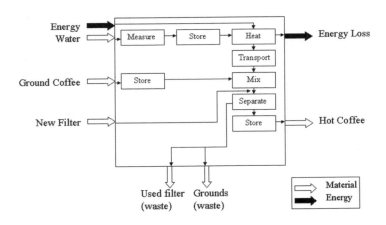

Figure 4: Illustrative Function Relation Analysis for a Coffee Maker

7. Case Study: Computers

Computer "recycling" firms both recycle and reuse products. Some firms take discarded computers, make slight modifications, and place them in schools, nonprofits, and charities for extended lifetime use. Others "recycle" electronic equipment, extracting value from the components or high-value materials like gold and other precious metals. The emergence of these firms has diverted the flow of many computers from the municipal waste stream. However, consumers and businesses alike have shown a considerable unwillingness to throw away old electronic products. Instead, computers are often stockpiled in attics and storerooms until space is needed for another purpose. The existence of adequate storage space has contributed to the diversion of computers from landfills as well, as owners have had time to put off the disposition decision long enough for the recycling and reuse markets to mature.

The arrows in Figure 5 define the pathways of discarded computers. A new computer is purchased, and eventually becomes obsolete. At that time, there are four options to the owner of the computer. First, it could be reused. This means that it is somehow used again after becoming obsolete to the purchaser— possibly a result of being resold or reassigned to another user without extensive modification. Second, the original owner could store the computer. In this case, it is serving no purpose except to occupy space. Third, the computer could be recycled. We define this to mean that the product is taken apart and individual materials or subassemblies are sold for reuse or recycling. Finally, the computer could be landfilled.

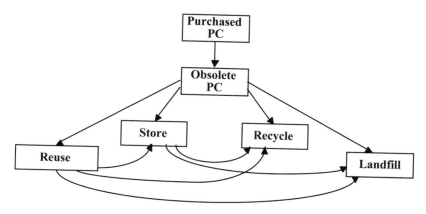

Figure 5: Flow Diagram of Computers

Matthews (1999) predicted over 680 million personal computers would be sold in the United States by 2005, but only 55 million computers would be landfilled and 143 million recycled. A large number of obsolete computers would still be stored in 2005, even though their value will only decrease over time, until they are worth only the sum of their raw materials. The residual value of materials in old electronic equipment soon after production is only 1-5 percent of the original cost of the equipment (MCC, 1996, Matthews, 1997). Storing an old computer instead of quickly reusing or recycling it is not a profit-maximizing or cost-effective solution. Holding on to an obsolete computer without getting some benefit out of it is akin to holding on to a stock of a company which is known to be going bankrupt—in either case you end up with nothing, and have full knowledge of this fact ahead of time.

7.1 Computer Design for Environment Programs

The key to improving successfully environmental quality of any product is to make informed decisions at the design stage. So-called Design for Environment (DFE) or Green Design programs maximize use of resources, and also ensure that corporate environmental goals are met in a timely manner. Most major computer manufacturers (Apple, HP, IBM) have environmental design programs in place and publicize their efforts. In addition, Compaq was selected to receive the 1997 World Environment Center Gold Medal for International Corporate Environmental Achievement in recognition of the company's exceptional performance in environmental, health and safety leadership, and proactive stance towards meeting international regulation far ahead of their competitors.

7.2 Modular Design and Upgradeability

Modular design and upgradeability are intended to alleviate some of the need to upgrade equipment constantly, and thus, to reduce potential waste. Although most computers can be partially upgraded by swapping components like larger drives, few computers exist with appropriate price-performance upgrade paths, and even fewer are able to be traded in for newer models. The only options on the Intel platform are generally limited to ranges of processor performance, and require relatively costly upgrades for little performance benefit (typically several hundred dollars for a modest gain).

However, Apple's PowerMac 7500 series was designed for upgradeability right out of the box. Even the original computer comes with the processor on a "daughtercard" attached to the motherboard. Upgrading is as simple as changing daughtercards and is very inexpensive—roughly $100 for twice the power. Although full upgradeability can never exist due to rapidly changing architectures, an option like this helps to extend the life of computers.

7.3 Component Reuse

In the absence of upgrade paths for most equipment, reuse needs to be seen as a viable option. Most subsystems (e.g., drives, memory, keyboards) are designed to last well beyond the five-year useful life of the overall computer system. This is an awkward situation as the whole system sits idle while its subsystems could be reassigned, yet the purchaser paid more for components, which will far outlast the system. Many of these components could be resold to increase the value.

7.4 Materials Selection

One of the more important reasons for concerning ourselves with materials selection is in preventing the use of toxic materials. Generally speaking, it will be impossible to remove all toxics from the design of computers. Overall, materials choices fall into three categories:

- Materials not necessary for operation (Class I)
- Materials necessary for operation and expensive to replace (Class II)
- Materials necessary but with no easy replacement (Class III)

Class I materials choices mentioned in a 1991 study included the lead shielding for CPU cases (Carnegie Mellon, 1991). Much progress has been made in this area. Manufacturers have switched to cases, which use more plastic for shielding, as well as using metals other than lead. Class II materials included PCP in capacitors, cadmium in batteries, lead solder on circuit boards, and mercury in batteries and switches. Some progress has been made in this category, but mostly through reduction efforts. Cadmium is still present in rechargeable portable computer batteries, as are traces of mercury, but each in lower quantities. Nickel-cadmium (NiCd) technology continues to be the most widespread choice in the industry, although other options such as nickel-metal-hydride (NiMH) exist. Lead solder is still a standard part of circuit board fabrication, but again, less is being used due to technology advances. Finally, Class III materials like phosphorous in monitors, copper-plastic interface cables, and silicon and arsenic in integrated circuits are still standard in products. Little progress has been made in removing these materials from design other than through reduction. Thankfully, projections of widespread use of gallium-arsenide (GaAs) technology have proved premature.

An interesting side effect of the continued use of metals in the design of computers is that they account for a high percentage of the end-of-life value of products. The more metals present (e.g., aluminum), the higher the reclamation value for a recycling firm. Ironically, as metals are successfully replaced, there will be less incentive for recycling to occur. Metals account for over 70 percent of the residual value of computers (MCC , 1996: Matthews, 1997).

Aside from materials selection improvements, progress has been made in subsystem recycling. This advance has come in part through legislation like the U.S. Environmental Protection Agency's 1992 decision to ban the landfill disposal of cathode-ray tubes (CRTs). As a result, monitor and CRT recycling has made great advances. This is significant because monitors contribute nearly 50 percent of the mass and volume of computer systems, and contain toxics— lead, phosphorus, cadmium and mercury. Glass, circuit boards, and wiring from both CRTs and standard televisions are reclaimed in great quantities every year (at least 85 percent of reclaimed monitors are recycled), reducing the volume of landfill waste from monitors (Envirocycle, 1997).

Even with these recycling technology advances, there are considerable obstructions to entering the market successfully. A company electing to reclaim old electronic products is classified as a "hazardous waste handler" by EPA regulations. Improvements need to be made which provide regulatory relief for companies and which seek both to reduce landfill waste and improve environmental quality. EPA's Common Sense Initiative is a good starting point for changing the perception and classification of recyclers as hazardous waste facilities.

7.5 Labeling and Materials Recovery

Individual firms have followed International Standards Organization (ISO) guidelines with respect to labeling parts. IBM has labeled all plastic parts of their computers so that they can be easily identified at end-of-life, using ISO specifications as well as supplier information. Such efforts have, for the most part, caused manufacturers to realize the benefits in reducing the number of materials used (namely, plastics) in their products.

In addition, the electronics industry has made considerable progress in setting up reverse logistic networks and reclamation facilities to extract value from end-of-life equipment. Digital, Lucent and IBM all have corporate centers in place to process obsolete electronic equipment.

7.6 Recycling Promotion

As mentioned above, used electronic equipment loses value quickly. Generally speaking, computers depreciate at a rate of 40 percent per year. Manufacturers are aware of this and realize the environmental burden of their products. Yet, there has been no major effort to adopt an industry-wide initiative to promote computer recycling. The Electronics Industry Association (EIA) would be a natural choice to organize such a program.

Endorsing such a program could be as simple as adding a line in user manuals or attaching stickers to all new computers informing users (a majority of whom are replacing equipment) of the value in recycling obsolete electronics while still valuable. The longer a disposition decision is delayed, the more costly it will be to the company, until eventually they will have to pay for removal. This type of endorsement could serve two purposes: to publicize the firm's environmental awareness and to increase the percentage of computers recycled.

Changes in government procurement and disposition procedures would be helpful as well. Currently there are restrictions in U.S. government procurement guidelines preventing purchase of recycled products. Also, many products purchased by the U.S. government cannot be donated or otherwise reused, requiring long-term storage of obsolete equipment.

7.7 Resource Recovery and Product Take Back

Although several major manufacturers have the ability to reclaim materials from products, third-party groups are doing most such reclamation. Although this inevitably meets the goal of preventing disposal, manufacturers thus have little incentive to try to design products that use nonvirgin materials. Resource recovery programs are critical to closing the loop towards having a steady supply of nonvirgin materials for manufacturers.

Large firms will sometime negotiate take-back pricing for old computer equipment (in the $50 range), but such a decision soon becomes moot, as charity organizations will give $100 or more tax credits for the same equipment. This fact underlies the economics of the situation—that personal computers are relatively expensive to recycle completely and there are small gains, whereas mainframe computers can be disassembled easily and with high returns. Note that this research has not even considered the potential environmental impacts or feasibility of software package recycling.

Firms with the logistics available to take back products should capitalize on this and incorporate outreach programs to fill capacity. Many firms donate old equipment to charity—why not promote recycling by launching "computer drive-off" programs, where empty trailers are left at schools to be filled with old equipment. In exchange for filling a certain number of trailers, the manufacturer provides "new" equipment to the school. Consumers have shown a remarkable willingness to provide computers for schools via grocery store receipt collection. Such programs could further inform the public about the incentives to recycling old equipment.

8. Conclusions

We have summarized the major design concerns for promoting closed-loop recycling, including avoiding toxic materials, easing disassembly, avoiding multiple material types, using recycled components and materials, and including information in products. We also described several examples of design changes that aid closed-loop supply chains.

Acknowledgment: The authors acknowledge Edwin Comparini for assistance in LCA and functional relations analyses and creation of illustrations.

References

Aluminum Association 2001, Economics and *Statistics, www.aluminum.org* Accessed May.

Antonsson, E. K. and J. Cagan. 2001, Introduction. *Formal Engineering Design Synthesis* (E. K. Antonsson and J. Cagan, eds.), in press: Cambridge University Press, NY.

Bhakuni. N.D., A.B. Trageser, S. Sundaresan and K. Ishii. 1991, Structural Optimization Methods for Aluminum Beverage Can Bottoms. Alcoa Technical Laboratories.

Boustead, I. and G.F. Hancock. 1979, *Handbook of Industrial Energy Analysis*. John Wiley & Sons.

Cagan. J. and C. M. Vogel. 2001, Developing Great Products. *Financial Times* Prentice Hall, Upper Saddle River, NJ.

Carnegie Mellon 1991, Design Issues in Waste Avoidance. Carnegie Mellon University Department of Engineering and Public Policy, Technical Report.

Container Recycling Institute 2001, www.container-recycling.org Accessed May.

Department of Commerce 1995, Statistical Abstract of the US Government Printing Office, Washington, DC.

Dreyfuss, H. 1967, *Measure of Man*. Watson-Guptill Publishers.

Envirocycle, Inc. 2001, http://www.enviroinc.com/env2.html Accessed May.

Hosford, W. F. and J. L. Duncan. 1994, The Aluminum Beverage Can. *Scientific America.* September, pp. 48-53.

Institute of Scrap Recycling Industries (ISRI) 2001, www.isri.org Accessed May.

Kirsch, F. W. and G. P. Looby. 1991, Waste Minimization Assessment for a Manufacturer of Aluminum Cans. *Envirosense.* U.S. EPA Environmental Research Brief, EPA/600/M-91/025, July.

Klausner, M. 1998, Design and Analysis of Product Take-back Systems: An Application to Power Tools. Unpublished Ph.D. Thesis, Department of Civil and Environmental Engineering, Carnegie Mellon University.

Klausner, M. and C. Hendrickson. 2000, Reverse-Logistics Strategy for Product Take-Back. *Interfaces.* May-June, 30(3), pp. 156-165.

Klausner, M., W. Grimm and A. Horvath. 1999, Integrating Product Take-back and Technical Service. *Proceedings of the 1999 IEEE International Symposium on Electronics and the Environment.* Danvers, MA, May.

Klausner, M., W. Grimm and C. Hendrickson. 1998, Reuse of Electric Motors of Consumer Products: Design and Analysis of a Usage Data Log. *Journal of Industrial Ecology.* Vol. 2, No. 2, pp. 89-102.

Klausner, M., W. Grimm, C. Hendrickson and A. Horvath. 1998, Sensor-based Data Recording of Use Conditions for Product Take-back. *Proceedings of the 1998 IEEE International Symposium on Electronics and the Environment.* Oak Brook, IL, May.

Lave, L. and C. Hendrickson. 1996, It's Easier to Say Green Than Be Green. *Technology Review.* Vol. 99 No.8, November/December, pp. 68-69.

Matthews, S. 1997, Unraveling the Environmental Product Design Paradox. *Proceedings of the 1997 IEEE Symposium on Electronics and the Environment.* San Francisco, CA, May.

Matthews, S., C. Hendrickson, F. McMichael and D. Hart (Matthews). 1999, Disposition and End-of-Life for Products: A Green Design Case Study. Green Design Initiative, Carnegie Mellon, http://gdi.ce.cmu.edu/gded-pc-case.pdf.

Matthews, D. 2001, Assessment and Design of Industrial Environmental Management Systems. Unpublished Ph.D. Dissertation, Department of Civil and Environmental Engineering, Carnegie Mellon, May.

Microelectronics and Computer Technology Corporation (MCC) 1996, *1996 Electronics Industry Environmental Roadmap.* Technical Report, February, Appendix I.

Otto, K. and K. Wood. 2001, *Product Design: Techniques in Reverse Engineering and New Product Development.* Prentice Hall, Upper Saddle River, NJ.

Pahl, G. and W. Beitz. 1996, *Engineering Design: A Systematic Approach.* 2nd ed., Springer-Verlag, New York.

Papalambros, P. and D. J. Wilde. 1988, *Principles of Optimal Design.* Cambridge University Press, New York.

Petroski, H. 1996, *Invention by Design.* Harvard University Press.

Sanders, Jr. R.E.; A.B. Trageser and C.S. Rollings. 1990, Recycling of Lightweight Aluminum Containers: Present and Future Perspectives. *Second International Symposium – Recycling of Metals and Engineered Materials.* Edited by J. H. L. van Linden, D. L. Stewart, Jr. and Y. Sahal. The Minerals, Metals, and Materials Society, pp. 187-201.

Sanders, Jr. R.E. and C.L. Wood, Jr. 1993, Aluminum Automotive Recycling and Materials Selection Issues. *SAE Technical Paper Series 930493.* International Congress and Exposition, Detroit, MI, March 1-5.

Simon, H.A. 1969, *The Sciences of the Artificial.* MIT Press, Cambridge, MA

Tilton, J. E. 1991, Material Substitution: The Role of New Technology. Chapter 15 *Diffusion of Technologies and Social Behavior*, edited by Nebojsa Nakicenovic and Arnulf Gruber, International Institute for Applied System Analysis, Springer-Verlag.

Trageser, A.B. and R.E. Dick. 1988, Aluminum Can Design Using Finite Element Methods, Presented at SME Can Manufacturing Technology Symposium, Schaumburg, IL, September 14-16.

Contacts:

Chris Hendrickson
Duquesne Light Company Professor of Engineering
Head, Department of Civil and Environmental Engineering
Carnegie Mellon University
119 Porter Hall
Pittsburgh, PA 15213-3890

Email: cth@cmu.edu

Francis McMichael
The Blenko Professor of Environmental Engineering
Department of Civil and Environmental Engineering
Department of Engineering and Public Policy
Carnegie Mellon University
Porter Hall 123G
Pittsburgh, PA 15213-3890

Email: fm2a@andrew.cmu.edu

H. Scott Matthews
Assistant Professor
Department of Civil and Environmental Engineering
Department of Engineering and Public Policy
Carnegie Mellon University
Porter Hall 118L
Pittsburgh, PA 15213-3890

Email: hsm@cmu.edu

THE ECONOMICS OF REMANUFACTURING

Geraldo Ferrer and D. Clay Whybark, Kenan-Flagler Business School,
University of North Carolina, at Chapel Hill, NC

1. Introduction

The cost of purchased parts and components is a very large fraction of direct manufacturing costs for many firms. Waste disposal is another cost element that has increased continuously. However, there is a strategy for reducing both cost elements simultaneously. Used components can serve either in manufacture of new products for maintenance purposes, or for manufacturing "equivalent to new" products. Hence, product recovery and remanufacturing can be an attractive means to decrease overall production costs.

For example, tires are among the industrial products with the largest generation of solid waste. Each passenger car leaves the assembly line with the equivalent of 30-40 kg of rubber and steel wire material as tires that are used for two or three years before being dumped. On average, automobiles last about 11-12 years using three sets of tires. Hence, if used tires are not reused somehow, each car dumps 10 kg of used tires in the waste stream each year. Fortunately, used tires are not necessarily useless. When they are replaced, many used tires retain some of the key characteristics required from a new tire, such as shape, rigidity, impermeability and lateral strength. Rubber reclaimers and tire retreaders have explored some of these properties. In many cases, surface adhesion is the only physical property lost by the tire during its first life. While the lack of adhesion renders a tire inappropriate for its original use, its remanufacture—also called retreading—is still viable. The total amount of oil saved per year by this method, and the resulting approximate savings in US dollars, are depicted below. (Source: American Retreaders Association, Bloomberg Oil Buyer's Guide).

United States	Retreaded Tires (units / year)	Oil saved per tire (liters / year)	Total oil saved (1000 liters)	Savings (1000 US$)
Passenger cars	5.300.000	17	90.000	9.900
Light trucks	7.200.000	36	259.000	28.490
Medium and heavy trucks	15.900.000	63	1.000.000	110.000
Specialty	870.000	140	121.000	13.310
Total	29.270.000	50	1.470.000	161.700

Table 1: Savings attributed to the retread business

Remanufacturing is described as "… an industrial process in which worn-out products are restored to like-new condition. Through a series of industrial processes in a factory environment, a discarded product is completely disassembled. Useable parts are cleaned, refurbished, and put into inventory. Then the new product is reassembled from the old and, where necessary, new parts to produce a fully equivalent—and sometimes superior—in performance and expected lifetime to the original new product" (Lund, 1983). Remanufacturing closes the material cycle, and provides the basis for a closed-loop supply chain. It focuses on value-added recovery, rather than just the recovery of the value of materials, i.e., recycling.

In discussing the economics of remanufacturing, our main concern is the economic feasibility of a remanufacturing operation. Therefore, we take a close look at the costs and the benefits associated with remanufacturing. This is different from discussing the technology of remanufacturing. We will not investigate the technical aspects, as long as they are not essential for discussing costs or benefits.

The economic feasibility of remanufacturing is dependent on three important components:
- The infrastructure of the reverse-logistics network
- The market for remanufactured products or components
- The design of the product

Creating a reverse logistics system—being able to generate and handle a sufficient return flow—is crucial to remanufacturing. Generating a steady return flow into the system can be achieved e.g., by leasing a product to a customer instead of selling it. Given a steady return flow, there remains the challenge of achieving economies of scale with picking up, packing and disassembling the used products.

Recovery of high-value parts and materials is not very useful, if there is no market for recovered and/or manufactured items. Product obsolescence plays an important role in this respect. For example, in the computer industry it is difficult to use remanufactured components such as memory chips, microprocessors or hard disks in new product lines, given the high rate of product change. There is limited demand for computer models of previous generations. The remanufacturer has to identify and reach a class of customers—such as schools—willing to purchase and operate machines using not-so-recent technology.

A disassembly operation usually employs a flexible workforce that varies with the flow of returned equipment. This characteristic is common to most disassembly operations where the return flow is not predictable or changes frequently. Nevertheless, the longer it takes to disassemble a returned product, the higher the labor costs. Thus, reducing the time spent on disassembly improves the operation's viability. Design plays an important role by making products easier to disassemble.

Remanufacturing is the recovery process that manufacturers of durable products should consider, either because of legislative pressure to ensure environmental protection, or because of the business opportunity inherent in reusing parts that would be discarded otherwise. Early activity in this area was limited to remanufacturing just a handful of capital goods. Now, pro-active manufacturers of several products have realized that it is possible to reduce the environmental impact that a product may have at its retirement and reduce the cost of future generations of the product. They have adopted "design for the environment" programs that have enabled economically sustainable remanufacturing activities, often coupled with a product line extension to serve a large segment of the market: customers of all-new products and of remanufactured products.

Introducing remanufacturing into an economy can have macroeconomic effects. One concern is the impact of remanufacturing on the demand for labor. There is a persistent argument whether remanufacturing activities have positive or negative impact on demand for labor. Although remanufacturing per se is labor intensive, it reduces the need for several outputs that are labor intensive as well. Yet it can be shown, that remanufacturing activity actually promotes the demand for labor. Another issue is whether remanufacturing promotes growth. Remanufacturing reduces the amount of interindustry interaction. As components of used products are reused, the amount of new components produced or bought from the same type is reduced. Suppliers of sectors subject to competition from remanufacturing sectors have their interindustry transaction significantly reduced. This situation is exacerbated if the sector is also subject to remanufacturing activity. Yet, one could argue that a reduction of interindustry transactions, with a given demand, results in a more efficient economy. Therefore, the overall impact of remanufacturing on the economy may give the impression of a reduction in growth, but actually there is an increase in the efficiency and demand for labor.

2. Economics of the Remanufacturing Process

There is a class of recovery processes that involves doing a series of replacement or repair activities until a major change must be made. In this section we look at this type of problem as a generic resource conservation issue. We raise the question of when "repair or maintenance" should cease and a replacement be made. This is a very general problem and, although we will deal with a specific example, it deserves a considerable amount of attention in the economics of conservation.

There are several examples of this managerial problem. For instance, consider the external paint on a commercial jet. The friction caused by the high speeds in air travel wears off some of the paint on the plane. As the paint gets chipped, there is a need to repaint the plane for performance and appearance reasons. Chipped paint increases the drag on an airplane, reducing speed and fuel consumption performance. Successive paint jobs increase the weight of the aircraft, also reducing performance. To avoid excessive performance degradation, the old paint should be completely removed before a complete paint job takes place. The management decision, in this example, is to define when to forego over-painting, to strip the old paint, and paint the airplane anew.

A similar management decision is required in the maintenance of the seats in buses and trains. These seats are often covered with an upholstery fabric. Over time, this fabric becomes worn, torn, dirty, and otherwise, beyond cleaning. At this point the seats can be reupholstered or replaced. If the basic seat (the core) is structurally sound, reupholstering is an acceptable alternative. The life expectancy of this second seat cover is usually shorter than the original for several reasons. It is hard to get as good a fit the second time. The core may have some wear that interacts unfavorably with the cover, and other factors may combine to increase wear and reduce the value of the recovered seat. Third, fourth or more recovering cycles may be justified, but at some point the core itself is in such bad condition that it must be replaced altogether, and the process starts over.

An industrial example comes from rotating turbines, used in gas compressors or in electricity generation. The bearings in these turbines are replaced as wear dictates. Over time, the shaft itself wears down, increasing the wear rate on the bearings. At some point in the bearing replacement cycle, the shaft itself may need to be repaired or replaced. Again, the management decision is when to make the investment in the shaft.

The example that we will use here comes from the tire industry. Specifically, we consider the question of when to stop retreading and replace the complete tire. Retreading the tires used on trucks, buses, construction equipment, and many other commercial vehicles is a widespread practice. In the past, it was quite popular even for passenger car tires, but that has waned. Retreading is so important for certain vehicles that the tire manufacturers invest in making tire casings that are especially suited for multiple retreading cycles without structural failure. Eventually, however, even modern tire cores must be replaced as they do deteriorate with successive retreads. As the core deteriorates, the expected life of the retread also decreases, suggesting that it may not be economical to retread the tire indefinitely.

In all of the examples presented above, there is a remanufacturing process. In repainting the airplane, the repaint job is the analog of remanufacturing. In replacing upholstery on the bus seat, the bus seat is remanufactured as is the turbine when the bearings in its shaft are replaced. A tire with worn down tread is taken into a retread facility to be remanufactured. In each of these cases, the decision is made either—to continue remanufacturing or to replace the core. We will analyze this decision in regards to tires as an example, and generalize our findings to suit other examples as well.

2.1 Retreading used tires

Much of the research about commercial vehicle tires concerns the development of casings that can live longer through a large number of retreads. A well-managed tire may be retreaded at least twice, lasting 500,000 km under US conditions. However, tire makers are working on the development of a tire whose carcass can live up to one million km (600,000 miles), with the help of two or three retreads.

	process VA	cum VA	cum VA/kg
in tread	$ 4.59	$ 11.15	$ 12.58
in casing	$ 10.05	$ 15.49	$ 15.92
total	$ 14.64	$ 26.64	$ 14.33

Table 2: Value-added from final production

Retreading is the only tire reclaim process that attempts to take full advantage of the value remaining in the used product. Table 2 shows that 60 percent of the value-added in the tire is in the casing, which hardly deteriorates during its first life. Hence, tire retreading brings the opportunity to recover all of this value-added, at a certain recovery cost. It is this large value-added still available that "finances" the retreading process.

For each remanufactured tire, one casing is reused. However, there are several stages in the retreading process where some material is lost. The current technology cannot eliminate these losses: the first one is the tire usage, when roughly 10 percent of the tire's weight is dissipated. The second loss occurs during pre-inspection process, because some of the incoming casings have been worn beyond repair. Then, some 10 percent of the weight of the tire is buffed away. The final inspection is responsible for eliminating the tires not successfully retreaded, for instance, because of vulcanization problems. The amount of virgin materials required for each retreaded casing, by weight, equals:

$$\text{Virgin Material Requirements} = (\text{Fraction Dissipated} + \text{Fraction Buffed}) \text{ Tire Weight} \quad (1)$$
$$\text{VMR} = (\text{FD} + \text{FB}) \text{ TW}$$

The virgin material costs should equal the price of a new tread, adjusted for differenct weights. That is

$$\text{Virgin Material Cost} = \text{VMR} * \text{Tread Cost} / \text{Treat Weight} \qquad (2)$$
$$\text{VMC} = \text{VMR} * \text{TrC} / \text{TrW}$$

Hence, when a casing is retreaded, its attributed value can be identified as the difference between the market price of the retreaded tire and the sum of two costs: the virgin materials required in the process and the retreading operating cost. Notice that not all casings entering the system are sold, and some of the virgin material is lost with the retreaded tires that do not pass final inspection. Hence, to calculate the used casing value, it is necessary to adjust for these losses, attributing a production yield for the retreaded tires that are not salable and for the virgin material that is lost in their production.

To give a general formula, we will in future call the part of a used product that is reused the core. In the case of tire remanufacturing, the core is the casing. The core value (CV) should be considered as the market value of the remanufactured product (MVRP) minus the material cost (VMC) and the process cost (PRC), respective to two yields: the yield adjusted to the loss incurred in the disassembly process (Y) and the yield adjusted to the loss incurred in the final inspection processes (Y_{insp}).

$$CV = MVRP*Y - (VMC + PRC)/Y_{insp} \qquad (3)$$

We can assume that a fraction of α is rejected during pre-inspection, and a fraction of β is rejected during final inspection. At the end of the process, all remanufactured products are inspected and a fraction β is rejected. Hence, $Y = (1-\alpha)(1-\beta)$ and $Y_{insp} = (1-\beta)$. The expression assumes that the type of material needed to retread a tire is the same as to make the tread of a new tire. Once equation (3) is solved, the unit value of any retreaded casing is calculated.

Retreaded tires have suffered from a credibility problem that poses difficulty in its expansion. Most of its market is from knowledgeable customers who can evaluate the product quality. These customers are the large fleet operators and frequent buyers of replacement tires. For them, tire replacement is usually the third largest item in the operating budget, right after personnel and fuel. Hence, using retreaded tires is a natural choice for profit improvement through cost reduction. Retreaded tires deliver the same mileage as comparable new tires, although they are sold with discounts between 30 percent and 50 percent. They

323

are supplied with the same warranty as standard tires. Moreover, tire retreading consumes less energy: it takes 26 liters of oil to make a new passenger car tire, but just 9 liters to retread it. Likewise, retreading a single heavy-duty tire may save up to 40 liters of oil.

Retreaded tires hold an 80 percent share of the replacement market for aircraft landing gears, since nearly all air carriers procure retreads when available. Off-road machines, such as earth excavators, are other big users of retreads. All tire types can be retreaded, including steel belt radial, mud and snow tires. Size is not a constraint either; for example, the front tires of the CAT 994 Loader, each tire weighing 4.5 metric tons, can be retreaded for an additional life expectancy of 5,000 hours. Among retreaded tire customers, there are civil and military fleets of many governments. In response to the US Environmental Protection Agency support to retreaded tires through its Federal Tire Program, the US Executive Order 12873 mandates commodity managers to take affirmative steps to procure retreaded tires.

Knowledgeable customers of retreaded tires include the US Postal Services (20 percent of its replacement tires), France's La Poste, other express courier companies (FedEx, UPS, etc.), and bus fleet operators. In all of these cases, tire procurement is an important management decision that may impact the company's profit. The very large fleets manage their tire consumption with regular retreading of a fixed pool of tires by a selected retreader. In this case, the retreader becomes a service provider and the tire is a valuable asset, carefully managed by fleet operators. In these instances, the casing is expected to live through at least two retreads; six retreads is not entirely uncommon. Similar policies are practiced by the users of specialty tires, such as for aircrafts or off-road vehicles. Among many criteria, fleet managers choose their retreaders based on their deadlines, which may vary between two and three days and seven to ten days for regular commercial tires. The outcome is that retreads command 41 percent of the replacement market of tires for commercial vehicles in the United States and 50 percent in Europe.

There are 1,385 retreading plants in the United States. About 70 of these plants belong to tire manufacturers and the others belong to independent owners, sometimes associated with a large franchiser. Retreading plants can vary in size from 20 tires/day to more than 2,600 tires/day. Some plants are specialized on a few segments (air, off-road), while others serve the long-haul trucking market as well as the light truck market. Only one market faces decline, that of passenger cars. This decline reflects the increased competition from inexpensive new tires, whose price differential from retreaded tires has been significantly reduced, and the common misconception that retreaded tires are unsafe.

Application	Quantity (thousands)	Weight (metric tons)
Heat generation	101,000	1,087,500
Civil engineering applications	13,500	145,500
Expor		
	12,500	134,500
Direct material use (punch, cut, stamp)	8,000	86,000
Ground rubber applications	3,373	36,500
Agriculture	2,500	27,000
Pyrolysis (thermal distillation)	500	5,500
Miscellaneous	1,000	11,000
Reclaim (non-retread)	142,373	1,533,500
Landfilled	110,626	1,191,500
All Used Tires	253,000	2,724,000

Table 3: Used tires applications in the United States
Source: American Retreaders Association (1996)

2.2 Applications for used tires

Used tires can have many destinations. Out of 283 million tires used in the United States in 1995, only 30 million were retreaded. The remainder had the destinations shown in Table 3. The table shows that 39 percent of all used tires are landfilled, while less than 11 percent of them are retreaded. Each application seeks a different property in the tire: the rubber's energy content, different physical characteristics (shock absorption, elasticity, impermeability, resistance to abrasion) or the chemical properties. However, these reclaim processes only use a small fraction of the value in the used tire. Only a small part of the physical, chemical and structural properties still remaining in the used tire are exploited in each of them.[1]

2.3   Direct material reuse

A small fraction of the scrap tires is consumed through direct reuse. The tire is cut, stamped or sliced to form welcome mats, muffler hangers, traffic cone weights, dock bumpers, as well as to secure covering for silos and outdoor storage. Some car manufacturers have included in their designs rubber components made of used tires, such as brake pads. It is a very limited market that takes advantage of part of the physical properties remaining in the rubber.

Some of the used tire physical properties, such as sound and impact absorption, suggest its use in construction. Whole tires have been used in reef and break-water construction, stabilizing embankments, as highway crash barriers and attenuating highway noise in urban areas. However, these applications can only absorb a small fraction of the used tires available each year. Other widely available recycled materials, such as used plastic bottles have been suggested for the same uses, thus reducing the opportunity to use recycled tire materials.

2.4 Granular rubber applications

Granular rubber can be obtained from three sources: from scrap tires, from reject tires and from retread buffings. When a used tire is buffed in the retread plant, a large amount of granular rubber is generated. Buffing is responsible for two thirds of all granular rubber available in the United States. Granular rubber is also obtained by grinding whole scrap or reject tires at room temperature or by a cryogenic method. Not all physical properties of the virgin rubber are preserved in the ground rubber, hence its utilization in the tire industry has been quite limited. So, there has been some research toward the development of a recycling process that allows reusing more of the rubber qualities still present in the used tires.

---

[1] EPA (1991) estimated that 66 percent of all used tried are landfilled, while 11 percent are retreated. Some of the difference is justified by the increased number of tires that are incinerated or used as asphalt additive. Nonetheless, both estimations should be read with caution.

Cryogenic grinding is one of the processes of grinding rubber— or any other polymer— without changing the polymer structure or the hydrocarbon content. The term "cryogenic" indicates that the rubber is vitrified in liquid nitrogen to about -200°C and pulverized with a hammer mill at an operating cost of $40/ ton of scrap tire. Approximately 70 percent of the tire content is yielded as rubber, 10 percent is steel and 15 percent is fiber. All products can be sold. The process is more advantageous for recycling scrap rubber and plastic before any mixture occurs; the polymer coming out of the grinding process reflects the variety of raw materials in the mix. Users of cryogenic granulated rubber include:

- contractors who make running tracks, tennis courts, and other sport surface,
- landscapers who use rubber as a soil amendment,
- manufacturers of rubber products who use recycled material as a filler,
- asphalt plants who use rubber as a modifying additive, and
- rubber devulcanization facilities.

Used tires can be ground at room temperature as well. The used tires are fed into a shredder that reduces then into 3/4-inch chips before a magnet separates the steel wires. The chips are further reduced by a granulator down to 600-800 μm crumbs. The finely ground rubber is reused as filler in applications where the superior qualities of virgin rubber are not required. The advantage over cryogenic grinding is in the lower cost.

Because the used rubber has already been vulcanized, the utilization of ground rubber presents a number of technical difficulties with degradation of the physical properties. A number of companies worldwide have developed methods to turn recycled rubber particles (crumb rubber) into a material that has physical properties and a processing behavior comparable to that of virgin rubber. This new trend has the potential of revolutionizing the rubber industry because crumb rubber will no longer be limited to applications in low-tech products. There is some evidence of progress in the development of bioreaction, which reduces this handicap and might allow the reuse of rubber into the tire industry. Bioreaction is a process that has the potential to improve the quality of the ground rubber, perhaps giving it the opportunity to return to the beginning of the production cycle as a new material. The objective of this technology is to avoid that ground rubber is forced into *cascade recycling,* but that it is allowed into a *like-for-like recycling* process.

Granular rubber is introduced in a bioreactor containing microorganisms that metabolizes its sulfur content, neutralizing its first vulcanization process. After the reaction is complete, the output is ready to be incorporated in a new rubber matrix to produce high-grade rubber for tires. However, the process is still in laboratory scale, with batch sizes of 45 kg. Primary figures say that the process may generate a profit margin of $10/ton of tire rubber. It is hoped that once the continuous process is fully developed, it may substitute some of the demand for virgin rubber materials.

One of the preferred applications for granular rubber is as filler in asphalt mix, absorbing 50,000 tons/year of ground rubber in the United States. Rubber is expected to increase durability and traction of highway pavement. If the technology is appropriately developed, there would be enough demand to absorb the totality of scrap tires generated in any country. There are two competing technologies: the rubber-modified asphalt concrete (RUMAC) includes about 3 percent by weight of ground rubber, replacing some of the aggregate in the original asphalt. The rubber is graded to specifications and uniformly dispersed throughout the mixture. The final asphalt is applied by conventional equipment. It was originated in the 1960s and has been tested in the Department of Transport of New York State since 1989. A complete analysis comparing the material costs with the expected life of the road surface for both the RUMAC and the standard asphalt is not available yet.

The alternative technology is the asphalt-rubber (A-R). It has been extensively used in some areas of the United States. In this process, conventional asphalt is blended with up to 25 percent of ground rubber, after complete separation of the steel and fibers, at 200°C. The outcome is a product of higher viscosity

2.5 Pyrolysis

Pyrolysis is the process of separating materials in the presence of heat and without air, avoiding oxidation. Strictly speaking, pyrolysis is the recycling process for used tires, regenerating the basic chemicals used to make a tire. It generates carbon black, zinc, sulfur, steel and oils; the polymeric structure is lost. The process has been researched since mid-70s. The pyrolysis of one ton of tires produces 350-420 kg of oil, 130-160 kg of char, 190-220 kg of steel, and 150-180kg of fiberglass. The char can be reprocessed into low-grade carbon black, which cannot be used in tire production. This technical difficulty is the major drawback against the implementation of a successful pyrolysis process.

All the products from the pyrolysis have a stable demand, however its operating cost is still not competitive. Nonetheless, a few small commercial plants have operated in the United States and in the UK. Eventually, if the supply of some of its output becomes restricted, pyrolysis may become an economical use for scrap tires, but this is not expected to happen in the near future.

2.6 Heat generation

More than 57 percent of a used tire weight is made of rubber and other organic materials. On average, the heat value of a used tire is around 33 MJ/kg. If a used passenger car tire weighs 7.2 kg, it contains at least 238 MJ of thermal energy, which can be useful in some dedicated facilities. The market value of coal with specific heat of 27 MJ/kg is about $45/ton, that is $1.60 for 1000 MJ. Assuming that the operating cost (other than fuel) of a heat generating facility using coal is the same as using whole tires, the incineration implies a valuation of $0.38 per used passenger tire. This section discusses two industries where used tires can be used as a coal substitute: thermoelectric plants and cement plants.

Tires are fed into the hearth of thermoelectric plants without any pretreatment or slicing. Once the system is operating, little additional investment is required, as long as it receives a constant supply of used tires.

This opportunity has been exploited by several plants. The Wolverhampton plant in the UK burns 94,000 tons of scrap tire to produce 144,000 MWh of electricity. Considering a (conservative) market price of $50 per MWh, each ton of scrap tire fed into this facility can generate $76 worth of electricity. Assuming an average of 138 passenger car tires per ton, this operation values them as no more than $0.55/unit. This process is an economically viable alternative for used tires that cannot be effectively retreaded, generating a large amount of by-products. Each ton of input (as tires) generates 287 kg of solid residue made of zinc oxide, ferrous slag and gypsum, each with a well-defined market.

In 1991 there was one 14-megawatt thermoelectric plant in California burning used tires. Three other plants, totaling 86 MW, were planned or under construction in the United States in the same year.[2] As a rule-of-thumb, these facilities produce 20 kWh of electric energy for each tire consumed. The energy generated is sold to the local utility company for rates ranging from 6 to 8.3 cents/kWh.

Under this valuation, an average used tire (commercial and passenger car sizes alike), contributes with a revenue of about $1.20-$1.66. Adjusting for the respective weights, this implies a contribution of $0.80-$1.10 per passenger car tire.

Feeding tires to Portland cement plants has the advantage that it does not generate any waste beyond what is usually generated by a standard cement production facility. Sliced tires are fed into the kiln with the other raw materials. The energy in the rubber provides the heat while the combustion residues are incorporated in the cement without compromising the product's quality. The ferrous material from the steel wire partially substitutes the large quantities of iron ore used in cement production. Several fuels are used in a cement plant, including coal, natural gas and oil. The rubber may provide roughly 20 percent of the heat required in the kiln, generally at a lower cost than the other fuels. The high temperature of combustion, around 1400°C, under appropriate supply of oxygen, ensures complete burnout of the organic material.

Several European cement plants have been burning used tires since the 1970s. The Heidelberg Zement plant in Germany consumes 50,000 tons/year, representing 20 percent of its need for fuel. A small number of North American plants consume used tires as fuel substitute. The Genstar Cement plant in California substitutes 25 percent of its energy needs with 20,000 tons/year of tire chips. Other plants have been operating successfully in the United States, Canada, Europe and Japan.

The Lafarge plant in France is the first experience in this country. It started with the capacity to burn 20,000 tons of used tires per year but this figure is not always reached, creating some difficulties in adjusting the process parameters to changes in the input composition. Moreover, the firm has difficulty obtaining a continuous stream of used tires, which underscores the importance of locating the plant at a location where used tires are easily available, such as near tire piles. _____

[2] Source: EPA (1991)

2.7 Single cycle tire recovery processes

Figure 1 shows the material flow, considered the main alternatives for tire reuse today. Landfill is included for completeness, although the material is not reused. We indicate bioreaction and pyrolysis with dashed lines, to remind that these technologies are not fully developed. However, these processes are worth considering because they might consume large amounts of used tires in the future. Some of the output ratios in this graph are:

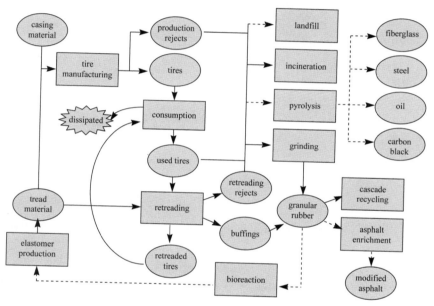

Figure 1: Material reclaim alternatives for used tires (today)

- Of all tires produced in a new-tire manufacturing process, about 3 percent are rejected.
- About 10 percent of a tire's original weight is dissipated in the road.
- About 10 percent of the used casings arriving at a retreading plant is rejected at one of the three inspection points (before buffing, at case repair, or after retreading).
- About 10 percent of a tire's original weight is removed during the buffing process.
- The pyrolysis of one ton of tires should produce 350-420 kg of oil, 130-160 kg of char, 190-220 kg of steel, 150-180 kg of fiberglass.

The diagram shows that tire retreading reduces the demand for casing material. Each tire coming out of a retreading plant is reusing a casing that would have to be manufactured otherwise. However, tire retreading increases the consumption of tread material because (1) the retreading procedure has higher reject ratio; (2) optimal retreading requires a reduction in tire life (the time between retreads is shorter than the single-usage tire life); and (3) the generation of significant amounts of ground rubber is unavoidable. Hence, an integrated tire reuse program should identify economical uses for ground rubber. In what follows we identify the value attributed to the casing whenever either alternative is adopted. Only the alternatives that can potentially absorb a significant amount of the used tires available today are considered.

2.8 The value of the casing in retreading

Formula 3 provided an approach for analyzing the value of a used core. If we apply this general formula to our example of used tires entering the retreading plant we get:

$$\text{Used Casing Value} = \text{Market Value of Retreaded Tire} * \text{Yield}$$
$$- (VMC + \text{Retreading Cost}) / \text{Partial Yield}$$
$$UCV = MVRT * Y - (VMC + RC)/Y_{insp} \tag{4}$$

,

The new tire in our calculations weighs 8 kg and is worth \$40. The retreaded tire is worth \$24. Figure 2 shows the material flow assuming that the tire is retreaded once, it has a second life and is finally disposed of. A fraction α of the used tires arriving at the retreading process is rejected during pre-inspection. Once the tread is vulcanized, retreaded tires are inspected and a fraction β is rejected. Hence, $Y = (1-\alpha)(1-\beta)$ and $Y_{insp} = (1-\beta)$.

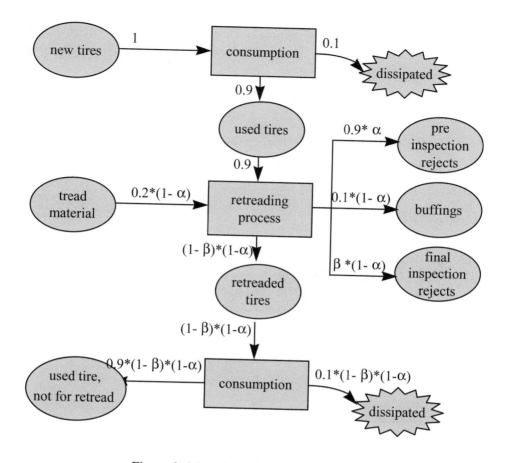

Figure 2: Material flow, single retreading

A used casing returning to the retreading facility provides an opportunity value that is exploited when it is effectively retreaded. The virgin material cost is given by equation (2). In a new tire, a tread weighs 2.5 kg. Appendix A estimates that it is worth $3.63. The tread material required for retreading a used tire weighs VMR = 0.2 * (1-α) * 8 kg = 1.52 kg. Adjusting for the different weights, VMC = $2.20. Assuming that α and β equal 5 percent, the yield is 0.9025. Apparently, the energy cost to vulcanize the tread-casing assembly, estimated as $0.10/tire, is approximately the same, whether the tire is produced new or retreaded. The retreading process includes other costly operations such as pre-inspection, casing preparation and buffing, nonexistent in the tire production process. These are labor-intensive operations. Based on interviews with professionals in the field, we estimate that these operations process on average 10-15 tires/man-hour, that is, no more than $7.00/tire. Applying these values in equation (4), it becomes:

$$UCV = MVRT * Y - (VMC + RC)/Y_{insp}$$
$$UCV = \$24 * 0.9025 - (\$2.20 + 7.10)/0.95$$
$$UCV = \$11.87$$

Hence, the retreading operation generates a contribution of $11.87 per casing. Alternatively, one may say that the opportunity value of each retreaded casing is $11.87.

This value should be read with caution because of a number of estimates that directly affect the result. As warned, it overlooks the transportation cost that the retreader might incur to collect used tires and the revenue from the sale of rubber crumbs or from tipping fees. More important, though, the operating yields are sensitive both to exogenous and endogenous causes. There is not much one can do about the exogenous changes in the yield. However, as the retreading technology progresses, the yield in the final inspection is expected to improve.

2.9 The value of the casing in heat generation

EPA (1993) evaluates the profitability of several ventures where used tires are burned as fuel. The intrinsic value of the used tire received at these facilities, drawing from some of the information available in that report, can be formu-lated as follows:

$$Profit = Tipping\ Fee + Revenue - Process\ Cost - Transport - Disposal$$
$$P = TF + R - PC - TR - D$$

In what follows, we use some of the numeric values estimated in that report to evaluate the material value of the used tire at the time of disposal, as a function of its application. Many of the incinerating operations benefit from tipping fees of up to $1.00 paid by tire dealers disposing of the used tires, which it is forced to collect from their customers. In some locations, a tire disposal fee is charged at the sale of each new tire; part of this resource is given as subsidy to the ventures that consume or recycle used tires, just as a tipping fee. In practice, power plants locate themselves close to large piles of tires landfilled in the past. The Filbin tire pile, outside the Oxford Energy's Modesto plant in California, guarantees a continuous operation for more than 10 years, along with the additional tires that the plant can collect during this period. Contrarily, the Lafarge cement plant in France depends on the incoming tires to fuel its operation. The difficulty in maintaining a continuous stream has made it difficult to tune the operation for a varying fuel mix. Hence, the income from tipping fees is not considered, since it may not be sustainable in the long run. For the same reason, transportation costs are overlooked, which is correct if regulation is strict and the tire owner is forced to dispose of the tires at approved locations.

Figure 3 shows the material flow leading to the incineration of used tires. The mineral by-products only occur in thermoelectric plants, since cement production would entirely absorb them. Clearly, incineration is an indirect recycling process: it treats the tires the same way as it treats the petroleum that originated it. Our analysis showed that each used passenger car tire may generate a revenue of $0.80 - $1.10 in a thermoelectric plant. Since the solid waste from this process can be commercialized, we assume that there is no disposal cost. EPA (1993) estimates that the operating cost of a thermoelectric plant equals $0.50 per average tire. Assuming activity-based costing (ABC), this figure is adjusted for the smaller size of the passenger car tire. Then, the operating cost of a thermoelectric plant becomes $0.33/tire. Substituting these values in equation (4) it becomes

$$P = TF + R - PC - TR - D$$
$$P = 0 + \$0.95 - \$0.33 - 0 - 0$$
$$P = \$0.62$$

In a cement plant, the revenue must be measured by the amount of traditional fuel that is diverted from the plant when tires are added to the mix. Earlier we indicated that the energy value of the tire, when compared to the price of coal, is $0.38/tire. Cement plants require that the tire is shredded before fed into the kiln. According to EPA (1993), this implies an additional cost of $0.18 - $0.24 per average tire. Adjusted for the size of the passenger car tire, this cost equals $0.12 - $0.16 per passenger car tire. Considering that there are no disposal costs, and assuming no transport or tipping fee, the used tire valuation in a cement plant is given by:

$$P = TF + R - PC - TR - D$$
$$P = 0 + \$0.38 - \$0.14 - 0 - 0$$
$$P = \$0.24$$

The analysis shows that when a used tire is incinerated, its intrinsic valuation is very low, which does not have to be true if the casing can be reused in a retreading process. Nonetheless, incinerating tires is the only commercial alternative to tire retreading today, especially for those tires that have been disposed of and are sitting in the huge landfills in Europe and the United States, or for those significantly damaged that cannot be retreaded. Next, we propose a "wiser" material flow for the tire industry: one that maximizes the recovery of the value-added still available in used tires at the time of disposal.

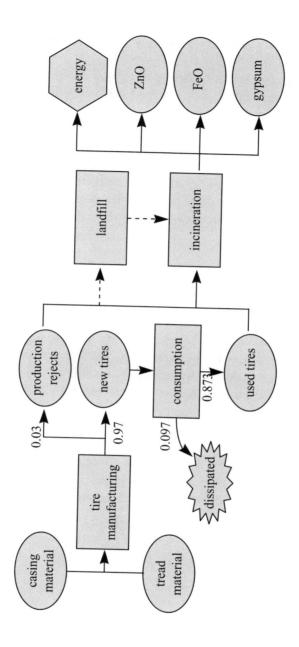

Figure 3: Material flow leading to used tire incineration

2.10 Multicycle tire recovery processes

Our vision of optimal tire utilization is to retread it a limited number of times until, eventually, it is shredded in the production of rubber crumbs or incinerated in a thermoelectric plant. If the bioreaction technology is fully developed, and the process can be implemented in an industrial scale, the rubber crumbs can be recycled into high-grade synthetic rubber in the production of new tires. Otherwise, the rubber crumbs can be added in the composition of asphalt, a process for which the technology still has to be perfected. At this date, none of these reuse methods can be fully evaluated because their respective technologies are not completely dominated. Meanwhile, heat generation is the best final use for tires.

Figure 4 balances the material flow of each consumed tire, assuming that each tire can be retreaded indefinitely, without loss in the length of tire life. In steady state, for 100 tires demanded in the market, 10 percent of the total weight is dissipated during consumption. Assuming that both the pre-inspection reject and the final inspection reject equal 5 percent, the system is in equilibrium if, for each 100 tires demanded in the market, 90.25 are retreaded and 9.75 are new. If each tire is allowed to be retreaded an unlimited number of times, the expected number of retreads per tire equals 90.25/9.75. Hence, on average, each tire is retreaded approximately 9 times before eventual rejection.

When the tire is originally produced, $25.36 is spent for an output worth $40. This represents a return on investment of 58 percent. If all tires follow the retreading cycle once— subject to being rejected at one of the inspection points —the expected revenue obtained from each casing equals

$$\$40 + 0.9025 * \$24 = \$61.66$$

The expected cost of manufacturing and retreading once each casing equals

$$\$25.36 + (\$2.20 + \$7.10) / 0.95 = \$35.15$$

Hence, the return on investment increases to 75 percent. Allowing unlimited retreading, the expected revenue from each casing from the time it is first manufactured until it is eventually rejected equals

$$\$40 + \frac{90.25 * \$24}{9.75} = \$262.15$$

Likewise, the expected cost of manufacturing and retreading each casing an unlimited number of times, until eventually rejected, equals

$$\$25.36 + \frac{90.25 * (\$2.20 + \$7.10)/0.95}{9.75} = \$115.98$$

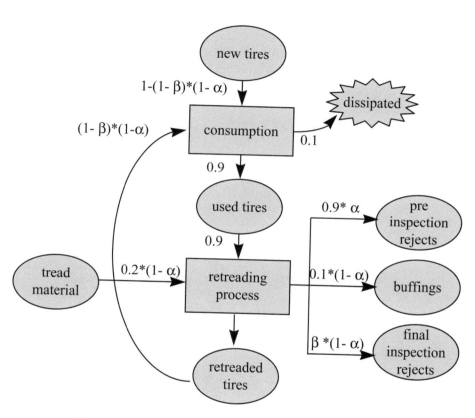

Figure 4: Material flow, unlimited retreading per casing

This represents an expected return on investment of 126 percent. If n is the maximum number of retreads that a casing is allowed to receive, it is simple to show that the expected revenue and the expected cost per core is given by the expressions

Expected Revenue (*n*) = New Product Revenue
+ Value of Remanufacture Product
* Expected Number Retreads(*n*)   (5)

$$ER(n) = NP + RV * \frac{Y - Y^{n+1}}{1 - Y}$$

Expected Revenue (*n*) = New Product Cost
+ Remanufactuing Cost in each cycle
* Expected Number Retreads(*n*)   (6)

$$ER(n) = NP + RC * \frac{Y - Y^{n+1}}{1 - Y}$$

where $Y = (1-\alpha)*(1-\beta)$ is the expected total yield. Substituting different values of *n* in the expressions with the values of new tire revenue and cost and re-treaded tire revenue and cost, the graph in Figure 5 is generated. Consequently, the net remanufacturing gain (NRG) after n cycles equals

$$NRG = NP - NC + (RV - RC) * \frac{Y - Y^{n+1}}{1 - Y} \qquad (7)$$

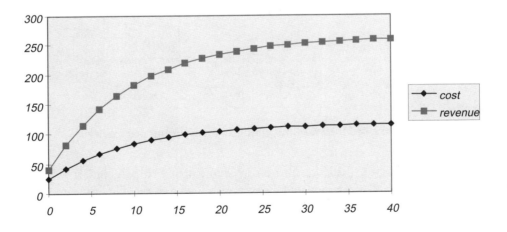

Figure 5: Expected revenue and cost when the casing is allowed to be retreaded *n* times, assuming that durability is not affected by the number of retreads

In practice, the tire cannot be retreaded more than a limited number of times. The pre-inspection rejection rate tends to increase with the number of times that the tire is retreaded, because of the fatigue of the casing structure. In order to ensure that a large number of tires pass the pre-inspection process, practitioners reduce the time between retreading as the number of retreads increase. Suppose that a tire is retreaded three times before it is finally disposed of. Some in the industry use the rule-of-thumb that the length of the three tire lives should be in the proportion 1:0.8:0.7. If the retread life length is reduced, one should expect that its value is reduced in the same proportion. Hence, for analytical convenience, we propose a recursive rule for estimating the life length of a retread such that the rejection rate is not altered:

$$RR_n = Z * RR_{n-1}$$
$$RR_0 = NTR$$

where Z is the rate of life reduction at each retread event. Under this assumption, equation (5) becomes:

$$ER(n) = RR_0 + Y * RR_1 + ... + Y^n * RR_n \qquad (8)$$

$$= \sum_{i=0}^{n} Y^i RR_i = NTR * \sum_{i=0}^{n} Z^i Y^i$$

$$ER(n) = NTR * \frac{1 - Y^{n+1} Z^{n+1}}{1 - YZ}$$

Notice that for each additional retread, one should compare the expected additional revenue with the expected additional cost. The optimal policy allows retreading up to n times if and only if the expected additional cost of retreading n times is less than the expected additional revenue. Moreover, the expected additional cost of retreading $n+1$ times is greater than the expected additional revenue. This translates to

$$\begin{cases} Y^n Z^n NTR > Y^n RC \\ Y^{n+1} Z^{n+1} NTR < Y^{n+1} RC \end{cases}$$

The solution to this problem is given by the integer n satisfying

$$n = \left\lfloor \frac{\log(RC/NTR)}{\log(Z)} \right\rfloor \tag{9}$$

where $\lfloor X \rfloor$ equals the largest integer less than or equal to X. Applying the value of retread cost (RC = $9.79) and the new tire revenue (NTR = $40) with several values of Z in equation 8, the recommended number of retreads for each tire is about four or five times, depending on the rate of reduction of the time between retreads (Z) required for maintaining the yield rate at a constant level (Y). The results are in the grid below:

Z	0.7	0.71	0.72	0.73	0.74	0.75	0.76	0.77	0.78	0.79	0.8
n	3	4	4	4	4	4	5	5	5	5	6

Notice the simplicity of equation (8). The information it requires is easily available to the fleet manager or to the tire lessor. For the sake of illustration, let Z = 0.78. Then, the tire is retreaded five times with respective life lengths in the proportion

1:0.78:0.60:0.48:0.37:0.29

Using equations (6) and (7), the expected revenue is $118.67, and the expected cost is $61.74, which represents a return on investment of 92 percent. The net remanufacturing gain will then be equal to:

$$NRG = NP \sum_{i=0}^{n} Y^i Z^i - RC \sum_{i=0}^{n} Y^i$$

$$\Rightarrow NRG = NP \frac{1 - Y^{n+1} Z^{n+1}}{1 - YZ} - RC \frac{1 - Y^{n+1}}{1 - Y} \tag{10}$$

2.11 The economics of remanufacturing multimodule products

The determination of optimal recovery policies of multimodular products is harder to generalize because each module will usually wear differently in the field. Without loss of generality, most industrial products result from the assembly of several modules, including

> a casing or a frame
> functional module
> functional connectors (cables, hoses, pipes, belts, chain
> structural connectors (nuts, bolts, welds, rivets)

Each module has a similar architecture, including a number of assemblies, functional connectors and structural connectors. The functional modules are the most critical when we design the remanufacturing process, because these modules are usually the ones with highest value-added. Therefore, these are the ones where the designer should dedicate most of his ingenuity. For example, consider a room air conditioner, composed of eight main components:

1. compressor
2. electric motor
3. external air fan
4. internal air blower
5. external air condenser
6. cold evaporator
7. electric controls
8. outer box

A sustainable recovery process for each of these components can be developed separately, especially if the product was designed for the environment. However, the recovery yields and the ideal recovery cycles will certainly differ. It is an obvious example of when a local optimization will not lead to a global optimization. In order to extract the most value from used air conditioning units, the manager has to identify a recovery procedure that extends the life of individual parts as well as the value of the global unit in each disassembly-reassembly operation. The remanufacturer has to standardize the recovery procedure as much as possible such that, it is hoped, all units are disassembled to recover the same prespecified set of subassemblies or modules. Once the recovery is completed, these subassemblies and modules are stored in a common inventory where they become available for the reassembly phase of the

343

remanufacturing process. This whole procedure comes with a significant challenge: each subassembly in the bill-of-materials has a different recovery yield, recovery costs and life lengths.

The recovery cost of an air conditioner with m modules is a function of the cost (K) to disassemble and separate all modules, the cost (RC_i) to recover individual modules, the probability (Y_i) that the item can be effectively recovered, and the replacement cost (P_i) of that part, in case it cannot be recovered. The expression is

$$EC = K + \sum_i^m Y_i RC_i - \sum_i^m (1 - Y_i) P_i \qquad (11)$$

Likewise, the value of the recovered air conditioner is a function of the replacement value of individual modules and the value-added (VA) associated with the assembly process. It can be represented as

$$ER = VA + \sum_i^m P_i \qquad (12)$$

Comparing these expressions, net remanufacturing gain can be expressed as

$$NRG = VA - K + \sum_i^m Y_i (P_i - RC_i) \qquad (13)$$

Each individual module recovery should be less costly than that module's replacement cost ($RC_i < P_i$). Modules that don't satisfy this condition should be discarded rather than remanufactured. In addition, the NRG is a function of the difference between the value-added associated with the recovered product's assembly and the disassembly-reassembly cost ($VA - K$). If this difference is not positive, remanufacturing is probably not the recovery process indicated for this product. If the market permits, however, these modules could be recovered for the secondary market of replacement parts.

As the product matures, the parameters in equation (2) may change. Typically, the recovery yield decreases over time. The more cycles that the module goes through, even the most robust components will accumulate some fatigue, and the probability that the module is recoverable decreases. Therefore, the remanufacturing manager should track the recovery yield and the recovery costs to ensure that the process remains economically viable. Further investment in design for the environment will allow easier disassembly and extended life-lengths, improving the net remanufacturing gain.

3. Economics of Remanufacturing Logistics

Remanufacturing also requires special transportation and handling for the used goods. This could require an organizational infrastructure even more complex than that for new products. Reverse logistics is the term that has been given to the process that retrieves products and components from customers and returns them to a reprocessing facility. Once the user has decided to trade in or retire a durable good, the existence of an efficient reverse logistic system is necessary if remanufacturing is intended. This process can involve intermediate collection points and the processing facility, which can be the original plant or some other location.

There are a number of important management decisions in designing and operating the reverse logistics system. They appear very much like distribution logistics decisions, but may require a finer geographical partition. It is known that the distribution system for both consumer and industrial markets is quite complex. The collection systems can be even more so. They must take into account the need to achieve economies of scale in transporting and storing a large number of products and components in different wear states.

The remainder of this section contains a discussion of some major logistic issues and their effect on product remanufacturing. We discuss the development of the transportation and storage network that feeds the remanufacturing operation, the handling and packaging required to satisfy a variety of product models and wear states, and the selection of disassembly facility locations.

3.1 Transportation and storage

Researchers have tackled many of the scheduling and inventory management problems appearing in forward logistics. One very difficult problem is to identify the most efficient distribution network, the number and location of central and regional warehouses, and all related parameters.

With these challenges in mind, the remanufacturer devises a reverse logistics scheme to collect the used items needed for its products and targeted market. In many cases, it is appropriate to develop this collection network separate from the distribution system. The transportation network must match the availability and location of used products (called *cores*) and the demand for remanufactured parts. It must also reflect the remanufacturing strategy adopted by the firm. For example, the network might need to serve decentralized disassembly activities because of low economies of scale in many of the remanufacturing tasks.

In some cases, the transportation system achieves higher efficiency by aggregating the reverse flow of several products to several remanufacturers of similar products from several sources. One example of a multifirm network is the one developed for the collection of used "ready-to-use" cameras in Europe. In each country or geographic region in Europe, a different OEM (original equipment manufacturer) coordinates the collection of used cameras from photo development laboratories to an independent warehouse where the products are sorted by brand and model. Subsequently, the sorted lots are sent to the respective companies for remanufacturing. In France, the separation of used cameras is performed under the auspices of a philanthropic organization. Once sorted, lots of disassembled or entire cameras are shipped to the respective manufacturers according to their brands. The OEMs have had some camera parts returning to the assembly line up to four times since they were originally produced.

Another example of a multiproduct network is the system developed by IBM for the collection of used computers in Europe. IBM business units in different countries have disassembly facilities to collect used IBM products in their geographic region. They perform a first level disassembly of all products containing reusable components, and deliver them to the corresponding subsidiary for the appropriate recycling or remanufacturing process. The rest of the product, with lower reuse value, is shredded to berecyled locally. With this procedure, IBM avoids large shipping costs by transporting only the most valuable components across long distances.

These examples of reverse logistics systems were developed to suit the firms' remanufacturing strategies and currently available resources. Used equipment has little or no value before the recovery process occurs. Hence, it is crucial to assure that the volume and the quality of the used material is worth the transportation cost. By aggregating the collection of ready-to-use cameras from different manufacturers, it is easier to achieve economies of scale in all geographic regions. By separating the valuable components of used computers before shipping, IBM assures that only worthy material is transported.

3.2 Handling and packaging

Since the firm has already developed a distribution system, it is reasonable to ask why not use the return trip as the backbone of the collection system? Coupling the forward and the reverse logistic system is appealing. However, the forward distribution operation has to fit the reverse logistics needs. In reverse logistics, the volume of returned goods can be quite variable over time and the variability of their physical state increases handling complexity. Moreover, there can be more locations for retrieving used products than for delivering new ones. Finally, the destination of the returned used good might differ from the original production site.

Usually, forward distribution is better suited for handling large volumes of the same item at each OEM, transportation and receiving node in the network. Hence, they may have difficulty achieving economies of scale dealing with the diversity of used items returned for remanufacturing. In addition, those firms that have tried to couple reverse with forward logistics have encountered a few barriers. For instance:

a) **Handling process:** The operator may not have the appropriate culture or incentive to handle used products correctly. Used products are at least as fragile as the new ones. If the used product is handled without care, some of the value still remaining may be lost inadvertently.

b) **Loading and unloading:** Transport operators are organized to provide one-way service. Truck loading and unloading procedures are more complex if, at each stop, there is material being loaded and unloaded.

c) **Delivery location:** The point of delivery of the new product and the point of collection of the used product (even at a single site) are not necessarily the same. In such circumstances, the material handling would have to be reorganized in order to allow an efficient collection procedure.

d) **Substitution process:** The delivery time of the new product is not necessarily the same as the time that the old product is ready for disposal. Machines that depend on complex installation or setup procedures have to be installed and operational before the old machine is decommissioned.

e) **Retirement process:** The customer may decide not to retire the old product immediately after the acquisition of the new one. The product discontinuation may be gradual, and the retirement decision is deferred to "sometime in the future." For instance, the buyer may prefer to experience a momentary capacity expansion, even if this is not economically efficient.

We elaborate on these issues here. Product variety is much greater in reverse logistics than in forward logistics. Even if collection and distribution are coupled, and only one product family of a single manufacturer is transported, the product variety during collection remains greater than during distribution. If for no other reason, this occurs due to the short duration of the product life cycles.

For instance, suppose that a manufacturer adopts a certain design for about two years. Once in the market, the customer uses the product for five to ten years before disposal. This implies that the new product is handled by the forward logistic function during the first two years, but the reverse logistic handles the used product during seven years thereafter. If this process repeats itself for several product generations, the reverse logistics system deals with 3.5-times as many models as the forward logistics system. Hence, as long as there is no loss in the system (all used units are returned) and different customers use similar products for different lengths of time, the reverse logistics provider handles more variety than the forward logistics provider.

Handling used products during transport to the collection warehouse and stocking them with other goods bound to the same remanufacturer adds further difficulty. If the used product is handled roughly, some of the value still remaining may be destroyed. The logistics provider has to recognize that the used product is inherently more fragile than the new product, because its structural integrity may have been compromised during use. Hence, a handling system must be developed in order to avoid further deterioration of the used product and to protect the remaining value.

When the forward logistics provider receives the merchandise, it is appropriately packaged, ready for distribution. The situation is quite different at the time of collecting the used product at the customer's site. Generally, the user does not bother to package the used good when it is retired. If the contractor does not do it, the product is transported without protection. Hence, it may be necessary to develop a packaging system that can be used by the logistics contractor at the customer site, before moving the product. It may be as simple as having the reverse logistics contractor bring packaging material to the customer's site and package the used product.

In some cases, a new package may have to be designed for the return trip. The package has to satisfy some basic constraints like content protection, high re-usability and low cost. In addition to these, there may be other constraints specific to the remanufacturing environment. The package has to be simple to use in the field and compatible with many product models. This simplicity is required to prepare swiftly the used product for the return trip to the plant. Since the product variety is likely to be large, the packaging must be suffi-ciently flexible to deal with a diversity of models. There are different ways to deal with the packaging problem:

a) Design a comprehensive handling, packaging and storage system, ca-pable of handling many product models without loss of efficiency.

b) "Internalize" the product, through leasing contracts with pre-defined contract lengths, or through comprehensive maintenance contracts, in-ducing the customer to return the product in good physical form at the end of a predetermined time.

c) Reduce the variability of product life by imposing the product's retire-ment date or creating incentives for fixed-time replacement.

None of these solutions is a cure-all, and all of them require special attention. All of them have been used in different instances, however. Flexible packages are easier to develop for lightweight and sturdy goods, such as printer car-tridges, beer bottles and ready-to-use cameras. Many firms place large elec-tronic equipment on pallets and wrap them with plastic film for collection. Xerox manages the return of its large photocopiers by means of leasing con-tracts. This ensures that returning machines have approximately the same age, creating no surprises to the transport contractor or to the remanufacturing shop. Occasionally, some firms develop take back schemes to promote the sales of newer models. A firm may adopt this strategy on a permanent basis to balance the volume of returned products, reduce the variance of the mix, and improve the handling and recovery operations.

3.3 Disassembly facility location

Once the collection system is in place and the sorting capabilities developed, the next activity is disassembly. One of the critical questions for this activity is where it should be done. One obvious choice is at the processing facility to which the material is brought after collection. For widely distributed products, this could mean a large number of disassembly facilities, all requiring skilled labor. At the other extreme, bringing all the items back to a central facility or the original manufacturing site might increase transportation costs. Also, adding disassembly activities to an assembly plant could so complicate the work environment that processing efficiencies would be lost.

The question of where to disassemble is similar to the question of plant or warehouse location. There are trade-offs between transportation, facility and processing costs that vary with the number and locations of the facilities. Observations of empirical decisions provide mixed results. Some firms, like Pitney Bowes, contract with third-party providers for disassembly. They have determined that the costs for transportation, labor and processing are greater inside the company than outsourcing with a third party, where other manufacturers can help build the contractor's volume to provide economies scale for everyone. Creative ways of collaborating with similar companies, competitors and third-party providers can help in developing an efficient system.

4. Summary

Two clear themes run through this chapter. The first is concerned with the economical aspects. The second has to do with the logistics requirements for effective remanufacturing. For both, sound decision making and management oversight is required. General guidelines are proposed for the development of logistics systems that return the used products and disassemble them. The development of these systems, either independently or in concert with other firms, is a prerequisite to effective material recovery. We gave some examples of independent, collaborative and third-party solutions.

For the economic aspects, the class of remanufacturing problems that concern rebuilding a core for a certain number of cycles, and then replacing it with a new product was considered. Typical of this type of problem is the retreading of truck tires or the repainting of jetliners. A general expression for the value of a core was provided and the trade off between the rate of deterioration of the core, the cost of remanufacturing, and the cost of a new product was evaluated. For a particular set of assumptions concerning these parameters, a closed-form expression for the determination of the optimal number of economically viable cycles of core remanufacturing was presented.

A specific example from the tire retread industry was provided. Applying the expression to the industry data indicated that the number of viable cycles was generally longer than the number observed in practice.

One clear conclusion comes from this and other work in the remanufacturing area. It is possible to extend profitably the overall product life cycles for products that would ordinarily go to the landfill. It does take creativity in the design of the products and the logistics systems. The orchestrated adoption of design for the environment, extended product durability and reverse logistics capabilities will improve the parameters driving the economics of remanufacturing operations. In so doing, the firm will create new profit opportunities and will lead us closer to the elusive goal of sustainability.

Acknowledgment

The authors wish to thank Enno Siemsen, whose comments that helped improve the content of this chapter.

References

Ayres, R.U., G. Ferrer and T. Van Leynseele (1997), Eco-Efficiency, Asset Recovery and Remanufacturing. *European Management Journal,* Vol. 15, No. 5, 557-574.

Biddle, D. (1993), Recycling for Profit: the New Green Business Frontier. *Harvard Business Review* (November-December 1993): 145-156.

Corbett, C.J. and L.N. Van Wassenhove (1993), The Green Fee: Internalizing and Operationalizing Environmental Issues. *California Management Review* 36:1 (Fall 1993), 116-135.

Ferrer, G. (1997), The Economics of Tire Remanufacturing. In *Resources, Conservation and Recycling* 19, 221-255.

Ferrer, G. and R.U. Ayres (2000), The Impact of Remanufacturing in the Economy. In *Ecological Economics* 32, 413-429.

Ferrer, G. (2001), On the Widget Remanufacturing Operation. Forthcoming in *European Journal of Operational Research*.

Ferrer, G. and C. Whybark (2000), Communicating Developments in Product Recovery Activities: Processes, Objectives and Performance Measures. *The Handbook of Environmentally Conscious Manufacturing*, edited by Chris Madu, Kluwer Academic Publishers.

Ferrer, G. and C. Whybark (2000), From Garbage to Goods: Successful Remanufacturing Systems and Skills. *Business Horizons* 43 (6 - November 2000)

Ferrer, G. and V.D.R. Guide, Jr. (2002), Remanufacturing – Case Studies and State-of-the-Art. Forthcoming in *Handbook of Industrial Ecology*, Robert U. Ayres and Leslie Ayres, Editors.

Graedel, T. E. and B.R. Allenby (1996), *Design for Environment*. Prentice-Hall, Upper Saddle River, NJ.

Krikke, H. (1998), *Recovery Strategies and Reverse Logistic Network Design*. Thesis, University of Twente, Enschede, The Netherlands.

Lund, R.T. (1983), Remanufacturing: United States Experience and Implications for Developing Nations. Washington, DC, The World Bank.

Ottman, J. (1997), *Green Marketing: Opportunity for Innovation*. NTC Business Books, Chicago, IL.

Romine, R.A., M.F. Romine, and L. Snowden-Swan (1995), Microbial Processing of Waste Tire Rubber. Presented at the meeting of the American Chemical Society on October 17-20.

Sarkis, J. and A. Rasheed (1995), Greening the manufacturing function. *Business Horizons*. Sep. 38:5, 17-28.

Sharfman, M., R.T. Ellington and M. Meo (1997), The next step in becoming 'green': Life-cycle oriented environmental management. *Business Horizons*. May/June 40:3, 13-22.

Thierry, M., M. Salomon, J. Van Nunen and L. Van Wassenhove (1995), Strategic Issues in Product Recovery Management. *California Management Review* 37(2 - Winter 1995): 114-135.

Contacts:

Geraldo Ferrer
Operations, Technology and Inovation Management Area
Kenan-Flager Business School
The University of North Carolina at Chapel Hill
McColl Building - Campus Box 3490
Chapel Hill, NC 27599-3490

Email: geraldo_ferrer@unc.edu

D. Clay Whybark
Operations, Technology and Inovation Management Area
Kenan-Flager Business School
The University of North Carolina at Chapel Hill
McColl Building - Camp7s Box 3490
Chapel Hill, NC 27599-3490

Email: clay_whybark@unc.edu

Managing Product Returns for Remanufacturing

V. Daniel R. Guide, Jr., Pennsylvania State University, USA
Luk N. Van Wassenhove, INSEAD, France

1. Introduction

Recoverable product environments are environmentally conscious systems where products are returned from end-users to be reused. Reuse options include value-added recovery (i.e., repair and remanufacture) and material recovery (i.e., recycling) (Thierry et al., 1995). These options prevent waste by diverting materials from landfills and conserve natural resources (energy and materials). Recoverable product systems are also profitable. In the US there are over 70,000 remanufacturing firms with total sales of $53 billion (USD) (Lund, 1998). These firms directly employ 350,000 workers and average profit margins exceed 20 percent (Nasr et al., 1998).

In the European Union a number of recent legislative acts, known as producer responsibility laws, require manufacturers to collect and reuse their products. The requirements for firms doing business in the EU are clear, and these regulations may also act as entry barriers for firms not aware of the changes required for reverse logistics activities. Firms designing products for reuse may have a competitive advantage in lower costs and enhanced market share due to the growing consumer awareness and preferences for environmentally conscious products (Kodak, 1999; Xerox, 1999).

Several authors have cited a need for careful economic analysis of the potential benefits of environmental activities (Reinhardt, 1999; Esty and Porter, 1998). Firms are often encouraged to offer environmentally friendly products (i.e., recoverable products) as a demonstration of corporate citizenship. However, this may prove to be an unrealistic expectation since a rational firm will only engage in profitable ventures, those that increase shareholder wealth. Further, it may not be reasonable for every original equipment manufacturer (OEM) to engage in reuse activities. The fastest growing firms in electronics and telecommunications may need all the available capital to invest in core activities. In addition, the stock market is expecting high returns from these sectors, and firms may require high return on capital expenditures or favorable economic value analyses (EVA®). It may be rational for an OEM not to engage in reuse activities, to subcontract the reuse operations, or encourage start-up corporate spin-offs to assume the responsibility. The decision whether or not to engage in reuse activities directly, indirectly, or not at all should be driven by a thorough economic analysis of the costs and benefits of such a program. In the event that recovery is mandated, a careful economic analysis is required to determine the best way to do the recovery.

Despite the potential profitability of reuse and the legislative requirements, there are no integrated decision frameworks to advise decision makers about the economic viability of various reuse options. We seek, in part, to develop the foundation for analyzing the potential profitability of reuse options. Specifically, we develop a framework for analyzing the profitability of reuse activities, and show how the management of product returns influences operational requirements. The framework is based on our experiences with companies that presently use an ad hoc trial and error approach for analyzing the potential of reuse activities. We intend the framework to serve as a structured method for examining reuse alternatives, and to serve as the foundation for further research that would lead to explicit relationships and perhaps closed-form optimizations within our framework.

A firm operating a recoverable product system relies on the return of used products as the basic input (raw material) to a reuse system (repair, remanufacturing, cannibalization, recycling). The return rate of used products has been regarded as an exogenous process that cannot be controlled by the firm. We hypothesize that return rates may be influenced by actions taken by the firm, and this decision, when appropriate, should be a conscious choice. Product acquisition management addresses several essential issues (see Figure 1). First, we intend to show that product acquisition management determines whether reuse is a value-creation activity for a specific firm. Second, if reuse activities are profitable, to maximize, revenue the appropriate method for managing product returns should be selected. Third, operational issues, such as facility design, product planning and control policies, and inventory policies, are dependent on the method selected to manage product returns. Fourth, product acquisition management activities help show the potential economic benefits of identifying and developing new markets for reused product, and to balance the return rates with market demands. We will focus on the first three issues in this research and recognize

EVA® is a registered trademark of Stern Stewart & Co.

that while the development of new markets is crucial to the success of product reuse, it is not the focus of our present research.

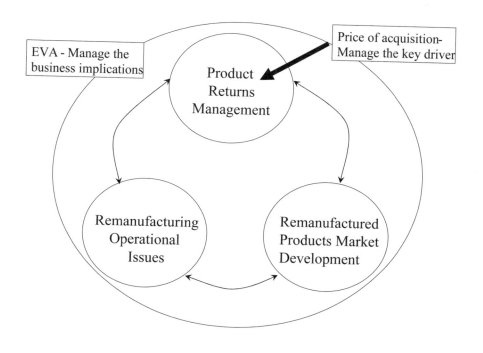

Figure 1: Product Acquisition Management

This view represents a fundamentally new approach to the economics and operations of reuse activities. Traditionally, research efforts have focused on ways to minimize the loss associated with reuse; e.g., cost minimization models. This traditional view of reuse activities requires that firms seek to create new markets for used products, but passively accept product returns. We propose a structured method for valuing the potential economic attractiveness of reuse activities.

In this manuscript we focus on the concept of product acquisition management, and how this concept may be used in several contexts. Product acquisition management is a key input to assessing the potential economic attractiveness of reuse activities, and as a foundation for operational planning and control activities. We reject the idea that firms must passively accept product returns, and show that a system for control exists. The idea that a firm may control the quality, quantity, and timing of product returns has a profound impact on the understanding of how reuse systems may be profitable in some cases. We also show that this new approach leads to many research issues that remain unanswered.

We begin with a literature review in the following section. In subsequent sections, we present an overview of the product returns process and choices, a detailed discussion of product acquisition management activities, and a discussion of research needs.

2. Research Literature

We refer the reader to Fleischmann et al. (1997), and Guide et al. (2000) for complete literature reviews. We note that much of the previous research concerned with reuse activity focuses on a particular functional area or activity, such as network design (Krikke, 1998; Krikke et al., 1999; Spengler et al., 1997), shop floor control (Guide and Srivastava, 1998; Guide et al., 1997), or inventory control (Inderfurth, 1997; van der Laan, 1997; van der Laan et al., 1999). No published research explicitly considers the problem of managing or controlling products returns. The research literature has a number of restrictive assumptions. First, all of the models assume that product returns are an exogenous process. An exogenous process, in this case, refers to the assumption that return rates, quality, and timing are all outside the direct control of the firm. The firm passively accepts all returns, and the returns process itself is a black box operation. Second, when product returns are explicitly considered, return rates are assumed independent of sales rates. The sole exception to this assumption is Kelle and Silver (1989), who assume a time-lagged return rate. Finally, although several authors (Fleischmann et al., 1997; Guide et al., 2000) have called for a more integrated approach to logistics planning, no such research has appeared.

Under the classic assumption of exogenous, uncontrollable return rates and quality, there is research showing that remanufacturing operations are more complex to plan, manage, and control than traditional manufacturing operations (Guide and Srivastava, 1998; Guide et al., 1997). The primary reason for this complexity is the high degree of variability in the quality of used products that serve as raw materials for the production process. This variability makes the tasks of materials planning, capacity planning, scheduling, and inventory management complex and difficult to manage. Managing this high amount of variability is expensive for the firm since decoupling the system requires higher investments in materials, equipment, and labor.

We also note there is evidence that some remanufacturing firms actively control the quality, quantity, and timing of product returns (Guide 2000). This evidence shows that the classic assumption that a firm must passively accept product returns with no ability to influence returns quality, quantity, and timing is not valid. Given the high cost of complexity, it is logical that firms have developed methods for controlling the product returns process. In the following section we discuss product returns and provide detailed examples of product acquisition management.

3. Product Returns

In the past, the EU has been a diverse set of differentiated markets driven by many different cultures and tastes. This market segmentation has made product reuse difficult because of the lack of volume of standardized consumer goods. However, with the adoption of the Euro as a common currency, unified markets are rapidly developing across the EU in some sectors that are not cultural, e.g., consumer electronics (PCs, cellular telephones, personal stereos), and automobiles. The consumer electronics markets have the greatest growth potential for reuse activities since volumes are high and product life cycles are increasingly short. In general, several trends have made producer responsibility legislation increasingly popular. Millions of products are produced annually with shorter product life cycles, and this leads to a huge number of obsolete products entering the waste stream. The final disposition of these products poses an enormous problem for the environment, and a large potential stream of used products for reuse operations.

Legislation in the United States tends to encourage, rather than mandate, reuse activities. The recycling industry in the United States is an example of such a system where legislation encourages reuse via tax credits, or municipalities assume collection responsibilities. However, individual states have banned the landfill of cathode-ray tubes and some electronics equipment, and the number of states banning specific types of products from landfill is expected to grow.

There are two primary systems for obtaining used products from the end-users for reuse: the *waste stream* system and the *market-driven* system. The waste stream system relies on diverting discarded products from landfills by making producers responsible for the collection and reuse of their products. A market-driven system relies on financial incentives to motivate end-users to return their products to a firm specializing in the reuse of those products.

In the waste stream system, firms passively accept all product returns from the waste stream. Unable to control the quality of returns, firms often consider the large volumes of returns a nuisance, and naturally tend to focus on the development of low-cost reverse logistics networks. The result of the product returns mandates and policies is a large uncontrolled volume of used products flowing back in increasing volumes to the original equipment manufacturers. Firms are ill-prepared to cope with the complexity of product returns and end-of-life disposition, and are seeking ways to minimize their losses.

In the European Union (EU) a number of recent legislative acts, known as producer responsibility laws, require manufacturers to assume responsibility for the end-of-life disposition of their products (Guide et al., 2000). For instance, in Germany, the Commercial and Industrial Waste Avoidance and Management Act (KrW/AbfG) requires that the producer is responsible for the end-of-life disposition of their products, including reuse and recovery. The Ministerial Bill of Ordinance on Disposal of Information Devices (IT-Geräte-V) is an agreement whereby manufacturers of electrical and electronic equipment (specifically information technology devices) take responsibility for the recovery and end-of-life disposition of their products (Gotzel et al., 1999). In The Netherlands, the electronics waste act has similar requirements. Some legislative acts may require the end- user to return the used product to a collection system for reuse. The used car ordinance in Germany requires that the last owner of an automobile deliver it to a collection center (Gotzel et al., 1999). The requirements for firms doing business in the EU are clear, and these regulations may act as entry barriers for firms not aware of the changes required for reverse logistics activities.

In a market-driven system end-users are motivated to return end-of-life products by financial incentives, such as deposit systems, credit toward a new unit, or cash paid for a specified level of quality. Firms are able to control the level of quality of returned products since acceptance of returns is conditioned by standards. Market-driven systems are common in the United States because of the profitability of remanufacturing (Guide, 2000). Firms using a market-driven approach for product returns focus mainly on high value industrial products (Guide, 2000; Nasr et al., 1998). However, there are exceptions; the system for remanufacturing automotive parts has been well established since the 1920s. As the auto parts industry illustrates, there is also money to be made with high-volume, low-value products (see Kodak's [1999] description of its single-use camera program for another example of high-volume, low-value products). A growing number of firms are interested in the consumer electronics segment, and this is the largest growth area in remanufacturing in the United States.

A combination of the market-driven and waste stream approaches is also possible. Product returns may be mandated or encouraged by legislative acts, but firms may still encourage the returns of products in known condition by offering incentives. A firm using a pure waste stream approach or a pure market-driven approach will have facilities with different operational characteristics and managerial control problems.

In contrast, the two systems result in extremely different views of reuse activities. In the waste stream system, cost reduction is encouraged and the fundamental issue is to minimize the amount of money the firm loses. The market-driven system views reuse as a profitable economic proposition. Past research has focused almost exclusively on the waste stream approach to reuse activities and it is logical that the modeling efforts are aimed at cost minimization. In the following section, we examine the operational implications of the two pure product acquisition management approaches.

4. Impact of Product Returns on Operational Characteristics

The waste stream and market-driven approaches lead to facilities with different operational characteristics. In the waste stream approach, Case 1 (Figure 2), the first significant difference is the lower quality, on average, of used products arriving to the facility. These used products also have large variances in quality, quantity, and timing. Since there is no effort made to control the incoming quality of used products, additional facility space is required to store, sort, and grade the returned products. A large number of units will need to be disposed of since a high proportion of units will not be recoverable for remanufacturing. Incoming products to the remanufacturing shops will have high variability in routings and in required processing times. This high variability will lead to long queues at work centers, unpredictable lead times, and low throughput.

The overall high levels of variability make this remanufacturing facility diffi-cult to plan, control, and manage (Guide and Srivastava, 1998; Guide et al., 1997). Operating expenses will be greater since additional labor and machine costs are required. The facility will most likely resemble the process-based, classic repair job shop with jumbled product flows. These types of shops are difficult to plan, manage, and control.

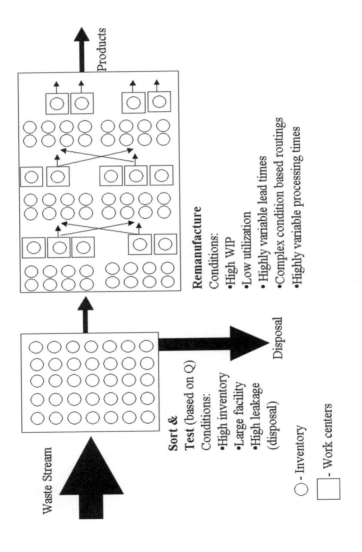

Figure 2 - Case 1: Waste Stream

A firm actively controlling the incoming level of quality, Case 2, by using a market-driven approach (see Figure 3), has several significant operational benefits. Products will be sorted and graded before entering the remanufacturer's possession. The size of the facility reserved for arriving used products will be less than the waste stream case since products will be tested to ensure that quality standards are met. Lower amounts of used product inventory will be needed and disposal costs will be decreased. The variability of routings and processing times required will be reduced because of the higher levels of incoming quality. This lower variability will result in shorter queues, better machine and labor utilization, and more predictable flow times. Throughput for the facility will increase with no additional machines or labor, and machine and/or labor costs may be lower for higher volumes of output. The facility layout appears as a flowshop, with dominant product flows made possible by more standardized routings. When a market-driven approach is used, the overall task of planning, controlling, and managing a facility is simplified. This should lead to a more productive and cost-effective system.

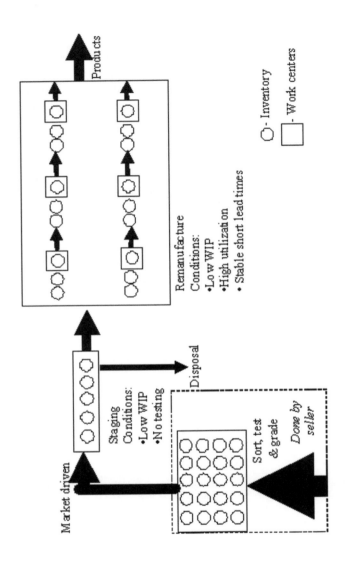

Products

Remanufacture
Conditions:
• Low WIP
• High utilization
• Stable short lead times

Disposal

Staging
Conditions:
• Low WIP
• No testing

Market driven

Sort, test & grade

Done by seller

◯ - Inventory

▢ - Work centers

364

We suggest that market forces will drive companies to evolve management systems that allow greater control. This natural evolution is shown in the example that follows, referring to a cellular telephone remanufacturer, that has developed a method for obtaining used products that allows greater control over the profitability of their operations.

5. Product Returns at ReCellular, Inc.

ReCellular, Inc. is a third-party remanufacturer of mobile telephones located in the United States. The company has been in business for almost ten years and has remanufactured over one million phones since its inception. The process of product acquisition management has evolved from a system of buying discarded mobile phones in bulk from cellular airtime providers, to a system of offering established prices for phones with a specific nominal level of quality. The information in this section was gathered through in-depth interviews with the president of ReCellular, Charles Newman.

The original system of acquiring used mobile phones involved getting cellular airtime providers to collect and send the discarded phones to ReCellular. The phones were acquired for a minimal acquisition price, but there were other substantial costs. This method required an extensive sorting, testing, and storage area since the phones arrived in unknown condition. Labor costs were high because of the labor-intensive tasks of sorting and grading. Phones often were sold as scrap or disposed of since the quality level was poor and the cost to remanufacture high. Many phones were missing recharging systems, and had physical damage. Gradually the system has evolved to the present method of setting a price for a known level of quality (see Tables 1 and 2). Each seller that ReCellular purchases cellular telephones from has an established level of nominal quality and prices are based, in part, on this level of quality. The seller's level of quality is relatively consistent based on the source of used cellular telephones. ReCellular's purchasing agents must spend a substantial amount of time with a seller in the beginning to explain how phones are graded and priced. The seller is then responsible for ensuring that the phones are of acceptable levels of quality before sending them to ReCellular.

The shift to a more focused, intelligent purchasing system has lead to a number of benefits for ReCellular. This product acquisition management strategy has enabled the firm to reduce the need to sort and grade phones in-house. It has also served to reduce the level of variability for inputs to the system, making many management tasks more predictable. In short, ReCellular has moved from a Figure 2 situation to a Figure 3 situation.

An analogy may be drawn with the evolution of quality management practices. Prior to the advent of total quality management systems and just-in-time systems, firms attempted to screen the level of incoming quality of parts and materials by the use of sampling and inspection schemes, and setting acceptable standards for vendor's average outgoing quality levels. When ReCellular began remanufacturing cellular telephones, there was no attempt to control incoming levels of quality. The lots were screened at ReCellular, and cellular telephones of unacceptable quality were disposed of or sold to scrap dealers. Since the Japanese quality movement, firms focus more on preventing quality problems rather than inspection. Firms have gone from systems with percentage defective to parts-per-million defective, with no inspection. This has allowed the direct, synchronized, feed of parts to production lines with no intermediate storage. The quality movement has made systems with shorter lead times and less work-in-process possible. The shift in product acquisition management practices at ReCellular may be seen as evidence of rapidly evolving management control systems in remanufacturing and reuse.

Nominal Quality Level	Description
1.	Passes a functional and electrical test with minimal cleaning, produces a nice looking phone. Phones show no water or physical damage and have a good antenna, display, lens, keypad, and a working primary charging system.
2.	Passes a functional and electrical test and with cleaning and buffing can produce a phone that is acceptable in appearance. Phones show no water or physical damage and have a good antenna, display, lens, keypad, and a working primary charging system. Keypad and plastic may show some fading or ' uniform discoloration.
3.	Passes a functional and electrical test but will require some amount of rework to make this phone usable. Phone has a good display and working keypad. Phones may have some physical damage and may show signs of wear that will require the replacement of some parts.
4.	Phones may have the same physical appearance as a grade 1 phone, but the lens may have some scratches. These phones failed the test or did not power up. Many of these phones are repairable and should produce a good yield with some technical knowledge.
5.	Phones have the same physical appearance as a grade 2 phone, but failed the test or did not power up. Many of these phone can be repaired and should produce a good yield with some technical knowledge.
6.	Phones have failed the test or did not power up. Phones have some damage but can be used for part salvage.

Table 1 : Nominal Quality Metrics for Grading Mobile Telephones

Preliminary Pricing	1	2	3	4	5	6
Ericsson DH336/338	$33	$31	$29	$25	$20	$15
Motorola Startac 3000	$85	$75	$65	$55	$35	$25
Nokia 5100/6100 series	$110	$105	$100	$90	$80	$60
Sony CMRX100	$40	$35	$30	$25	$15	$10

Table 2: Prices Offered for Specific Mobile Phones with Specific Levels of Nominal Quality

6. Management of Product Returns

As can be seen from the cellular telephone example, it is possible for a firm to manage the quality of product returns by offering financial incentives. In our example, the remanufacturer may choose not to buy cellular telephones of a lower quality. The seller may respond by offering the lower quality cellular telephones for a lower price, or finding a buyer that will accept the lower levels of quality. This makes the development of cascade reuse systems possible. A seller (broker) of used products may grade the returned products and price the product accordingly. Firms that require used products as inputs for reuse operations then select the price and quality that enables the firm to make an acceptable level of profit. Firms with lower financial rates of return will be able to use products that may be unacceptable (unprofitable) for firms requiring higher rates of return.

There are many types of incentive systems used by firms in the US remanufacturing sector, including deposits, credit toward a remanufactured or new unit, cash for product returns, and leasing (Guide, 2000). The product returns management process allows a planner to set a price the firm is willing to pay for a used product. This acquisition price is the direct cost to the firm and will be greater than zero, but presumably less than the cost of a new product. There are other indirect costs, such as the logistics costs, which include collection, transportation, storage, and sorting. A firm may offer an attractive enough incentive so that the end-user is motivated to return the product to a reuse site, thus eliminating collection costs. The cost of logistics in this case will be greatly reduced. Product sorting will occur at the time a used product is offered, and firms will not accept products below a minimal quality level. A market driven approach will encourage the formation of cascade reuse systems, where products unprofitable for one firm to remanufacture may be offered to firms willing to recycle materials.

In order for market-driven returns to operate effectively, firms will need to develop tests to measure product quality; otherwise, consumers will be motivated to return inferior quality products for a premium payback. The higher the value of the used item, the greater the incentive for a firm to develop a better inspection system. Firms and consumers may benefit from the development of formal bidding systems that match reuse firms' needs with potential sources of used products. The Internet is a logical location for an on-line bidding system focused on product reuse, and several such sites are presently in operation (e.g., http://www.buyreman.com).

Products obtained from the waste stream will have no direct cost for obtaining the products; however, there are logistics costs associated. Countries mandating producer responsibility ensure that firms will have sufficient quantities of product returns, but the producer bears the cost associated with developing and maintaining a reverse logistics network. The quality of product that is returned via the waste stream is highly uncertain since individual users must decide when to return a product for reuse. Presumably, products returned as part of the waste stream will be of lower average quality than products returned from a market-driven system. The problem becomes one of sorting products that may be economically reused from products that are only fit for recycling or landfill. Secondary sorting may be required when only parts from selected end items may be reusable. Firms must maintain large amounts of inventory prior to sorting and provide a large enough facility for storage of the returned items.

We hypothesize a given price yields a distribution of nominal quality of the returned products. By a distribution of nominal quality, we mean that classes of quality are defined, and returns may be graded so as to fit into one of the quality classes, and a frequency distribution fit to the number of items in each of the quality classes. There is evidence that product returns have a distribution of nominal quality (Krikke et al., 1999). The nominal distribution of quality is conditional on the acquisition price paid for the used product, although the exact relationship is unspecified at this time. The cost to remanufacture a used product is inversely related to the cost of acquisition since the quality of the used product will determine the amount of material replacement and labor content, among others. By examining various levels of average nominal quality and the associated acquisition cost, a firm may be able to determine what minimum level of quality is necessary for reuse to be economically attractive.

The selling price for a remanufactured good may be constrained by the market's willingness to purchase remanufactured goods. A firm may determine the profit margin for a given level of nominal quality. This information may be used for an economic value analysis to determine if remanufacturing is economically feasible.

7. Economic Value Added

Reuse activities may not be economically attractive for all firms, and a manager should be able to determine the most attractive option for their firm. Economic Value Added (EVA) provides a robust method for determining the potential profitability of reuse opportunities. EVA measures the difference between the return on a company's capital and the cost of that capital (Young, 1997). A positive EVA indicates that value will be created for the firm's shareholders that satisfies their expectation; a negative EVA shows that value will not be created.

We posit that EVA can be of benefit to a manager in examining whether sufficient value is created via reuse activities, and that EVA may be used to determine the best product acquisition management decisions. We assume that the market for remanufactured products exists and that we know the price/quantity relationship; i.e., for a given price a remanufacturer knows how many remanufactured products will be sold, and commits to deliver this quantity. We can now use an EVA what-if analysis for this situation where revenue is fixed. We will show below that the acquisition price is a driving variable in the level of the EVA.

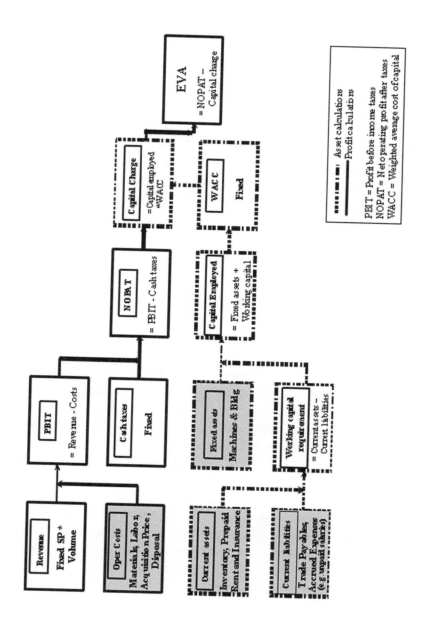

EVA
= NOPAT −
Capital charge

Capital Charge
= Capital employed
*WACC

WACC
Fixed

Capital Employed
= Fixed assets +
Working capital

NOPAT
= PBIT − Cash taxes

PBIT
= Revenue − Costs

Cash taxes
Fixed

Fixed assets
Machines & Bldg

Working capital
requirement
= Current assets −
Current liabilities

Revenue
Fixed SP *
Volume

Oper Costs
Materials, Labor,
Acquisition Price,
Disposal

Current assets
Inventory, Prepaid
Rent and Insurance

Current liabilities
Trade Payables,
Accrued Expenses
(e.g. unpaid salaries)

Legend:
Asset calculations
Profit calculations

PBIT = Profit before income taxes
NOPAT = Net operating profit after taxes
WACC = Weighted average cost of capital

Figure 4 shows the flow of decisions in our EVA calculations. The shaded boxes are affected by alternative product acquisition management decisions (note that for reasons of clarity, we have chosen to keep our EVA discussion relatively crude and simple). The key to controlling the potential profitability is the quality of used products the firm desires (see Figure 5). By changing the minimal acceptable quality level for used products, the price for acquisition changes. The price of acquisition acts as a driver for many of the cost relationships. The price of acquisition directly affects operating costs (via the costs of acquisition, labor, replacement materials, and disposal costs). A higher nominal quality of returned products will decrease the labor content, the replacement materials, and the disposal of products that are not economically recoverable. However, increasing the price paid for products may increase operating expenses as higher prices are paid for higher levels of quality. A higher level of nominal quality may also decrease a firm's investment in fixed assets (via machines and buildings). Since the condition of products is more predictable with a higher level of quality, less storage space and machine capacity are required (see Figures 2 and 3). The impact of quality on current assets is less clear since higher quality will affect inventories in two ways. First, the total amount of inventory held by the system will decrease due to lower variance. Second, the value of acquired products (the raw materials) will increase because of higher acquisition costs. Of course, current assets and liabilities may also be influenced by decisions like buying or renting (e.g., storage space).

In any case, it is not conceptually difficult to analyze the relative EVA impact of product acquisition management alternatives, given the approximate relationship between nominal quality and acquisition price. The EVA shows, with minimal information, whether or not a firm should consider remanufacturing activities. The impact of using a wide range of levels of nominal quality may be simulated since each level of quality has an associated acquisition price. The challenge is to determine the exact relationship between the cost of acquisition and the levels of nominal quality. At present, the exact relationships are unknown and managers are currently using simple ad hoc estimates. However, these estimates provide managers with enough information to run rough EVA calculations. The Hewlett-Packard Company (Davey, 1999) presently uses a trial-and-error EVA approach to analyze the potential profitability of reuse activities. The manager uses pessimistic, neutral, and optimistic estimates in doing the calculations, and simulates the regions around each of these estimates to get an answer that is reasonably robust to changes in the input values. Companies may not be able to specify exactly the functional relationships we propose using, but the managers are capable of defining a number of reasonable alternatives and making estimates based on these. Experienced managers possess expert knowledge that makes these approximations acceptable in a business setting. A manager can simulate the impact of various scenarios to determine if remanufacturing is an attractive option for a firm, and determine what investment in quality is optimal for the individual organization.

A firm may lower the costs of reuse and choose to lower the selling price. By changing the selling price, we change the quantity sold, and hence the overall EVA may be used to examine a large number of scenarios by altering the input (acquisition), as well as the output (market) side. If enough information is known about the relations shown in Figure 5 to specify the mathematical relationships, then an overall optimization may be done for the decision process. The specifying of the mathematical relationships is a topic for further empirical and modeling research that would lead to explicit relationships and perhaps closed-form optimizations within the EVA-product acquisition management framework we propose.

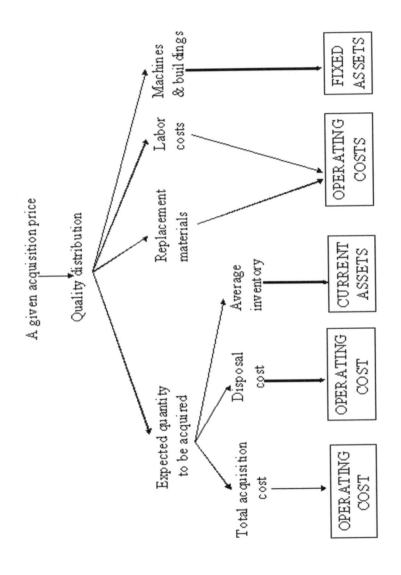

Figure 5: A simple view of the impacts of acquisition price

Since individual firms have different requirements for the weighted average cost of capital (see DeBono, 1997 for a complete discussion), the decision may be unprofitable for a large firm in a market where high returns are required by stockholders, but profitable for smaller firms where lower returns may be acceptable. The EVA approach explains why for some firms reuse is very profitable, and for others it is not economically attractive. EVA also shows that the price of acquisition may be a powerful control lever on the potential profitability of the reuse systems.

8. Implications and Future Research

There are strategic implications of product reuse activities that are not addressed by the EVA, and they deserve consideration. A firm must consider the risks inherent in not controlling the reuse of their products. Disassembly of used products provides essential information about the durability and reliability of products during the life of the product. This information may be used in developing the next generation of higher quality products, and to assist designers in dematerialization efforts. The confidentiality of product characteristics may produce information asymmetries and competitive advantages. The authors know of one remanufacturer that provides these product details back to the OEM in a cooperative agreement.

A firm must also consider the competitive advantages in adopting a green image. At present, very little research showing the effects of a green image on sales is available. An additional marketing-related strategic concern is the cannibalization of new sales. No studies have been done showing the effect of remanufactured sales on new product sales. There are risks in providing remanufactured products that may compete for sales, and these risks should be better understood.

We recognize that our approach to EVA could be refined. The functional relationships detailed in the previous section should be specified mathematically. This would allow a careful optimization of the EVA process. Other refinements are possible and encouraged. Operational implications require a better understanding of the relationships between the costs of remanufacturing, quality, and acquisition price. Specifically, we need to be able to specify the functions for acquisition prices, quality, and remanufacturing costs so that optimization models may be developed.

The areas shown in Figure 1 all deserve close attention. Market development is an unexplored area and little is known about consumer preferences and attitudes toward remanufactured products. The development of secondary markets for remanufactured products (e.g., selling remanufactured laser printers to universities and school districts) also deserves close attention. A strategic question is whether remanufacturing provides product differentiation and the competitive advantages that accompany it. Additionally, firms must consider the interaction between remanufactured product sales and the product life cycle of the product itself.

Managing product returns requires a better understanding of price as an incentive to return products. Present research on quality and price is structured from the manufacturer's point, not the end-user. Another consideration is whether a given acquisition price will result in sufficient quantities of returned products.

Models that consider the dynamics between the areas of market development, product returns management, and operational issues should be carefully considered. A hierarchical approach to planning and control in this environment could produce an insightful managerial tool. Other optimization models incorporating search algorithms may also be useful in this type of environment.

Given the lack of detailed information and theory available, the first requirement is for sound empirical research to define better the relationships and cost functions. Only after a thorough understanding of the actual conditions may refined models be developed. We believe that product acquisition management represents an evolution of the understanding of reuse systems. The firms that emerge as industry leaders will need to develop a quantifiable model for the business of reuse and we believe this work is a first step in this direction.

9. Conclusions

We have presented a fundamentally new approach to the economics and operations of reuse activities. Traditionally, research efforts have focused on ways to minimize the loss associated with reuse; e.g., cost minimization models. This traditional view of reuse activities requires that firms seek to create new markets for used products, but passively accept product returns. We proposed a framework, based on the EVA concept, to value the potential economic attractiveness of reuse activities. The concept of returned product quality acts as a driver in our framework.

We also have shown that product acquisition management may serve as a foundation for operational planning and control activities. We reject the idea that firms must passively accept product returns, and show that a system for control exists using returned product quality as the system regulator. The idea that a firm may control the quality and quantity of product returns has a profound impact on the understanding of how reuse systems may be profitable in some cases. We also show that this new approach leads to many research issues that remain unanswered.

References

Davey, S. (1999) World Wide Product Returns Manager, Hewlett-Packard Company. Private communication with the authors.

DeBono, J. (1997) Divisional cost of equity capital, *Management Accounting* (UK), November, 40-41.

Esty, D. and Porter, M. (1998) Industrial ecology and competitiveness: Strategic implications for the firm, *Journal of Industrial Ecology*, 2(1) 35-43.

Fleischmann, M., Bloemhof-Ruwaard, J.M., Dekker, R., van der Laan, E., Van Nunen, J.A.E.E. and Van Wassenhove, L.N. (1997) Quantitative models for reverse logistics: A review, *European Journal of Operational Research,* 103(1) 1-17.

Gotzel, C., Weidling, J., Heisig, G., and Inderfurth, K., Product return and recovery concepts of companies in Germany, Preprint Nr. 31/9 1999, Fakultät für Wirtschaftswissenschaft, Otto-Von-Guericke-Universität Magdeburg, Germany.

Guide, Jr., V.D.R. (2000) Production planning and control for remanufacturing: Industry practice and research needs, *Journal of Operations Management*, 18(4) 467-483.

Guide, Jr., V.D.R., Jayaraman, V., Srivastava, R., and Benton, WC (2000) Supply chain management for recoverable manufacturing systems, *Interfaces*, 30(3) 125-142.

Guide, Jr., V.D.R., and Srivastava, R. (1998) Inventory buffers in recoverable manufacturing, *Journal of Operations Management* 16(5) 551-568.

Guide, Jr., V.D.R., Srivastava, R. and Kraus, M. (1997) Product structure complexity and scheduling of operations in recoverable manufacturing, *International Journal of Production Research* 35(11) 3179-3199.

Inderfurth, K. (1997) Simple optimal replenishment and disposal policies for a product recovery systems with leadtimes, *OR Spektrum*, 19(2) 111-122.

Kelle, P. and Silver, E.A. (1989) Purchasing policies for new containers considering the random returns of previously issued containers, *IIE Transactions*, 21, 349-354.

Kodak (1999) *1999 Corporate Environmental Report*, Rochester NY: The Kodak Corporation.

Krikke, H.R. (1998) Recovery strategies and reverse logistic network design, PhD Thesis, Institute of Business Engineering and Technology Application (BETA), Universiteit Twente, Enschede, The Netherlands.

Krikke, H., Van Harten, A. and Schuur, P. (1999) Business case Océ: Reverse logistic network re-design for copiers, *OR Spektrum*, 21(3) 381-409.

Lund, R., Remanufacturing: An American resource, *Proceedings of the Fifth International Congress for Environmentally Conscious Design and Manufacturing*, June 16 - 17, 1998, Rochester Institute of Technology.

Nasr, N., Hughson, C., Varel, E. and Bauer, R. (1998) *State-of-the-art assessment of remanufacturing technology*, Rochester Institute of Technology, National Center for Remanufacturing, Rochester, NY.

Reinhardt, F. (1999) Market failures and the environmental policies of firms, *Journal of Industrial Ecology*, 3(1) 9-21.

Spengler, TH., Püchert, T., Penkuln, T. and Rentz, O. (1997) Environmental integrated production and recycling management, *European Journal of Operational Research*, 97(2) 308-326.

Thierry, M., Salomon, M., Nunen, Van J. and Van Wassenhove, L. (1995) Strategic issues in product recovery management, *California Management Review*, 37(2) 114-135.

van der Laan, E. (1997) The effects of remanufacturing on inventory control. Ph.D. Series in General Management 28, Rotterdam School of Management, Erasmus University, Rotterdam, The Netherlands.

van der Laan, E., Salomon, M., Dekker, R., and Van Wassenhove, L. (1999) Inventory control in hybrid systems with remanufacturing, *Management Science*, 45(5) 733-747.

Young, D. (1997) Economic value added: A primer for European managers, *European Management Journal*, 15(4) 335-343.

Xerox, (1999) *1999 Environment, Health and Safety Progress Report,* Webster, NY: The Xerox Corporation.

Contact:

V. Daniel R. Guide, Jr.
Department of Supply Chain and Information Systems
The Smeal College of Business Administration
The Pennsylvania State University
509 Business Administration Building
University Park, PA 16802-3005

Email: dguide@psu.edu

Luk N. Van Wassenhove
The Henry Ford Professor of Operations Management
INSEAD
Boulevard de Constance
77305 Fontainebleau Cedex
France

Email: Luk.Van-Wassenhove@insead.edu

Author Index